N. BRUNO

Principles of
WOODWORKING

WILLIAM F. HOLTROP, ED. D.

AND

HERMAN HJORTH, M. S.

THE BRUCE PUBLISHING COMPANY • MILWAUKEE

Library of Congress Catalog Card Number: 61–11832

© 1961 THE BRUCE PUBLISHING COMPANY

Made in the United States of America

Preface

During all ages wood has played an important part in the development of mankind. It enters, directly or indirectly, into the construction of more manufactured articles than any other material, and there is not an engineering project nor construction job of any kind, in which wood is not used in some way.

A material which enters so extensively into every phase of life is of tremendous economic value to all civilized nations. The woodworking industries in this country, particularly the building and furniture industries, are among the most important, because they employ thousands of highly skilled workmen, designers, and artists, to produce useful as well as beautiful articles of wood. Other thousands are engaged in the distribution and selling of these products, and still other thousands in the manufacture of the numerous tools and machines used in woodworking.

This text is intended not only for the use of students in secondary and vocational schools and colleges, but also for adults who have taken up the study and practice of woodworking as a hobby.

Fundamental tool processes, common to all woodworking trades, have been compiled and arranged in family groups. With these as a basis, cabinet-making has been emphasized throughout the book, because of its universal interest and appeal, and because this phase of woodworking is probably most frequently elected by students and hobbyists.

All tool operations have been described and written in the form of instruction sheets. These have been further supplemented with related information about materials, tools, and machinery, and by a chapter on furniture selection, design, and planning.

The teacher of woodworking will find the subject matter — both instruction sheets and related information — in convenient form for assignments.

Special attention is called to the method of planning and analyzing various tool operations involved in the construction of an object. By following this method, any cabinet job may be analyzed and reference made by number to topics describing the various tool operations. After the students have become acquainted with the book, they should do their own thinking and formulate their own plans for approval by the teacher.

The review questions at the end of each chapter should be of value to the student in testing his knowledge of a given topic, and to the teacher to see whether his students have mastered the subject matter. A prepared key to these questions may be obtained from the publisher.

It is the sincere hope of the author that the increasing number of "home woodworkers" will find this book helpful, and that it will contribute to their interest and pleasure in craftsmanship. May they experience that satisfaction and joy of achievement which comes with a piece of work well done.

HERMAN HJORTH

Preface to the Revised Edition

In this new edition of PRINCIPLES OF WOODWORKING, the aim has been to increase its usefulness. This has been done in the following manner:

By first contacting the many manufacturers of woodworking machines and related tools and equipment and checking their products for obsolescence and improvements. Tools, machines, and materials found obsolete were eliminated and replaced by more current ones.

By replacing many of the illustrations which from the standpoint of dress had become dated. Wherever it seemed appropriate for clarity of description and execution of operations, new illustrations were inserted.

By adding significantly to the completeness of a number of chapters. For example, to Chapter 1, "History of Woodworking Tools and Machines," some interesting illustrations and descriptions of early American machines were added. Chapter 3, "Machine Tools" now features a number of the multipurpose machines which have become so popular in recent years. In Chapter 7, "Gluing and Clamping," glues, particularly the recently developed synthetic ones, are discussed in greater detail. In Chapter 11, "Upholstery," a new and versatile material, foam rubber, is discussed and illustrated in detail.

By re-writing most of the material in Chapter 15, "Wood" and presenting here numerous recent research findings. Wood continues to assume an ever greater importance in our modern society. A product which at one time seemed scarce is now abundant because of carefully planned conservation and tree farming.

By substituting the chapter, "Applied Projects" with a chapter on "Project selection, design, and planning." Projects presented complete with drawings, bills of material and plans of procedure, encourage copying and leave little room for one's imagination and creativity. This new chapter shows how projects should be selected and designed along accepted lines. Techniques of identification and layout are presented which should prove both helpful and effective.

Finally, by introducing a completely new chapter on "Modern Coated Abrasives."

It is the sincere hope that this revised volume of PRINCIPLES OF WOODWORKING will continue to prove helpful to those interested in woodworking and wood technology, whether they are students in high school, college, apprentices in the trade, or hobbyists.

WILLIAM F. HOLTROP

Santa Barbara, California
April 1, 1961

Acknowledgments

The author expresses his thanks and appreciation to the many companies in the woodworking industry who so splendidly co-operated in the preparation of this book. A number of their representatives spent considerable time and effort in preparing copy on certain topics or by making valuable suggestions by reviewing parts of the original text.

The assistance of the following persons and companies is gratefully acknowledged:

American Brake Shoe Co., Kellogg Division, Rochester, N. Y., 467

American Screw Co., Willimantic, Conn., 308

American Walnut Manufacturing Association, Chicago, Ill., 527, 573, 574, 575

Amerock Corporation, Rockford, Ill., 316, 317, 318, 325, 328

Atlas Press Co., Kalamazoo, Mich., 145

Barnard, John, *The Handy Boy's Book,* Lock & Co., London, 337

Bassett Furniture Industries, Inc., Bassett, Va., 414

Beaver Manufacturing Co., Inglewood, Calif., 163

Behr-Manning Co., Troy, N. Y., 145, Ch. 12

Black Brothers Co., Grand Rapids, Mich., 577

Black and Decker Manufacturing Co., Towson, Md., 91

Boice-Crane Co., Toledo, Ohio, 58, 59, 60, 77

Boston Gear Works, Inc., North Quincy, Mass., 99

British Columbia Lumber Manufacturing Assn., Vancouver, B. C., 507

Brodhead-Garrett Co., Cleveland, Ohio, 17

California Redwood Association, San Francisco, Calif., 506

Carter Products Co., Inc., Grand Rapids, Mich., 71, 72

Clarks Sanding Machine Co., Muskegon, Mich., 116

Crescent Machine Co., Leetonia, Ohio, 164

Delta Power Tool Division, Rockwell Manufacturing Co., Pittsburgh, Pa., 51, 60, 61, 65, 70, 72, 76, 78, 79, 80, 81, 85, 99, 100, 101, 102, 103, 105, 112, 114, 123, 124, 125, 126, 127, 146, 151, 154, 155, 191, 204, 251, 261, 343, 352, 356, 357, 358, 361, 365

Dependable Machine Co., Greensboro, N. C., 135, 136

The DeVilbiss Co., Toledo, Ohio, 465, 466, 467, 468, 469

De Walt Division, American Machine and Foundry Co., Lancaster, Pa., 90, 127, 128, 129, 130, 131, 132

Douglas Fir Plywood Assn., Tacoma, Wash., 194, 248, 318, 329

Drexel Furniture Co., Drexel, N. C., 184, 194, 227, 247

Ekstrom, Carlson and Co., Rockford, Ill., 107, 114

Fine Hardwoods Association, Chicago, Ill., 517, 518, 520, 523, 526

Foley Mfg. Co., Minneapolis, Minn., 162

Greenlee Bros. and Co., Rockford, Ill., 93, 94, 95, 97, 168

Hanchett Manufacturing Co., Big Rapids, Mich., 156, 166

Handy Manufacturing Co., Chicago, Ill., 133

Hibben, Thos., *The Carpenter's Tool Chest,* J. B. Lippincott Co., Philadelphia, Pa., 1, 2, 3, 5

Huther Brothers Saw Mfg. Co., Inc., Rochester, N. Y., 67, 156

Magna Power Tool Corp., Menlo Park, Calif., 117, 118, 119, 120, 121, 122

Mattison Machine Works, Rockford, Ill., 111

Max Manufacturing Co., San Jose, Calif., 162, 169

Mercer, Henry C., The Bucks County Historical Society, Doylestown, Pa., 337

Metropolitan Museum of Art, New York, N. Y., 4

National Lumber Manufacturing Association, Washington, D. C., 515

National Rubber Bureau, Washington, D. C., 413, 415, 416, 417

New Britain Machine Co., New Britain, Conn., 92

Nicholson File Co., Providence, R. I., 47, 140, 141, 142

Oliver Machinery Co., Grand Rapids, Mich., 58, 59, 63, 71, 77, 80, 81, 82, 85, 86, 87, 88, 96, 102, 105, 110, 111, 113, 134, 160, 164, 338, 339, 341

Onsrud Machine Works, Inc., Chicago, Ill., 106, 109, 133

Porter-Cable Machine Co., Syracuse, N. Y., 108, 112, 116, 117

Quennell, M. and C. H. B., *Everyday Life, in the New Stone, Bronze, and Early Iron Ages,* G. B. Putnam's Sons, N. Y., 336

Sackner Products, Inc., Grand Rapids, Mich., 421

H. B. Smith Machine Co., Smithville, N. J., 116

Stanley Electric Tools, Division of Stanley Works, New Britain, Conn., 18, 19, 20, 28, 29, 30, 32, 33, 34, 35, 36, 39, 41, 42, 43, 44, 45, 46, 48, 108, 109, 140

The Tannewitz Works, Grand Rapids, Mich., 62

U. S. Department of Agriculture, Forest Service, Washington, D. C., 513

Walker-Turner Co., Inc., Plainfield, N. J., 342, 386

Washington Steel Products Inc., Tacoma, Wash., 324, 330, 331, 332

West Coast Lumberman's Association, Portland, Ore., 532, 534, 535, 536, 537, 539, 553, 563, 564

Weyerhaeuser Forest Products Co., St. Paul, Minn., 528

Wheeler, Charles G., *Woodworking for Beginners,* G. P. Putnam and Sons, N. Y., 16, 50, 54

B. D. Whitney and Son, Inc., Winchendon, Mass., 86, 103, 104

S. A. Woods Machine Co., Boston, Mass., 7, 8, 9, 10, 11

Woodworker's Tool Works, Chicago, Ill., 104, 163

Wm. Zinsser Co., New York, 457, 458, 459, 460

Arthur W. Priaulx, Public Relations Director, West Coast Lumberman's Association, for his valuable help in the preparation of Chapter 15, "Wood."

Miss Mary Rosa for doing the extensive typing for this revision.

Robert C. Smitheram, Jr., for preparing new photographs.

Contents

CHAPTER 1

History of Woodworking Tools and Machines

The first woodworking tools were made of stone about 300,000 years ago (Fig. 1). Stone axes, wedges, scrapers, saws, and drills, used at that early age, have been found all over the world. The oldest of these tools were very crude, but the ones made during the latter part of the stone age were

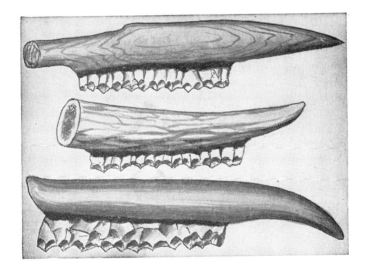

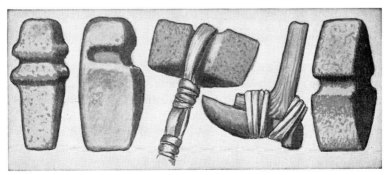

Fig. 1.   Upper: Stone saws with handles of wood or horn.
Lower: Axes from the ground stone age.

1

Fig. 2. Flaked flint tools from the new stone age.

ground to beautiful shapes, on other stones, and some of them were even polished (Fig. 2).

Metals were first used by the people in that part of the world now called the Middle East. The first metal tools were made of copper. Then someone discovered that, by adding a small amount of tin, the metal became harder and therefore more serviceable. This was the beginning of the bronze age when the ancient cities of Troy, Babylon, Ur, Thebes, and others were built. The first bronze tools were cast in one-piece stone molds and were rather crude (Fig. 3). The next step in the development was the two-piece mold with both halves alike. Tools and utensils found during comparative recent excavations show that these ancient peoples — Sumerians, Assyrians, Egyptians, and others — possessed a high degree of manual and artistic skill and made a distinct contribution to the advancement of civilization. Written records and pictures describe how carpenters, smiths, and other artisans worked and what tools they used (Figs. 4 and 5).

When the bronze age began is not definitely known, but a complete set of carpenters' tools, about 5000 years old, have been found on the island of Crete. Similar finds have been made at other points in this region. At the end of the bronze period — about 3000 years ago — when people first began to use iron, most of the carpenters' tools had been invented with exception of the plane and the brace (Fig. 6).

Although much superior to bronze, iron tools at first were not well liked. The early Romans were allowed to use iron for farm implements only,

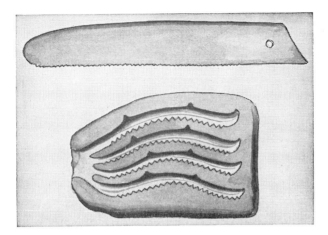

Fig. 3. Upper: Nine-inch bronze saw found in Switzerland. Lower: Stone mold for casting bronze saws found in Sweden.

and no workman was allowed to use iron tools in the building of Solomon's temple. Bronze tools, therefore, continued to be used together with iron tools for many years.

The ancient Romans were the first people to make saws with regular shaped and set teeth. They also invented the plane, made both tang and socket chisels, and developed the claw hammer. In fact, the carpenters' tools found in the ruins of Pompeii are a good deal like the ones used by present-day carpenters.

During the Middle Ages, the early iron tools, especially the saws, were improved in quality. Not until the fifteenth century, however, were the brace and boring bits invented.

Fig. 4. Egyptian furniture makers. The carpenter on the left is using an Egyptian bow saw.

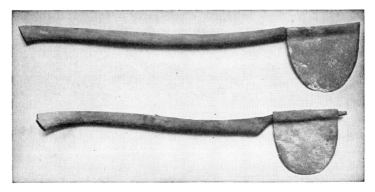

Fig. 5. Upper: Egyptian adze. Center: Egyptian saw.
Lower: Egyptian ax.

In the Middle Ages workmen in the different trades grouped themselves and formed trade associations or guilds. There were three stages or grades in the guilds, the apprentice, the journeyman, and the master. An apprentice usually began to learn his trade at the early age of twelve. His parents made

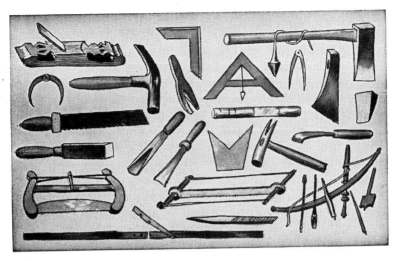

Fig. 6. Roman tools.

a contract with a master, to whom they paid a fee for which the master in return fed and clothed the boy and taught him the skills and knowledge of his trade. In the early days a master could have only one apprentice besides his own son or nephew.

An apprenticeship lasted from one to twelve years, depending upon the necessary skills and knowledge to be acquired in a particular trade. At the end of the time of learning, the apprentice had to pass a stiff examination before he could become a journeyman and receive wages for his work. If a journeyman had sufficient ability and capital to set himself up as a master, he was required to work several years in one of the larger cities to gain experience. He then had to pass a very rigid test to demonstrate his skill, knowledge, and character, before he could proclaim himself a master.

The guilds were established for the protection and welfare of their members. These members were taken care of when sick and were given employment when out of work. On the other hand, the guilds had many stringent rules of conduct and workmanship which they enforced by frequent and careful inspections of the shops. Poor work and materials were destroyed and heavy fines imposed; a man might even be condemned to death for bad and dishonest workmanship. In this way, craftsmanship during the Middle Ages was kept up to a very high standard of excellence.

By the time machinery was invented, however, the guilds had fallen into disrepute and gradually disappeared. Masterships were sold by officers of the state without regard to ability, and shops were inherited from father to son. The master himself became more of a businessman, employing many people, and less of a craftsman working with his apprentices and journeymen.

The development of woodworking machinery began about 150 years ago. While some primitive sawing machines, driven by hand, water, or wind power, had been used in different localities during the Middle Ages, it was not until the end of the eighteenth century that the forerunners of our present woodworking machines were built. The greatest inventions in this field were made in England by Sir Samuel Bentham, who discovered the principle of *rotary cutting,* which is used in all modern planers, jointers, shapers, and molders.

The machines built by Bentham were very crude according to modern standards, having only heavy timber frames bolted together to support the cutting element and its bearings. Not until the middle of the nineteenth century were woodworking machines made entirely of metal.

It is a curious fact that this crude machinery was first used in prisons where it enabled unskilled men to plane, saw, and bore as well and much faster than skilled woodworkers. The machines proved such a success that they were introduced in the shipyards where the work of building wooden ships was speeded up many times.

The first circular saw was invented in Holland, but was not successful, owing to the difficulty of making bearings and saw blades. The band saw was invented by Newberry and was patented in England in 1808 (Fig. 7).

Undoubtedly the best way to form some idea as to the appearance of these earlier woodworking machines is to leaf through the pages of a 100-year-old

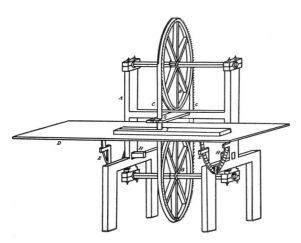

Fig. 7. The first endless band saw patented by William Newberry of London, England, in 1808.

machine catalog. Although not many of these catalogs are still in existence, the author was fortunate in obtaining one for the express purpose of acquainting himself with these early machines.

The following illustrations with a brief description were secured from the 1884 illustrated catalog of planing, molding, and sawing machinery as manufactured by the S. A. Woods Machine Co., of Boston, Massachusetts. By this time this company had been in business for 30 years.*

Wood-Frame Saw Table, With Self-Oiling Saw Arbor and Cone Bushing (Fig. 8)

DESCRIPTION: "These tables, made from the best of kiln-dried hard wood, are accurately framed together and secured by joint bolts. The top is glued up from narrow strips of rock-maple or beech, which being fastened to cross cleats cannot warp or split. Each table is fitted with a patent self-

Fig. 8.   Wood-frame saw table.

oiling saw arbor with cone bushing, so that saws with holes of different size may be used. The top is hinged to the rear end of the frame and is adjusted with a crank and held in position by clamps. It is fitted with a splitting gauge, and an adjustable cut-off gauge is furnished when the machine is to be used for both splitting and cutting off."

This particular saw table was manufactured in six (6) different sizes. Smallest size, 2 ft. 6 in. by 3 ft. 6 in. Largest size 3 ft. 6 in. by 6 ft.

* Source: Illustrated Catalogue of Woodworking Machinery, 1884, S. A. Woods Machine Co., Boston, Massachusetts. Courtesy: L. B. Carlson, Vice-President and Chief Engineer.

Fig. 9.   Early band saw.

No. 3 Band Sawing Machine (Fig. 9)

DESCRIPTION: "The above cut represents our new Band Sawing Machine, which is now offered to those in want of a first-class machine as being second to none. The frame is heavy, with cored sections, and capable of resisting great strain without yielding. The wheels are 38 inches in diameter; are light and strong, having wrought-iron spokes with bent wood rims covered with rubber; are perfectly balanced, running in long bearings that are easily adjusted in any direction. The table is usually made of iron, but may be made of wood if preferred, which reduces the price. The iron table may be tipped for sawing on a bevel, and if so ordered will be fitted with a gauge for straight work which may readily be removed. The upper wheel may be adjusted to guide the saw to the center, or any desired part of the rim, and a compensating spring insures an equal tension to the saw at all times. The shipper will receive the belt from any direction. The machine will work 13 inches thick and has a sweep of 37 inches. Tight and loose pulleys on machine are 14 x 4 and should make 350 revolutions per minute."

Band saws of a later date showed definite improvement from the standpoint of safety. But it was well into the twentieth century that the operator was protected from breaking blades by means of protective upper and lower wheel guards.

Improved Jointing and Facing Machine (Fig. 10)

DESCRIPTION: "The base of the machine being cast in a single piece (in pedestal form) presents a neat appearance, and gives great strength and solidity, and also provides a useful tight-closing receptacle for wrenches, tools, etc. The frame being a single casting and resting firmly on the base, prevents all possibility of twisting or straining the moving parts in securing the machine to the floor.

"The tables are planed perfectly true, and being heavily ribbed with a 2½ inch box rib extending entirely around them cannot warp or spring. Each table is adjusted on inclined planes, which experience has taught us is the most reliable way to hold them and keep them in close proximity to the knives. By merely loosening a thumb-screw either table may readily be drawn back, giving access to the cutter-head, and allowing molding cutters to be used when desired. The tables are steel faced, which prevents breaking or chipping the edges and allows them to be made very thin, which admits of a narrower opening, and this is essential to good work and the safety of the operator, as is well understood.*

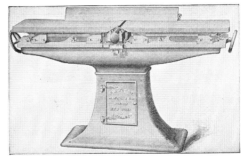

Fig. 10. Improved jointing and facing machine.

"The head is of steel, made from solid forging, with long bearings running in improved self-oiling boxes, and being tapped on two sides for straight knives, and slotted on two sides for molding, grooving, and irregular cutters, allows a great variety of work to be quickly and accurately performed.

"The cutterhead boxes are yoked together and therefore always in line,

* NOTE: Jointer guards of any form or shape are completely lacking.

and either end of the cutter-head yoke may be adjusted, which is a most important feature and not found in other machines of this class, as it allows one end of the head to be raised should the knives wear faster on the back side or next to the gauge as they usually do, and saves resetting the knives. The table is fitted for rabbeting, and in every detail it will be found a superior machine.

"The gauge may be set at any bevel, and can be swung diagonally across the cutters when desired.

"The cutterhead revolves at a speed of 4500 revolutions per minute."

Improved Patent Combination Planer (Fig. 11)

To plane 24 inches wide, 16 inches thick and from 8 feet upward, as ordered.

DESCRIPTION: "This machine is too widely and favorably known to require an extended description in this place, but we have recently greatly improved the general construction, and introduced many valuable and important features, and shall be pleased to furnish those who may desire a descriptive circular of these improvements.

Fig. 11. Improved patent combination planer.

"As a dimension planer for getting stock out of wind, it has no equal, doing the work perfectly, and three times as rapidly as the 'Daniels' will do the same work. The machine can also be used for planing off stock as thin as $\frac{1}{16}$ of an inch, by removing the dogs and placing the stock to be planed on the carriage, and adjusting the pressure roll so as to keep the stock firmly to the carriage, running it back and forth at will, while a complete board surfacer may be had by swinging the feed-roll attachment into place.

"The above cut shows the manner in which the feed-roll attachment is used for surfacing boards, and some details not shown in the cut of the Extra Heavy size.

"The receiving pulley is 14 x 6, and should make 630 revolutions per minute. Loose pulley will be furnished when ordered. The belting required for this machine is as follows: for cylinder belts, 35%12 feet of 4-inch; for feed-works, 26%12 feet of 3-inch, and 23%12 feet of 2½ inch."

No. 1 Four Roll Combined Molding, Planing, and Matching Machine (Fig. 12)

For working heavy moldings and gutters of every description.

DESCRIPTION: "The machine represented here is the largest and heaviest built in America, and is provided with all the adjustments and improvements. As now constructed its superiority is conceded by all who are familiar with its merits. For car and job shops it is especially valuable, as by the application of our Patent Hinged Chip-Breaker, it becomes a superior planing and matching machine for the class of work noted above. The change of plates and heads for either molding or matching is made in a few minutes' time, while the additional expense is of small moment when compared with the benefits derived. When used for working gutters the under head is belted at both ends (as shown by cut) and driven from a friction-shaft. For ordinary work we recommend driving the under cylinder by one cross belt on the opposite side of the machine direct from the driving shaft. We, however, construct them for belting either way.

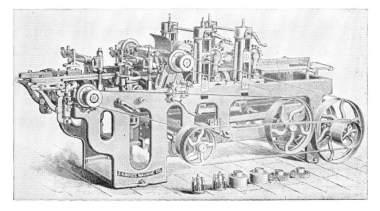

Fig. 12. No. 1 four-roll combined molding, planing, and matching machine.

"Tight and loose pulleys on machine are 14 inches in diameter for 6-inch belt, and should make 600 revolutions per minute, giving the cutter-head 3800. When arranged for belting the under cylinder at both ends, the belting required will be as follows: the cylinder belts for top cutter-head, 33⅞₁₂ feet of 4-inch; two under cylinder belts, 32⅝₁₂ feet of 4-inch, for both matcher belts, 35⅞₁₂ feet of 3-inch; one feed belt, 13¹⁰₁₂ feet of 3-inch. When the underhead is belted only at one end, the belts will be the same as on our No. 1 two roll moulding machine."

The descriptions of the machines listed above should give the reader some idea of their early development. Especially when they are analyzed and compared with the newer machines described in succeeding chapters, one should generally gain a deeper appreciation of our present-day technological age and particularly of the woodworking industry.*

REFERENCES:

The Carpenter's Tool Chest by Thomas Hibben (Philadelphia: J. B. Lippincott Co.)

Modern Machine Woodworking by William F. Holtrop and Herman Hjorth (Milwaukee: The Bruce Publishing Co.)

S. A. Woods Machine Co., Illustrated Catalogue of Woodworking Machinery, 1884, Boston, Mass., 58 pp.

REVIEW QUESTIONS, CHAPTER 1

Possible score 35 points

Your score . . . . . .

PART I. COMPLETION QUESTIONS.   Complete the following statements:

1. The first woodworking tools were made of stone about . . . . years ago.
2. Metals were first used by people in that part of the world now called . . . .
3. The first metal tools were made of . . . .
4. It was discovered that this metal could be hardened by adding a small amount of . . . .
5. About 5000 years ago a complete set of carpenter's tools was found on the island of . . . .
6. Carpenter's tools, a good deal like the ones used now, have been found in the ruins of . . . .

---

* NOTE: For the historical development of the wood-turning lathe, see Chapter 9, "Wood Turning."

7. The brace and boring bits were not invented until the ....
8. As early as the Middle Ages, tradesmen formed their own associations or ....
9. After having been an apprentice and journeyman for a number of years, a tradesman could become a ....
10. Depending upon the necessary skill and knowledge to be acquired, apprenticeships lasted from one to .... years.

PART II. TRUE-FALSE QUESTIONS.   Indicate, by circling T or F, whether the following statements are true or false:

11. At the end of his learning period, an apprentice automatically became a journeyman   T   F
12. Through rigid inspection, craftsmanship during the Middle Ages was kept up to a very high degree of excellence.   T   F
13. Early trade associations disappeared as machinery was invented.   T   F
14. Some primitive sawing machines were used during the Dark Ages.   T   F
15. Forerunners of our present woodworking machines were built toward the end of the eighteenth century.   T   F
16. The greatest, early inventions in this field were made in France.   T   F
17. Sir Samuel Bentham discovered the principle of rotary cutting.   T   F
18. Such machines as circular saws and band saws operate on the principle of rotary cutting.   T   F
19. The first endless band saw was invented by Newberry in London, England.   T   F
20. The Dutch are credited with inventing the first circular saw.   T   F

PART III. MULTIPLE-CHOICE QUESTIONS.   Select, by encircling the correct letter, the answer which completes each statement:

21. The S. A. Woods Machine Co. is located in:
    A. New York N. Y.
    B. Philadelphia, Pa.
    C. Boston, Mass.
    D. Chicago, Ill.
22. Early circular saws had tops glued up from strips of:
    A. Walnut
    B. Rock maple
    C. Gum
    D. White pine
23. Bronze is formed by adding one of the following to copper:
    A. Silver
    B. Brass
    C. Steel
    D. Tin
24. One of the following was not invented by the early Romans:
    A. Brace
    B. Saws
    C. Chisels
    D. Claw hammer

25. The principle of rotary cutting applies to all but one of the following machines:
    A. Planers
    B. Saws
    C. Jointers
    D. Molders

PART IV. MATCHING QUESTIONS. Match the terms to the left with the description to the right by placing the correct letter in the parentheses. See sample answer:

26. (D) Samuel Bentham
27. (   ) S. A. Wood Machine Co.
28. (   ) Newberry
29. (   ) Strips of rock maple
30. (   ) Splitting gauge
31. (   ) Bent wood rims
32. (   ) Tool receptacle
33. (   ) Bronze
34. (   ) Boring bits
35 (   ) Rotary cutting

A. Inventor of the band saw.
B. Early name for what is now called splitter guard.
C. A part of early jointers.
D. Inventor of the principle of rotary cutting.
E. Invented during the fifteenth century.
F. Applies to planers, jointers, and molders.
G. Used on early band-saw wheels.
H. A leading manufacturer of woodworking machinery.
I. Used to glue up saw tables.
J. A mixture of copper and tin.
K. Invented by the Romans.

CHAPTER 2

Hand Tools

The woodworker uses a large variety of hand tools. Every workman should be familiar with the tools which he uses. He should know their proper names, the purpose for which each is used, and how they are sharpened and kept in good condition.

In this chapter a brief description is given of the most commonly used hand tools. In a later chapter the sharpening of tools is explained in more detail.

1. The bench is a tool or appliance of the utmost importance to the woodworker. The best type of bench has a top that is constructed of narrow strips of hardwood, glued and bolted together. In this way warping is prevented. It usually has a recess or trough in which tools may be placed while working. The top is bolted to a frame consisting of four legs braced securely with cross pieces. This frame is often fitted with one or more drawers (Fig. 1).

Woodworkers' benches at the turn of the twentieth century were simpler than those now in use (Fig. 2). To accommodate the ends of long boards, they were supported on wooden or iron pegs. Notice the various holes drilled in the side of the bench to hold these pegs. In order for the vise to hold

Fig. 1.
Workbench.

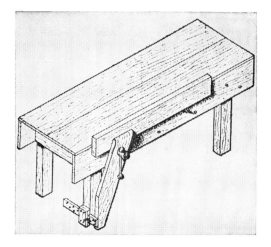

Fig. 2.   Early one-vise workbench.

thick stock, it was necessary to make an adjustment at the bottom by moving two pegs over one or more notches. The bench shown in Figure 3 is a distinct improvement over the one shown above. By means of a tail vise and bench stops it was then possible to hold long flat boards securely on the bench top. Also a storage drawer was added for the convenience of supplies and small tools.

In the modern school woodworking laboratory one often finds two-station workbenches of the type as shown in Figure 4. The six lockers underneath serve conveniently for the day-to-day storage of student's projects and parts. Figure 5 shows a modern four-station workbench with six lockers in the front and six in the back. Particularly in large classes, benches of this type with their excellent storage facilities are highly desirable.

The bench top is equipped with a side vise and sometimes also with a tail vise. These vises are made either of wood or iron. They have a central screw and parallel guide bars, one on each side of the screw (Fig. 6). Some iron vises are of the "continuous-screw" type and others of the "quick-acting"

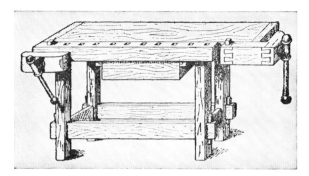

Fig. 3.   Early two-vise workbench.

Fig. 4. Modern two-station workbench with six individual storage lockers.

Fig. 5. Modern four-station workbench with twelve individual lockers.

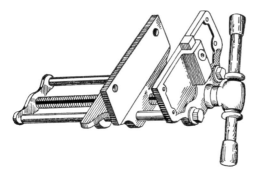

Fig. 6.   Quick-acting vise.

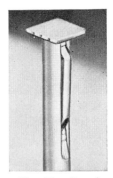

Fig. 7.   Bench stop with spring clip.

type. On some quick-acting vises a section of the screw thread is cut away throughout the entire length of the screw. This permits the movable vise jaw to be pulled in or out when the screw is in a certain position. A partial turn to the right tightens these quick-acting vises.

Some vises are equipped with an adjustable dog, i.e., a piece of iron which fits into a slot in the vise jaw. It can be set flush with the top of the vise jaw, or raised above it. A corresponding bench stop, or bench dog (Fig. 7), fits into holes bored in the bench top so that a piece of wood may be clamped firmly between the bench stop and the vise jaw. A bench stop should not be confused with a bench hook, which is an all-wood device used for sawing and chiseling (Fig. 8).

Another wooden device used to do hand coping saw work is the jack board (Fig. 8).

Fig. 8.   Brush, bench hook and jack board conveniently stored.

A tail vise is a great convenience on a workbench, because it permits of clamping long pieces, such as table legs, for planing or mortising.

Measuring Tools

2. A rule is generally the first tool used by the woodworker. Rules are made in different lengths and of different materials. Those used by the woodworker are usually of the folding type, and measure from 2 to 8 ft. in length (Fig. 9). Rules are generally marked off on both sides in inches and subdivisions of an inch, but they are also made with inch divisions on one side and metric divisions on the other.

Fig. 9. Folding rule.

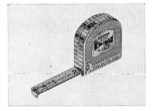

Fig. 10. Steel tape with push button lock.

Fig. 11. Steel tape.

3. Measuring tapes are used by carpenters, contractors, and architects. They are made of steel or cloth, and usually measure from 25 to 100 ft. in length (Fig. 10). Small steel tapes, 6 to 10 ft. in length, often are used instead of folding rules. They are divided into inches and feet, or meters and centimeters (Fig. 11).

4. Try squares are used for testing the squareness of lumber, and in checking the squareness of work being assembled, especially in places where the framing square would be too large. Try squares consist of two parts, the stock and the blade, which are firmly fastened together at right angles. The stock is thick and is made of wood or iron. The blade, which is thin, is made of steel and has an inch scale stamped on it (Fig. 12). Try squares are made in sizes of from 4 to 12 in., measured from the end of the blade to the stock.

5. Miter and try squares (Fig. 13) can be used at both 90 and 45 deg. **Combination squares** (Fig. 14) combine the equivalent of several tools,

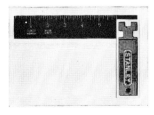

Fig. 12.
Try square.

Fig. 13.
Miter and
try square.

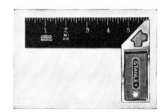

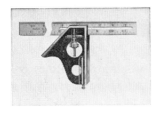

Fig. 14.
Combination
square.

Fig. 15.   Sliding T bevel.

such as: straightedge, plumb, level, outside try square, inside try square, marking gauge, depth gauge and miter square.

6. Sliding T bevels (Fig. 15) are similar to try squares, but differ in that their blades are adjustable to any angle. They are used for laying out angles other than right angles, as, for instance, on corner braces, dovetails, or side rails for chairs.

7. The steel square measures 16 by 24 in., or 18 by 24 in., and is of the same thickness, about ⅛ in., throughout. The 24-in. part is called the "blade" or "body," and is 2 in. wide. The 16- or 18-in. part is called the "tongue," and is 1½ in. wide. The "face" of the square is the side on which the manufacturer's name is stamped. The steel square is a very important tool, especially to the carpenter, who uses it in laying out the many different cuts employed in roof framing, stair building, oblique joints, etc. The cabinetmaker uses it mostly for testing the flatness of large surfaces (Art. 225) and for testing for squareness in gluing. The uses of the steel square are so numerous and varied that whole books have been written on this subject.

Besides the divisions of the inch into eighths, tenths, twelfths, sixteenths, and thirty-seconds, which are marked on the inside and outside edges on both sides of the square, the following tables are marked on it: brace measure, octagon measure, board measure, rafter table, and the divisions of 1 in. into 100 parts.

8. The brace measure and octagon table are marked on opposite sides of the tongue. The brace measure consists of a series of three numbers. Two of the numbers are placed one above the other, and a third to the right of these as $\frac{48}{48}$ 67^{88} (Fig. 16). This means that a square having a

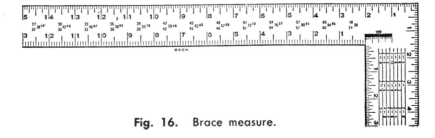

Fig. 16.   Brace measure.

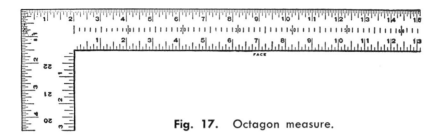

Fig. 17. Octagon measure.

side 48 in. or 48 ft. long, has a diagonal 67.88 in. or ft. long, as the case may be.

9. The octagon measure (Fig. 17) consists of a number of divisions marked along the center of the tongue. If an octagon is to be made from a square board having a side of 10 in., the octagonal shape is laid out as follows: Locate the center points on each of the four sides of the square. Set a pair of dividers equal to 10 of the spaces on the steel square, and lay off this distance on each side of the center divisions. Connect all these points across the corners of the square board, and the octagon has been completed.

The following is a simple way to lay out an octagon from a square:

1. Draw the diagonals of the square.

2. With half the diagonal as a radius, and a corner of the square as a center, draw an arc from one side of the square to the other. Repeat the process from the remaining corners.

3. Connect the end points of the arcs across the corners of the square to complete the octagon (Fig. 18).

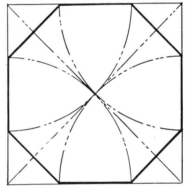

Fig. 18. To lay out an octagon from a square.

10. The board measure is marked on the blade of the square, and enables one to read off the number of board feet a board or timber contains without making any calculations (Fig. 19). Under the 12-in. mark, on the outer edge of the steel square, is a column of figures which refers to the length of the boards to be calculated. The other numbers on the inch scale, to right and left of the 12-in. mark, refer to the width of the boards.

To use the scale, read off the length of the board to be calculated, follow this line to the number indicating its width, and the result is found in the column of figures under that number. For example, a board is 7 in. wide

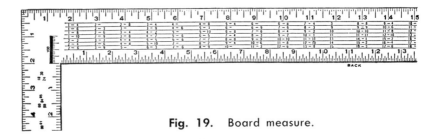

Fig. 19. Board measure.

and 10 ft. long. Find 10 under 12 on the third line; follow to the left and stop under 7. The result, 5 ft. 10 in., is found on the third line under 7. For boards larger than 15 ft., divide the length into two smaller parts, find the board feet for each of these, and add the results. For example, to find the number of board feet in a board 10 in. wide and 17 ft. long, divide the length into 8 and 9, and follow these lines to the left until 10 is reached. An 8-ft. board contains 6 ft. 8 in. and a 9-ft. board 7 ft. 6 in. Adding these figures gives a total of 14 ft. 2 in. The scale is based on 1-in. boards. For 2-in. planks, multiply the results obtained by 2.

A board 12 ft. long contains as many board feet as it is inches wide. Similarly, a 6-ft. board contains half as many board feet as it is inches wide. For this reason the numbers 6 and 12 have been omitted from the column under the 12-in. mark.

11. The rafter table is not found on all squares, but when it is given it is stamped on the blade (Fig. 20). It can be used only for roofs having standard pitches.

Before explaining the rafter table, the terms "run," "rise," and "pitch" of a rafter must be understood. By the "run" is understood the level distance below any rafter, usually half the width of the building; by the "rise," the vertical height of the rafter over the top of the walls; and by the "pitch," the ratio between the rise and twice the run. The pitch is equal to the rise

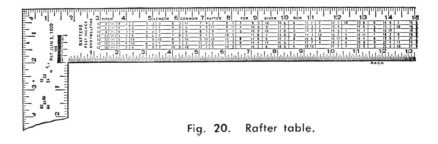

Fig. 20. Rafter table.

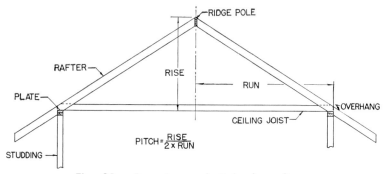

Fig. 21. Run, rise, and pitch of a rafter.

divided by twice the run (Fig. 21). A run of 12 ft. and a rise of 6 ft., therefore, give a pitch of $\%_{24} = \frac{1}{4}$. A run of 18 ft. and a rise of 6 ft. give a pitch of $\%_{36} = \frac{1}{6}$, and so on.

To use the table, determine the pitch of the roof, and read off the length of the rafter under the number on the inch scale corresponding to the length of the run. For example, a roof having a run of 12 ft. and a rise of 8 ft. has a pitch of $\frac{1}{3}$. The length of the common rafter found under 12 on the third line is 14 ft. 5½ in.

Some manufacturers of steel squares use a different form of rafter table, which shows the length of both common, hip, valley, and jack rafters. The length, however, is given per foot run only, which means that the number found on the steel square must be multiplied by the length of the run in order to obtain the total length of the rafter.

If the pitch is irregular, as 15-ft. run and 10-ft. 6-in. rise, the length of the rafter may be found by measuring across the square from 10½ on the tongue to 15 on the blade. If this measurement is made with another square, using the twelfth scale and counting each inch as a foot and each twelfth of an inch as a full inch, the length is immediately obtained in feet and inches. This method is also very convenient for measuring the length of braces.

By placing the square on the side of the rafter or brace with the numbers

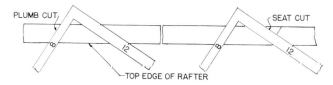

Fig. 22. Method of obtaining angles for cutting a rafter or brace.

indicating rise and run in line with one edge, the proper angles for cutting are obtained (Fig. 22).

12. A marking gauge is made of wood or steel. The one most commonly used consists of a square, wooden bar or beam, about 8 in. long, on which a wooden block or head slides (Fig. 23). This block can be fastened at any point of the bar by means of a brass setscrew bearing against a brass shoe. The block, on the better grade of gauges, is protected from wear by a piece of brass set flush with its surface. The bar is graduated in inches and provided with a steel point or spur fastened near the end with a screw. The spur must be filed to a fine point.

This tool is used for marking or gauging widths on narrow pieces of wood, such as table legs, etc. When using it, move the gauge away from you, and tip it slightly forward, keeping the block in contact with the edge or face of the board at all times.

As the spur may be easily bent out of place, most workmen disregard the graduations on the beam and measure the distance to be gauged from the spur to the face of the block with an ordinary rule.

An attachment for marking along curved edges consists of a bent piece of brass fastened to the block of the gauge.

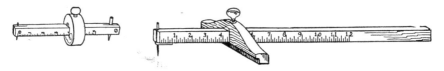

Fig. 23. Marking
gauge.

Fig. 24. Panel gauge.

13. A panel gauge is similar to a marking gauge, but has a longer block and a beam 17½ in. long (Fig. 24). It is used for gauging the width of larger pieces, such as panels.

14. A slitting gauge is similar to a panel gauge, but has a handle in addition to the block (Fig. 25). It has a knife instead of a spur and is used for cutting thin stock.

15. A mortising gauge is a marking gauge with two spurs, which can be spaced at different distances and mark two parallel lines at the same

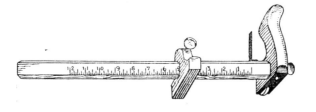

Fig. 25. Slitting
gauge.

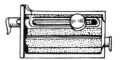

Fig. 26. Wooden mortising gauge.   **Fig. 27.** Butt gauge.

time. One type is made of rosewood and has an adjusting screw in the end of the beam (Fig. 26), which moves one of the points up or down as desired. The other side of the beam is fitted with a single point as on the ordinary marking gauge. This gauge is used chiefly for laying out mortises and tenons. Other types are made entirely of metal and have two bars.

16. A butt gauge differs from a mortising gauge in that its spurs are at the extreme ends of the beams. It can, therefore, be used in internal corners such as on a door jamb when gauging for the width of hinges. It is made of steel and has three spurs (Fig. 27).

17. Dividers or compasses consist of two slender steel bars or legs sharpened to a fine point and held together at one end either by a movable joint or a spring (Fig. 28). They are made in lengths from 6 to 10 in., and are used to scribe small circles. A pencil holder may be attached to one of the legs.

18. Trammel points consists of two steel points which can be fastened to a wooden stick or bar at any distance from each other (Fig. 29). They are used to scribe larger circles such as are needed for circular table tops. A pencil point can be fastened to one of the points. A finer tool for the same purpose, with bars made of steel, is used by draftsmen and is called a "beam compass." Trammel points may be improvised by driving two nails through a stick of wood.

19. Inside and outside calipers are similar in shape to dividers, but their legs are bent either inward or outward (Fig. 30). They are used chiefly in

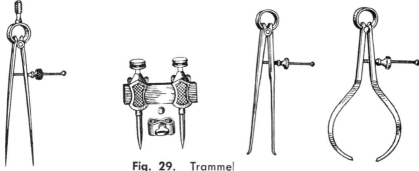

Fig. 28. Dividers.   **Fig. 29.** Trammel points.   **Fig. 30.** Inside and outside calipers.

Fig. 31.   Plumb and level.

wood turning for measuring the inside or outside diameters of turned pieces.

20. The plumb and level is used principally by the carpenter. It consists of a piece of wood, often brass bound, about 1⅜ by 3 by 26 in., into which a spirit-level glass is fastened horizontally (Fig. 31). As the glass is not quite filled, a bubble always remains. When this bubble is in the center of the glass, indicated by lines marked on it, the structure on which the level rests is absolutely horizontal or level.

Most levels also have one or two glasses set vertically to the length of the level. These are called "plumb glasses," and serve to determine if a wall or timber is placed plumb or perpendicular to the horizontal. Levels are also made with an iron body. They vary greatly in length.

21. A plumb bob is a piece of metal shaped like a boy's top (Fig. 32). A cord is attached to the thick end of the bob. It is used in building construction, to test the perpendicularity or plumbness of any structure or part thereof. Plumb bobs are also used on leveling instruments to enable the surveyor to place the instrument accurately above any point.

22. Summary.

For measuring length, we use the following tools:

1. Rules, steel or wood, straight or folding, from 2 to 8 ft. long.
2. Tapes, steel or canvas, from 25 to 100 ft. long.

For laying out angles, we use:

1. Try squares, with blades 4 to 12 in. long, for 90-deg. angles only.
2. Miter and try squares for 45- and 90-deg. angles.
3. Miter squares for 45-deg. angles only.
4. Sliding T bevels for any angle.
5. Steel squares for any angle. Steel squares have several tables engraved on the tongue and blade.

Fig. 32. Plumb bob.

For gauging lines parallel to an edge, end, or side, we use:

1. Marking gauges which mark a single line. Parts: block, beam, and spur.
2. Panel gauges which are large marking gauges.
3. Slitting gauges which cut through thin wood instead of marking.
4. Mortising gauges which mark a double line.
5. Butt gauges which can be set to three dimensions and are of steel.

For marking arcs and circles, we use:

1. Dividers for small circles and for stepping off measurements.
2. Trammel points for marking large circles.

For measuring the diameters of turned work, we use:

1. Inside calipers.
2. Outside calipers.

For laying out and testing horizontal and vertical surfaces, we use:

1. The plumb and level.
2. The plumb bob.

Saws

After measuring and laying out the portion of a board or plank wanted, the next step is to saw along the lines marked. Different types of saws are used for different sawing jobs. Some of the most common are as follows:

23. The ripsaw is used for ripping or cutting with the grain along a straight line. Blades of ripsaws vary in length from 20 to 28 in. They are always wider at the handle than at the end, in order to prevent them from bending or buckling when they are pushed through the wood (Fig. 33). The teeth of a ripsaw vary in size according to the fineness of the work to be done. Their size is indicated by the number of "points" to the inch; i.e., the number of teeth occurring in 1 in. less one. For example, a 7-point saw has 7 tooth points, but only 6 complete teeth in 1 in. The number of points a saw contains is stamped on the blade near the handle of the saw. The teeth of a ripsaw are shaped like chisel points, and their forward edges are at right angles to the length of the blade (see Fig. 6, p. 141).

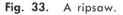 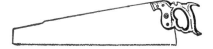

Fig. 33. A ripsaw.

24. The crosscut saw is similar in shape and appearance to the ripsaw. The only difference lies in the shape of the teeth, which are filed to a point instead of square across as on a ripsaw (see Fig. 8, p. 142). The number of points to the inch varies from 8 to 12.

The reason for this difference is that the wood fibers run lengthwise, and cannot be cut across smoothly except with a sharp knife point. A wider edge, like that of the teeth of a ripsaw, tears them apart and makes a rough and ragged cut. The wider-edged teeth, however, cut very smoothly in the same direction in which the fibers run, or with the grain. They also cut much faster than the teeth of a crosscut saw. This statement may be proved very easily and effectively by chiseling with and across the grain with a narrow chisel. A crosscut saw can be used to cut with the grain, but the work will proceed much slower than if a ripsaw is used.

All saws must be set. "Set" means to bend every other tooth to one side and the rest of the teeth to the opposite side. When the teeth are not set, the saw kerf, which is the slot the saw cuts in the wood, becomes too narrow for the saw blade to pass through without binding. Oiling or greasing the saw helps only momentarily. Setting the saw makes the saw kerf wider (Fig. 34; see Fig. 2, p. 140). A saw set (Fig. 3, p. 140) is used for setting hand saws.

The sharpening of saws is described in Article 128.

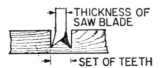

Fig. 34. Set of teeth showing clearance of saw blade.

Fig. 35. Backsaw.

Fig. 36. Dovetail saw.

25. The backsaw is a crosscut saw with a thin blade and fine teeth (Fig. 35). A heavy piece of steel fitted over the back of the thin blade prevents it from buckling. The blades of backsaws are from 8 to 18 in. long. Backsaws are used for finer work such as the cheek and shoulder cuts on tenons as described in Article 193.

26. The dovetail saw is a backsaw with a thinner, narrower blade and finer teeth (Fig. 36). The handle of a dovetail saw is like a chisel handle. The length of the blade varies from 6 to 12 in. It is used for extremely fine work such as the cutting of dovetails, as described in Article 211.

27. The compass saw is shaped like a ripsaw, but its blade is so narrow that it can cut on curved lines (Fig. 37). It is particularly useful in cutting a section from within a board or panel. A hole is bored near the line to be cut and the pointed end of the saw is inserted in this hole.

28. The keyhole saw (Fig. 38) is a smaller and finer compass saw.

Fig. 37. Compass saw.

Fig. 38. Keyhole saw, with blades for wood, metal cutting and pruning.

29. The turning saw consists of a very narrow blade, about 3/16 in. wide, which is held under tension in a frame (Fig. 39). It has ripsaw teeth and is used for cutting curves, as the blade usually can be revolved in the frame. It can also be set in the frame so that it cuts either on the pulling or the pushing stroke.

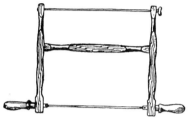

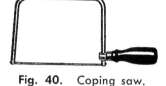

Fig. 40. Coping saw.

Fig. 39. Turning saw.

30. A coping saw is a very small turning saw usually having a metal frame (Fig. 40). It is used for sawing out fretwork patterns, and for coping moldings (Art. 208).

31. Miter boxes are made of either iron or wood. The iron miter box consists of a cast-iron frame fitted with a large backsaw, which is held perpendicular to the work by metal guides (Fig. 41). It can be adjusted to cut at any angle. It is used chiefly for mitering moldings and in picture-frame work. It is also very useful for cutting small pieces of wood at right angles.

32. A hack saw is not properly a woodworker's tool, but it is often a very convenient tool to have in the shop. It has a narrow blade set in a long, narrow metal frame, and is used for cutting metals (Fig. 42).

33. Summary. The fineness of a saw depends upon the number of *points to the inch. Set* means to bend the teeth to alternate sides to increase the width of the *saw kerf* and prevent binding. Common saws may be easily remembered when grouped in pairs.

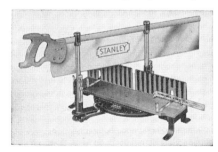

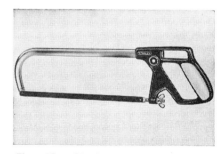

Fig. 41. Iron miter box and saw.

Fig. 42. Hack saw. Spare blades can be stored in the frame.

Ripsaw is used for sawing along the grain. Teeth are like serics of chisels.

Crosscut saw is used for sawing across the grain. Teeth are like knife points.

Backsaw is a fine crosscut saw used in making joints.

Dovetail saw is a smaller backsaw used for making dovetail joints.

Miter-box saw is a large backsaw used in iron miter boxes.

Compass saw is a small pointed ripsaw used for interior cutting.

Keyhole saw is a narrower compass saw used for interior cutting.

Turning saw has a narrower saw blade held in a wooden frame. It is used for cutting curves.

Coping saw is a small turning saw held in a metal frame. It is used for cutting curves.

Hack saw is a machinist's tool used for metal only.

Planes

After measuring and sawing a piece of lumber to rough dimensions, it is generally planed to finished dimensions.

Planes, like saws, are made in many different forms for different planing jobs. Some of the most common types are as follows:

34. The wooden plane is the oldest type of plane (Fig. 43). It consists of a heavy cutting iron wedged in a block of hardwood. Although used very little in this country, it nevertheless has some advantages over the iron plane which are well worth noting. The most important of these is that shavings from resinous woods do not adhere to the sole or bottom of the wooden plane as they do to iron planes. It is also lighter in weight, which is an important consideration if the plane has to be used for any length of time, and finally, it is cheaper and will not break if it should fall to the floor. The disadvantage of the wooden plane, however, is the difficulty of setting the plane iron correctly.

Fig. 43.
Wooden
plane.

Fig. 44.
Jack plane.

35. The jack plane is the most useful, all-round plane in the woodworker's kit (Fig. 44). It is 14 or 15 in. long, and consists of an iron body to which the plane iron can be clamped. The bottom of the plane, which is either smooth or corrugated, is called the "sole." The front part of the sole is called the "toe," and its rear part, the "heel." A casting, called the "frog," is screwed to the iron body near its center. A wooden knob is screwed to the forward part of the body, and a handle to its rear part.

The plane iron, which in a jack plane is 2 in. or 2¼ in. wide, consists of two parts, the cutter and the cap. The latter is screwed to the back or flat side of the cutter, and is used to stiffen it and to break up the shavings. The plane iron is clamped to the frog by means of another iron, corresponding to the wedge in a wooden plane, called the "lever cap." The cap is fastened about ¹⁄₃₂ in. from the cutting edge of the blade. It must fit perfectly, otherwise shavings will be forced in between the two irons and "choke" the mouth of the plane. The plane iron can be adjusted to the depth of the cut by means of a brass screw engaging a wishbonelike casting. This is called the "Y adjustment." The plane iron can be adjusted laterally or level with the sole of the plane, by a lever riveted to the top of the frog (Fig. 45).

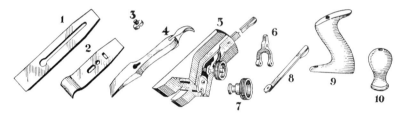

Fig. 45. Plane parts. 1, cutter iron; 2, plane-iron cap; 3, cap screw; 4, lever cap; 5, frog; 6, Y adjustment; 7, Y-adjustment screw; 8, lateral-adjustment lever; 9, handle; 10, knob.

The sole of the plane keeps the thickness of the shaving uniform. If the board to be planed is uneven, it prevents the cutting iron from touching the hollow parts until all the high parts have been leveled off. Therefore, the longer the sole, the straighter the edge that is produced. The shavings enter through a narrow slit called the "throat" or "mouth." This slit is in the sole just forward of the cutting iron. The toe of the plane presses down on the wood in front of the shaving being taken, thus preventing it from splitting ahead. The width of the throat can be narrowed by moving the frog forward.

When planing an edge or a narrow board, the entire sole of the plane should be in contact with the wood to produce a straight edge. The tendency among beginners to hold the plane obliquely should be avoided and discouraged. Oblique cutting is a little easier, but it does not produce a flat surface, because only a small part of the sole is in contact with the wood.

36. The fore plane (Fig. 46) is built exactly like a jack plane, but is 18 in. long and has a plane iron 2⅜ in. wide.

37. The jointer is also like the jack plane, but is 22 to 24 in. long, and has a plane iron 2⅜ or 2⅝ in. wide (Fig. 47). The latter two planes are used for leveling larger surfaces and for jointing the edges of boards to be glued.

Fig. 46. Fore plane.

Fig. 47. Jointer.

Fig. 48. Smooth plane.

38. The smooth plane is of the same construction as the above-named planes, but it is shorter, being from 5½ to 10 in. in length (Fig. 48). It also has narrower plane irons, from 1¼ to 2 in. It is used for planing smaller pieces and for very fine work.

Jack, smooth, fore planes, and jointers may be obtained either with smooth or corrugated bottoms.

39. The circular plane differs from the others in that it has a flexible bottom 10 in. long, which can be adjusted to either convex or concave curves (Fig. 49). It is used on curved work, such as round table tops and aprons.

Fig. 49. Circular plane.

Fig. 50. Block plane.

Fig. 51. Bullnose rabbet plane.

40. The block plane is a small plane from 4 to 8 in. long (Fig. 50). It has only a single plane iron, which is placed at a very low angle with the beveled side up. The lever cap is generally curved so that it fits smoothly within the hollow of the hand. This plane is used for planing end wood and in places where an ordinary plane could not be used.

41. The bullnose rabbet plane is about 4 in. long, and has the plane iron fastened to the extreme front of the body (Fig. 51). It is used for small and fine work.

42. The rabbet and fillister plane is an iron plane used for planing grooves or rabbets on the edges of a board (Art. 170). It has both a depth and a width gauge, as well as a spur, which scores the wood in advance of the plane iron, thereby preventing splitting (Fig. 52).

Fig. 52. Rabbet and fillister plane.

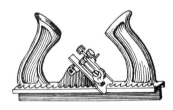

Fig. 53. Matching plane.

43. A dado plane is similar to a rabbet plane, but is used for cutting across the grain.

44. A matching plane is used for matching boards; i.e., plowing a groove on the edge of one and a tongue on the edge of the other. It has two cutters, a plow and a tongue cutter (Fig. 53).

Fig. 55. Universal plane.

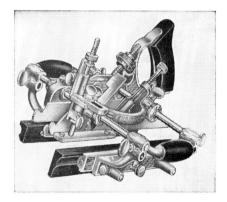

Fig. 54. Router plane.

45. The router plane (Fig. 54) is used for removing the wood between two sawed or chiseled edges such as dadoes (Art. 172) or grooves. The plane iron is lowered after each cut. It is furnished with a ¼-in., a ½-in., and a smoothing cutter.

46. The universal plane (Fig. 55) is used for planing a variety of different shaped moldings, beads, flutes, etc. Some planes have as many as 55 different and interchangeable cutters. The universal plane takes the place of as many wooden molding planes, because each molding plane can produce only one molding shape. The universal plane is rather complicated and difficult to set. With the many small and portable shapers available, the universal plane is not used so much at present.

47. Plane gauges are made both for iron and wooden planes. They can be attached to the sides of smooth, jack, fore, or jointer planes, and enable the operator to plane bevels or chamfers of any angle on the edge of a board without the continuous use of bevel or try square (Fig. 56).

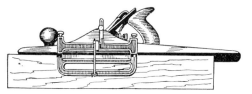

Fig. 56.   Gauge attached to plane.   **Fig. 57.**   Iron spokeshave.

48. The spokeshave is like a plane with a very short bottom (Fig. 57). It is, therefore, suitable for smoothing curves that are too small for a circular plane. Spokeshaves are made in many patterns, generally with an iron body. One type, the *patternmaker's spokeshave,* is made of wood (Fig. 58). The sharpening of plane irons is described in Article 129.

Fig. 58.   Patternmaker's
spokeshave.   **Fig. 59.**   Cabinet scraper.

49. Scrapers are of two kinds: those sharpened like a plane iron and held in an iron frame or plane body (Fig. 59), and those that have square edges and are held in the hand only (Fig. 60). The first class is called "cabinet scrapers" or "scraper planes," and the last type is called "hand scrapers" (Art. 132). Hand scrapers having curved edges are called "molding scrapers."

The action of a scraper can be likened to that of a piece of broken glass, whose sharp edges will cut fine shavings from a piece of wood. The scrapers are sharpened so that a fine, hooklike edge is formed which produces only very thin shavings.

Scrapers are used for smoothing a surface after it has been planed. Cross-grained and highly figured woods must always be scraped. As they usually can be planed only across the grain, the only tool that can be employed for smoothing them is a scraper. Veneers generally are not planed, but scraped.

All cutting and scraping should be finished before sanding. There is a good reason for this; for no matter how fine the sandpaper may be, tiny particles of quartz from the sandpaper become embedded in the surface of the wood. This is not noticeable either to the hand or eye; nevertheless these particles are sufficient to dull the edge of a sharp tool immediately.

Fig. 60. Hand scraper.

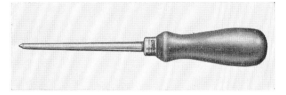

Fig. 61. Burnisher for hand scraper.

The sharpening of cabinet and hand scrapers is explained in detail in Articles 131 and 132. A necessary tool for this operation is a burnisher (Fig. 61).

50. Summary. Advantages of a wooden plane are: resinous shavings do not stick to the bottom; it is lighter in weight, cheaper, and unbreakable.

Four iron planes constructed exactly alike and differing only in size are: smooth, jack, fore, and jointer planes. Other common planes are: circular, rabbet, bullnose, block, router, and universal planes.

A spokeshave is often mistaken for a cabinet scraper, because these tools look a good deal alike, but a spokeshave is in fact a small plane. Scrapers are of two kinds, those with square edges and those with beveled edges.

Chisels

When a board has been planed to dimensions, the next operation usually is to join it to some other board or part of a structure. A chisel, in conjunction with other tools, is indispensable in the construction of most joints made by hand. It is indeed one of the most important and most used of woodworking tools.

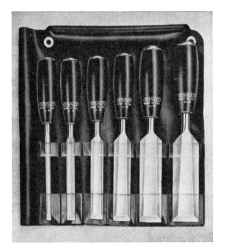

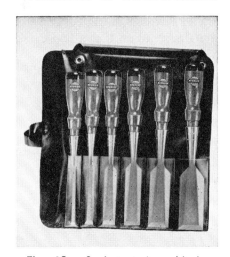

Fig. 62. Tang paring chisels.   **Fig. 63.** Socket paring chisels.

According to their construction, chisels may be divided into two general classes: *tang chisels,* in which part of the chisel enters the handle (Fig. 62), and *socket chisels,* in which the handle enters into a part of the chisel (Fig. 63).

According to their use, chisels are divided into the following classes:

51. The firmer chisel, which has a strong blade, may be used for both heavy and light work (Fig. 63).

52. The paring chisel, which has a slender blade, is used mainly for hand chiseling (Fig. 62). This type of chisel usually is beveled along the sides, so that fine work can be done, such as reeding (Art. 278) which requires an extra-thin blade.

53. The framing chisel has a very heavy and strong blade, and is used in rough carpentry work and shipbuilding. It often has an iron ring around the end of the handle instead of a leather cap.

54. The butt chisel (Fig. 64) differs from the others only in that it has a shorter blade and, therefore, can be used in more inaccessible places. It is commonly used in chiseling gains for hinges.

The above-named chisels are made in widths of from ⅛ to 2 in.

Fig. 64. Butt chisel.

55. The mortise chisel, as its name implies, is used for chiseling mortises. It is, therefore, very thick just below the handle so that it will not break when it is used as a lever in forcing the shavings out of the mortise (Fig. 88, p. 229).

If the mortise is bored, it may be cleaned out and squared with an ordinary firmer chisel as described in Article 193.

The parts of a chisel are: the blade, on the end of which one bevel is ground; the shank, which is the upper narrow part of the blade; the socket, which is the end of the blade, shaped like a hollow cone, and in which the tapered end of the wooden handle fits. In tang chisels, the shank ends in a sharp point called the "tang," which is driven into the end of the handle. A projection on the shank, called a "shoulder," butts against the end of the handle and prevents the tang from entering farther. A brass or iron ring, called the "ferrule," fits on the lower end of the handle and prevents it from splitting. Chisel handles are often leather tipped to protect them from the blows of the mallet.

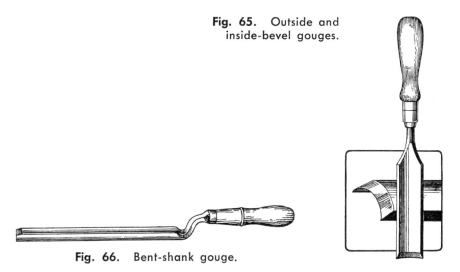

Fig. 65. Outside and inside-bevel gouges.

Fig. 66. Bent-shank gouge.

56. Gouges are like chisels, except that their blades are bent lengthwise, so that in cross section they appear as a part of a circle. If the bevel is ground on the convex side, they are called "outside-bevel gouges" (Fig. 65), and if it is ground on the concave side, they are called "inside-bevel gouges." Some inside-bevel gouges have a bent shank, which is of advantage in giving room for the hand. This type of gouge is called "bent-shank gouge" (Fig. 66).

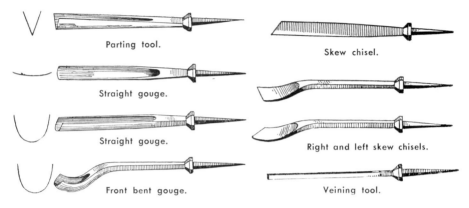

Fig. 67. Carving tools.

57. Carving tools (Fig. 67) are made in numerous different shapes. Many of these are gouges of different diameters and bend, others are chisels, but having two bevels; and still others have their blade bent lengthwise into a sharp angle, and are known as "veining tools." Veining tools are very useful, not only for wood carving, but also for two toning (Art. 289). Chisels with an oblique cutting edge are called **skew chisels** (Fig. 67). The sharpening of chisels is described in Article 129. For description of turning chisels and how to sharpen them, see Article 134.

58. The drawknife is used for rough cutting, especially on both edges, both straight and curved. It is a tool with a long blade whose cutting edge is on the side. At each end of the blade is a handle (Fig. 68). The operator grips the handles and draws the knife toward him.

Fig. 68.   Drawknife.

59. Summary.   According to their construction, chisels are divided into socket and tang chisels. According to their use, we have the following chisels: framing chisels for heavy, rough work; firmer chisels for all-round work; paring chisels for fine work; butt chisels for cutting gains for hinges, etc.; mortise chisels for cutting mortises.

Other types of chisels are: gouges, straight or bent shank with bevels ground either inside or outside; carving tools, wood-turning chisels, and the drawknife.

Boring Tools

The woodworking and metal trades distinguish sharply between bits and drills and between boring and drilling.

Woodworkers never say that a hole is *drilled* in wood, but use the term *bored* instead.

The woodworker uses bits for boring holes for screws, dowels, and hardware, as an aid in mortising and in shaping curves and for many other purposes. As was the case with saws, planes, and chisels, bits vary in shape and structure with the type of work to be done. Some of the most common bits are the following:

60. Auger bits are screw-shaped tools consisting of two main parts, the twist and the shank (Fig. 69). The twist ends in two sharp points, the nibs or spurs, which score the circle, and two cutting edges, the lips, which remove the shavings from within the scored circle. A small screw point, in the center of the cutting end, centers the bit and draws it into the wood (Fig. 70). The threads of this screw are made in three different pitches — steep, medium, and fine. The steep pitch means quick boring and thick chips, and the fine or slight pitch means slow boring and fine chips. For end-wood boring, a steep- or medium-pitch screw should be used because end wood is likely to be forced in between the fine screw threads, and that prevents the screw from taking hold (Fig. 70).

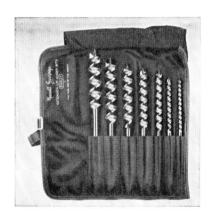

Fig. 69.
Auger bits.

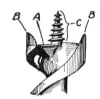

Fig. 70. End of auger bit.
A, lips; B, nibs; C, screw
medium pitch.

The shank ends in a square-tapered tang, which is held by the chuck of the brace. The sizes of auger bits are indicated in sixteenths of an inch and are stamped on the tang. Number 10 means, therefore, 10/16 or ⅝ in.; 4 means 4/16 or ¼ in., and so on. Auger bits are made in sizes from 3/16 to 1 in. by sixteenths of an inch. The common woodworker's set ranges in size from ¼ to 1 in.

61. Dowel bits are short auger bits 4½ in. long over-all. Ordinary auger bits up to 1 in. in diameter are from 7 to 9 in. long over-all.

62. Car bits and ship augers are auger bits from 18 to 24 in. in length.

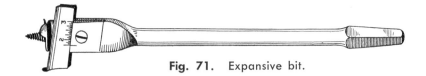

Fig. 71.   Expansive bit.

63. Expansive bits have a movable cutter, which is adjustable to bore holes of different diameters (Fig. 71). Expansive bits are made in two sizes. The largest size has three cutters, and bores holes up to 4 in. in diameter. On some expansive bits the cutter can be moved sidewise by means of a screw.

64. Foerstner bits have no twist and no screw. They cut with a sharp circular steel rim and two lips within this rim (Fig. 72). They bore very accurately, and are especially useful for boring thin wood and for endwood boring. Moreover, when boring near the end of a piece of stock, a Foerstner bit is less likely to split the wood than an auger bit, the screw of which is wedge shaped. Their sizes are stamped on the tangs in sixteenths of an inch.

Fig. 72.   Foerstner bit.

Fig. 73.   Gimlet bit.

65. Gimlet or German gimlet bits (Fig. 73) are used for boring holes of small diameters such as are needed when inserting screws in hardwood (see Art. 239). Their size, which varies from ¹⁄₁₆ to ³⁄₈ in. by thirty-seconds, is stamped on the tang. Number 6 stamped on the tang therefore means 6/32 or ³⁄₁₆ in. Their cutting edge is on the side and cannot be resharpened.

66. Twist bits are superior to gimlet bits. Their cutting edges are on the end and can be resharpened (Fig. 74). They range in size from ¹⁄₁₆ to ⅝ in. by thirty-seconds. The full fraction usually is stamped on the tang.

67. Twist drills are shaped like twist bits, but their cutting edges are not ground to as steep an angle. As the name implies, they are made for drilling in metal, but can also be used for wood. Twist drills used by machinists have only a round shank and can be held only in the chuck of a hand drill (Fig. 75). Twist drills used by woodworkers have a square shank like the

Fig. 74.   Twist bit.    Fig. 75.   Twist drill.

other bits and are called bit-stock drills. They break more easily than twist bits. Twist drills are made in the same sizes as twist bits with the full fraction usually stamped on the round shank.

68. The bradawl has the appearance of a small screw driver (Fig. 76). It is used for making holes into wood for screws and nails. The hole is produced by forcing the awl into the wood with a twisting motion. It should not be used in thin wood nor too near the edge. It forces the wood fibers apart, but does not cut any shavings.

Fig. 76. Bradawl.   **Fig. 77.** Rose countersink.

69. The countersink is a small, cone-shaped tool used for widening the end of holes bored for flathead screws (Fig. 77).

The combination wood drill and countersink (Fig. 78), performs three boring operations at once. The tool acts as a countersink, and drills the shank and pilot holes.

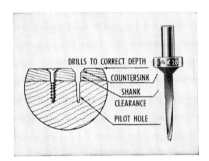

Fig. 78. Combination wood drill and countersink.   **Fig. 79.** Plug cutter.   **Fig. 80.** Circle cutter.

70. Plug cutters and circle cutters (Figs. 79 and 80) are used to cut circular disks from wood or leather. Such small disks are sometimes used to plug up holes in wood.

71. The plain brace is a tool used for holding a bit securely while boring a hole. At one end the brace has a chuck for clamping the bit. The chuck consists of two jaws and a sleeve which fits over the jaws and brings them together when turned to the right. At the other end is a knob which turns on ball bearings. The handle of the brace is shaped like a crank.

72. The ratchet brace (Fig. 81) is fitted with an attachment which permits boring in places where a complete turn cannot be made. The size of braces is given according to the *sweep;* i.e., the diameter of the circle that the handle makes in a complete revolution.

Fig. 82.   Bit-brace extension.

Fig. 81.   Ratchet brace.

73. A bit-brace extension is a steel rod having a small chuck on one end and a square shank like a bit on the other (Fig. 82). A bit, ⅝ in. or more in diameter, is inserted into the chuck of the extension, and this in turn into the chuck of the brace. The smallest hole that can be bored with this tool measures ⅝ in. Bit-brace extensions are made from 12 to 21 in. in length. The smallest hole than can be bored with the larger size measures ¾ in.

74. Auger-bit gauges of different types can be fastened to auger bits, and adjusted so that only holes of certain depths are bored (Fig. 83).

A wooden depth gauge (Fig. 84) can be easily made by any woodworker. It is especially useful on dowel bits which are too short for the regular auger-bit gauge.

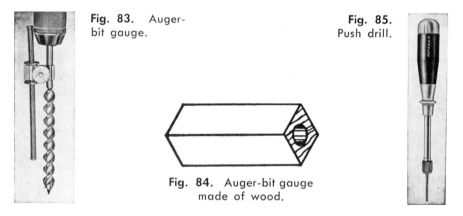

Fig. 83.   Auger-bit gauge.

Fig. 85.   Push drill.

Fig. 84.   Auger-bit gauge made of wood.

75. Automatic drills and reciprocating drills.   The automatic drill bores when it is pushed into the wood. The reciprocating drill bores both with the up and down strokes of the driver. A magazine for small drill points usually is found in the handle of these tools (Fig. 85). Fluted drills with specially shaped top ends are used with the automatic drill. Ordinary round-shank drills up to ³⁄₁₆ in. can be used with the reciprocating drill. They are used for rapid boring of small-size holes.

76. The hand drill (Fig. 86) is really a machinist's tool. Its chuck has three jaws and holds only straight-shank drills. When a brad has to be driven into hardwood, a hole may be bored for it with a brad of the same size held in the chuck of the hand drill. The head of the brad is cut off before inserting it in the chuck. In this way, fine drills, which break easily, are saved for more important work.

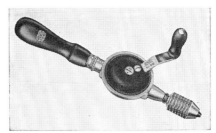

Fig. 86. Hand drill.

77. Summary. The most important boring tool is the auger bit. It has the following parts: screw, which centers the bit and draws it into the wood; nibs, which score the circle; lips, which cut the shavings; shank, and square tang. The sizes ³⁄₁₆ to 1 in., by sixteenths, are stamped on the tang.

Dowel bits are short auger bits; car bits are long auger bits. Screws of auger bits have fine, medium, and coarse threads.

Foerstner bits have no screw. They are useful for boring in end wood and thin stock. They are made in the same sizes as auger bits.

Expansive bits bore holes up to 3 or 4 in. in diameter.

Gimlet bits, twist bits, twist drills, and brad awls bore small holes for screws.

Countersinks enlarge the tops of screw holes for flathead screws.

Plug and washer cutters cut small disks of wood or leather.

Extension-bit holder is used for boring long holes ⅝ in. or more in diameter. The brace holds square-shank bits. Its parts are: chuck with sleeve and two jaws, ratchet, handle, and knob. "Sweep" means diameter of circle which the handle of the brace makes in boring.

Automatic drills and reciprocating drills are used for rapid boring of small holes. Fluted and straight-shank drills should be used. A hand drill is a machinist's tool.

Auger-bit gauges are used for boring holes to uniform depth.

Miscellaneous Tools

78. Plain screw drivers are made with blades from 2 to 18 in. in length. The blades in the better grades are welded to a long steel ferrule, thereby preventing the possibility of turning in the handle (Fig. 87). A long screw driver is more powerful than a short one, because the long handle gives more leverage. The end of the screw driver should be flat and square and it'should fit the slot in the screw to be driven. Screw drivers which are too thin for the slot or have rounded edges climb out of the slot and damage its edges.

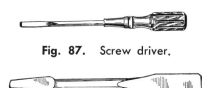

Fig. 87. Screw driver.

Fig. 88. Automatic screw driver.

Fig. 89. Screw-driver bit.

79. Automatic screw drivers are built on the same principle as automatic drills. A ratchet arrangement permits them to drive in one direction and release in the other. The best types can both drive and withdraw screws. They can also be locked so as to act as plain screw drivers (Fig. 88).

80. Screw-driver bits are screw-driver blades, the upper ends of which have been forged to a square, tapered shank (Fig. 89). They are used with a brace. These bits are 5 in. long and from ¼ to ½ in. wide at the point.

81. The claw hammer is the type of hammer generally used by carpenters and woodworkers. It has two parts, the head and the handle. The

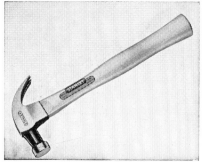

Fig. 90. Claw hammers: left, with neoprene grip; right, with wooden handle.

end of the head, used for striking blows, is called the face; the other end is the peen. The peen of this hammer is bent and shaped so that it can be used for pulling nails (Fig. 90). Hammers used in other trades have peens of different shapes used for other purposes, as for example, the ball-peen hammer. The face of the hammer often is slightly convex, or bell-faced, so that it will not make a circular mark on the surface of the wood after striking the last blow on the head of a nail. It is important to keep the face of the hammer clean and free from grease or glue, so that it will not glance off the head of a nail and bend it. It can be cleaned by rubbing it over a piece of emery paper. The size of the hammer is indicated by the weight of the head in pounds and ounces.

Fig. 91.   Crow or ripping bar.

When large nails must be removed from heavy timbers, the crow or ripping bar is an indispensable tool (Fig. 91).

82. Nail sets are small steel bars about 4 to 5 in. long and ¼ in. in diameter (Fig. 92). They have a cup-shaped point, and are used to set nails below the surface. The size of the point varies with the size of the nail to be set.

Fig. 92.   Nail set.

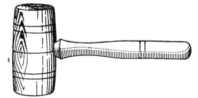

Fig. 93.   Mallet.

83. Mallets are wooden hammers (Fig. 93). As wood is more elastic than iron or steel, a mallet should always be used when driving on wood. The blows of a steel hammer would soon splinter a chisel handle and mar a joint to be driven together beyond repair. A mallet with a head 3 in. in diameter and 5 in. long is a good size for woodworkers.

84. Hatchets are used chiefly by carpenters in shingling and lathing. They have a short handle, a sharp edge for cutting shingles and laths to width and length, a hammer head for driving nails, and a slot for pulling them (Fig. 94).

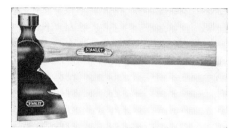

Fig. 94. Hatchet.

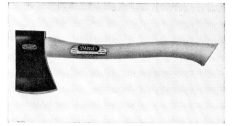

Fig. 95. Hunter's ax.

85. The ax and the adze have long handles which are held with both hands. The ax is used for felling trees and splitting log sections (Fig. 95). If it has two cutting edges, it is called a two-bitted ax (Fig. 96). The adze is used for squaring logs, in shipbuilding, etc. (Fig. 97).

86. Rasps and files are used by the woodworker for reducing and smoothing edges that cannot be easily worked with a cutting tool. Saw files and auger-bit files also are used for sharpening saws, auger bits, and the point on marking gauges.

Fig. 96. Two-bitted ax.

Fig. 97. Adze.

Files are made in more than three thousand different varieties. They have teeth or serrations of various degrees of fineness and pattern, but diagonally across their surfaces. Rasps have triangular projections, and cut much faster than files.

To clean a rasp or file see Article 141. Store them as shown in Figure 98.

Files are used in many different trades and for many different purposes. They are classified according to the shape of their cross section, as square, round, triangular, flat, half round, etc.; according to the manner in which the serrations or teeth are cut, as single cut (oblique parallel lines across the surface), double cut (two sets of parallel lines crossing each other obliquely), and open cut (oblique parallel lines, slightly broken); according to fineness of cut, as coarse, bastard, second cut, smooth, and dead smooth; according to length (not including the tang) usually from 3 to 14 in.; and according to outline, as blunt (having the same cross section throughout), and taper (Fig. 98).

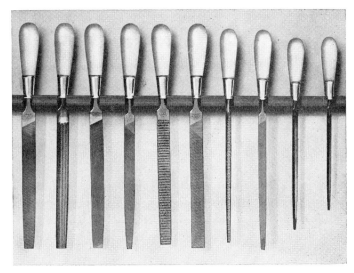

Fig. 98. Files and storage rack.

Flat files having no teeth on one or both edges are said to have one or two safe edges as the case may be.

The surface of rasps is covered with rough, triangular points or projections, called "teeth" (Fig. 99). Rasps cut faster but rougher than files. They should, therefore, be used before files. When measuring the length of files and rasps, the tang should not be included.

The use of rasps or files on wood should be discouraged, except on special work as chairmaking or where it is impossible or impractical to use a cutting tool.

The woodworker also uses various saw files, usually triangular, for sharpening saws, and the auger-bit file for sharpening auger bits (Fig. 100).

Recently a tool has been perfected, manufactured under the trade name "Surform," which at first glance looks like a typical wood rasp. Closer observation reveals that its cutting surface is made quite differently. This new tool is made of thin, hard tool steel. In the steel blade a series of razor sharp teeth have been cut. The openings made by the teeth serve for the quick disposal of filed particles. In operations where excess material must be removed without the need of a perfectly smooth surface, these tools

Fig. 99. Rasp.

Fig. 100. Single-cut auger bit file.

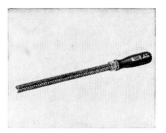

Fig. 101. "Surform" tools: left, flat, forming; center, plane; right, round file.

readily form the edges of plywood, wood, leather, plastics, composition board, asphalt tile, sheet rock, aluminum, copper, and even mild steel. The secret of this tool lies in the hardness of the steel used and the non-clogging feature. "Surform" tools are available in the flat file type, plane type, and the rattail or round file type (Fig. 101).

Clamps for holding the work together while gluing are made in various sizes and of several kinds. The most important are: bar clamps, C clamps, column clamps, and hand screws.

87. Steel bar clamps consist of a steel beam or bar fitted with a screw and crank at one end, and a steel head which can be moved along the bar and fastened to it by means of slots cut into its lower edge or side at short intervals (Fig. 102). Another type has a smooth bar, to which the steel head is clamped by means of steel disks and a spring. Steel bar clamps are made in lengths of 2, 2½, 3, 4, 5, 6, 7, and 8 ft. (Arts. 225, 226, 229, 230).

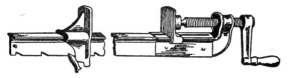

Fig. 102. Steel bar clamp.

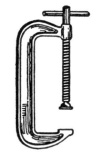

Fig. 103. C clamp.

88. C clamps, or screw clamps, sometimes called "carriage-maker's clamps," consist of a malleable-iron frame, bent in the shape of the letter C, and a steel screw with a swivel tip (Fig. 103). They are made in sizes which, when open, measure from 3 to 12 in.

89. Column clamps consist of a steel chain and a right and left screw. They are very useful when gluing together polygons, shaped columns, and any circular work such as the apron for a round table. The newer column clamps have either a steel or canvas band (see Fig. 13, p. 300).

90. Hand screws are most useful both in clamping up finished work and in holding work under construction (Arts. 159 and 205). They consist of two jaws made of hardwood and two steel spindles, the end and middle spindles (Fig. 104). They are opened or closed by grasping a handle in each hand and revolving the hand screw. The size of a hand screw is indicated by the length of the jaw in inches, the smallest being 6 in. and the largest 18 in.

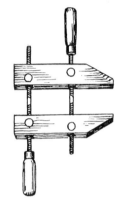 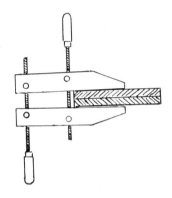

Fig. 104. Hand screw.   **Fig. 105.** Tightening hand screw.

When tightening up hand screws on straight work, the middle spindle should first be tightened so that the jaws hold firmly at that point, but are a little open at the end (Fig. 105). When the end spindle is now tightened, the jaws will come together at the end and be parallel.

Fig. 106. Carpenter's pincers.   **Fig. 107.** Tinner's snips.

91. Carpenter's pincers (Fig. 106) are used for pulling nails. A crescent wrench, tinner's snips (Fig. 107), cutting pliers or nippers (Fig. 108), and gas pliers (Fig. 109), although not woodworkers' tools, will be found very convenient and useful in the woodworking shop.

Fig. 108. Side-cutting
        pliers.

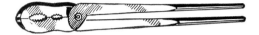

Fig. 109. Gas pliers.

92. Summary. Tools that cannot readily be classified or grouped together are:

1. Screw drivers, automatic screw drivers and screw-driver bits.
2. Carpenter's hammers having a rounded face called "bell face" and a claw for pulling nails called the "peen."
3. Nail sets with cup-shaped ends for driving nails below the surface.
4. Mallets used for driving on chisel handles.
5. Hatchets having a cutting edge, a hammer head, and a slot for pulling nails.
6. Axes and adzes for felling trees and squaring logs.
7. Files which are classified according to shape of cross section, length, serrations, fineness, blunt or taper, and safe edge.
8. Rasps which are coarse files with triangular-shaped teeth.
9. Clamps for holding work while gluing: iron bar clamps, C clamps, column clamps, and hand screws.
10. Carpenter's pincers for pulling nails, monkey wrench, tinner's snips, and pliers which are really metalworking tools, but convenient to have in a woodworking shop.

93. Tool Storage Facilities and Home Workshops. In recent years a great deal of thought has been given to the proper storage of tools, whether it is in the home workshop or in the school laboratory. The simple tool cabinet shown in Figure 110 was probably adequate half a century ago. But the modern home workshop with one or more power tools and their numerous accessories needs many more carefully planned storage facilities (Fig. 111).

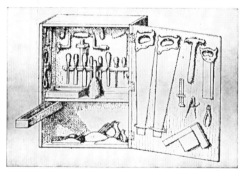

Fig. 110. Early one-door
tool cabinet.

Fig. 111.
Home workshop,
with Deltashop as
the main power
source.

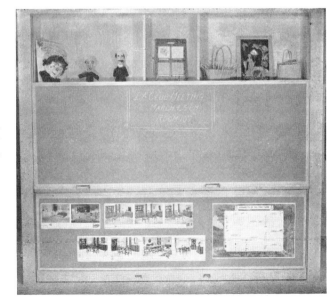

Fig. 112.
Sliding door
tool cabinet.

Fig. 113. Tool cabinet. Lower drawers for storage of supplies and small tools. Pivot doors provide additional tool storage.

Industrial arts teachers have for many years recognized the fact that the key to successful teaching is good planning and proper organization. Good tool storage is a part of good organization. Although this can be accomplished in many ways, the basic idea is to have a specific place for each tool.

Tools are often stored in wall cabinets, with vertical sliding doors (Fig. 112). Generally, when the cabinet is closed, the upper door can be used as a blackboard, while the lower door is made to serve as a bulletin board. When floor space is at a premium the closed tool cabinet may prove more suitable (Fig. 113). When the doors are opened, one can see at a glance that the tools inside have been placed with a minimum of space loss. Not

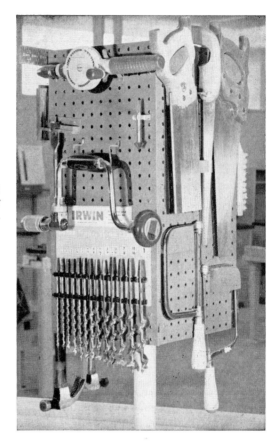

Fig. 114. Rotating
tool storage unit for
the general shop.

only are the back, sides, and doors used for tool storage, but also the two inside, pivoting doors.

Figure 114 shows a method of open tool storage. In a general shop where numerous activities are carried on, an elaborate tool cabinet is not necessary. The rotating storage unit shown here is placed in the center of a 4-station workbench. Some cabinets have casters, making it possible for the units to be rolled from one location to another. Particularly in elementary craftwork movable tool cabinets are popular. The limited amount of manipulative activity carried on in the grades does not warrant permanently installed tool cabinets.

With the continuing popularity of woodworking as a hobby and leisure activity, great strides have recently been made in the layout and design of home workshops. With the development of small individual and multi-purpose woodworking machines, a modern well-equipped home workshop often is a veritable show place. For example, the atmosphere of the basement workshop shown in Figure 111 seems much more conducive to creative family activity than the workshop of years ago (Fig. 115).

Fig. 115.   Early American workshop.

REVIEW QUESTIONS, CHAPTER 2

Possible score 55 points

Your score . . . . . .

PART I. COMPLETION QUESTIONS.   Complete the following statements:

1. Modern woodworking benches have from one to . . . . work stations.
2. For the convenience of students, modern workbenches are provided with storage . . . .
3. Modern bench stops can be adjusted for height by means of a . . . .
4. A handy device for doing hand coping saw work is a . . . .
5. To avoid cutting into the bench top, one should use a . . . .
6. Try squares consist of two parts, the stock and the ; . . . .
8. The steel or framing square is an indispensable tool to the . . . .
7. A testing tool that combines several tools into one is the . . . .

9. A geometric figure with eight equal sides is called an ....
10. A tool similar to a marking gauge but with a longer block and beam is called a ....
11. A tool especially used when gauging for the width and thickness of hinges is called a ....
12. A tool used to scribe large circles beyond the size that can be laid out with ordinary dividers is called ....
13. To measure the inside diameter of turned work, one uses ....
14. The tool used to cut with the grain along a straight line is a ....
15. The number stamped on a saw indicates the number of .... per inch.
16. Saw teeth, in order to cut properly, need a certain amount of ....
17. To cut moldings and picture frames at 45 degree angles, one best uses a ....
18. A most useful and all-round plane is the ....
19. Small planes from 4 to 6 in. long are called ....
20. To smooth a hard wood surface, after it has been planed, one uses a ....

PART II. TRUE-FALSE QUESTIONS. Indicate, by encircling T or F, whether the following statements are true or false:

21. A burnisher is a tool used to turn the edge of a scraper blade.   T   F
22. Butt chisels are like other chisels except that they have long blades.   T   F
23. Carving tools are made in a great variety of shapes and sizes.   T   F
24. Drawknives work best by pushing the knife edge away from the operator.   T   F
25. The speed by which an auger bit bores a hole is determined by the shape of the twist.   T   F
26. Numbers stamped on the tang of an auger bit indicate the size of hole that can be bored with the bit.   T   F
27. Dowel bits are longer than ordinary auger bits.   T   F
28. Twist drills are primarily used to drill holes in metal.   T   F
29. An auger bit gauge measures the size of auger bits.   T   F
30. The handle of many hand drills provides for convenient storage of drill points.   T   F

PART III. MULTIPLE-CHOICE QUESTIONS. Select, by encircling the correct letter, the answer which completes each statement:

31. To remove large nails from heavy timbers one best uses:
    A. Crowbar
    B. Claw hammer
    C. Hatchet
    D. Pliers
32. When sharpening the teeth of a hand crosscut saw one uses:
    A. A flat mill file
    B. A triangular file
    C. A round file
    D. A rasp

33. When clamping up a project with circular parts, one best uses:
    A. Canvas column clamps
    B. Steelbar clamps
    C. Hand screws
    D. C clamps
34. When removing surplus wood from a dado one uses:
    A. Rabbet plane
    B. Block plane
    C. Chisel
    D. Router plane
35. In roof construction, the level distance below any rafter, or half the width of a building is called:
    A. Pitch
    B. Slope
    C. Rise
    D. Run

PART IV. MATCHING QUESTIONS. Match the terms to the left with the descriptions to the right by placing the correct letter in the parentheses:

36. ( ) Rise
37. ( ) Pitch
38. ( ) Mortising gauge
39. ( ) Plumb bob
40. ( ) Saw kerf
41. ( ) Y adjustment
42. ( ) Sole
43. ( ) Rabbet plane
44. ( ) Molding scrapers
45. ( ) Tang

A. A marking gauge with two spurs.
B. The slot cut by the teeth of a saw.
C. Used to cut grooves or rabbets.
D. The ratio between the rise and twice the run.
E. The bottom of a plane.
F. Scrapers with curved edges.
G. The vertical height of a rafter over the top of the walls.
H. That part of a chisel that is driven into the handle.
I. Used to test the perpendicularity of a structure.
J. Wishbone like casting which helps to adjust the plane iron for depth of cut.
K. Used to plane a variety of different shaped moldings.
L. Removes shavings from within the scored circle.

PART V. PROBLEMS. Locate and calculate the answers to the following problems:

46. On a steel framing square locate the brace measure for squares with respective sides of 33, 42, 51, and 60 feet.
47. On the blade of a steel framing square locate the board foot measurements of boards 9, 10, 14, and 15 feet long, and respectively 4, 6, 8, and 10 inches wide.
48. If the pitch of a roof is determined by the ratio between the rise and twice the run, what is the pitch when rise and run are respectively:
    4 and 8 feet?   **6 and 18 feet?**

3

Machine Tools

During recent years there has been considerable progress in the field of woodworking machinery. Particular attention has been given to greater safety for the operator, and to convenience and ease in both the "setting up" and the operation of the machinery. Old types of production machines have been improved, and new types have been invented. Moreover, numerous types of portable machines have been developed.

For the home craftsman and hobbyist so-called multipurpose machines have been developed. These incorporate within one unit several operations generally performed by separate machines. From the standpoint of versatility, space requirement, and cost they are becoming increasingly popular. For a more complete discussion of them see pages 117–132 of this chapter.

Since woodworking machinery is very dangerous to operate, improvements and inventions that will safeguard the operator are of the greatest importance. Some of the most notable advances have been cylindrical cutter heads on hand planers, safety switches, improved guarding devices, and the elimination of fast-moving belts through direct motor drives.

Developments within the field of production machinery have completely revolutionized the furniture industry, and have made cabinet-making in its century-old form one of the disappearing trades. In large furniture factories, handwork has been reduced to a minimum, because machines have been invented which can be operated by semiskilled workers. Such machines perform practically all tool operations faster, better, and more uniformly than the skilled workman can by hand methods.

While a discussion of production machinery is interesting, both from a mechanical and a commercial point of view, it cannot be covered in this book, which deals mainly with handwork, hand tools, and the simpler and more commonly used woodworking machines and operations.

The development of the small and portable machines, on the other hand, is of interest to the manufacturer and the individual workman, as well as to students of woodworking, and the increasing number of amateurs, who find recreation, satisfaction, and joy in manual work. Large up-to-date factories have found it to their advantage to distribute a number of these small machines among their benchworkers, because they help to speed up production by eliminating practically all handsawing and planing.

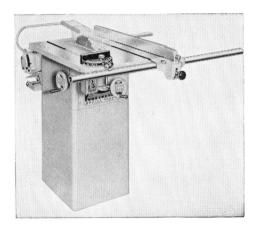

Fig. 1. 10-in. tilting arbor saw with full-floating, frictionless, rolling motor drive.

For the same reasons, contractors and individual workmen use them not only for sawing and planing, but also for routing, shaping, boring, and sanding.

This type of machinery has also become very popular in schools, especially those of junior grade where the work is usually limited to size.

A school shop equipped with woodworking machinery generally has a circular saw, a band saw or a jig saw, a jointer, one or more lathes, a drill press, and a tool grinder. These machines are basic, because they are the most useful in a general woodworking course and are in fact indispensable in any commercial shop. Trade, technical, and vocational schools may also have one or more of the following: a thickness planer, a cutoff saw, a mortiser, a boring machine, a shaper, a router, various types of sanding machines, and a wood trimmer.

96. The circular saw is, no doubt, the most useful and indispensable of

Fig. 2. Heavy-duty double-arbor universal saw.

Fig. 3. Variety saw with a mortising attachment.

woodworking machines. Besides the regular ripping and crosscutting operations, for which this machine is especially built, many other operations such
as cutting of grooves, rabbets, dadoes, tenons, miters, tapers, etc., may be
performed on the circular saw. On smaller machines shaping of straight
moldings may be done.

Circular saws are made in many sizes from the large production machines
to the small bench saws, which are fastened to heavy wooden tables or iron
stands in order to bring the saw table up to the proper working height, which
is about 36 in. (Fig. 1). The most common saws are the *universal* saw and
the *variety* saw (Figs. 2, 3, and 4).

A circular saw consists of a heavy casting to which an iron table with a
smooth, level surface is fastened. The universal circular saw, Figure 2, has
two saw arbors supported on a saw-arbor yoke, which can be revolved by
means of a handwheel, both when the machine is stationary and in motion.
Two saws, therefore, can be used on this machine at the same time, and
either one brought into action when desired. Each saw can be adjusted and
clamped at different heights above the table.

The variety saw has only one saw arbor. It is generally a smaller machine
than the universal saw, but is similar in construction (Fig. 4). Some variety
saws are equipped with a mortising and boring attachment (Fig. 3).

The older circular saws were belt driven, but the newer ones have what
is termed "a motor on arbor drive," which means that the saw arbor is the

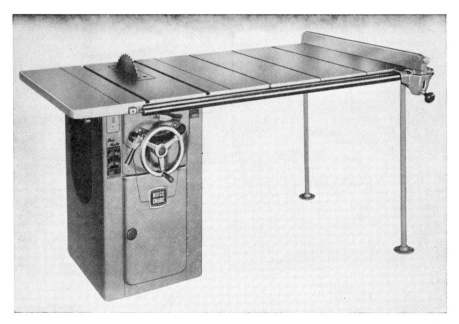

Fig. 4. Popular medium size 10-in. tilting arbor circular saw.

rotor of the motor (Fig. 5). Its projecting end has a *left* screw thread for the nut which clamps the saw blade between two large collars, one fixed to the arbor, the other loose. Since the saw arbor turns to the right or clockwise, it will be impossible for a "left" nut to work loose.

The table on some models consists of two parts. The larger one to the right of the saw blade is stationary and the smaller one to the left is movable

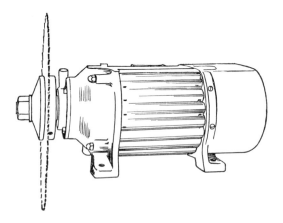

Fig. 5. Saw arbor as rotor of a motor.

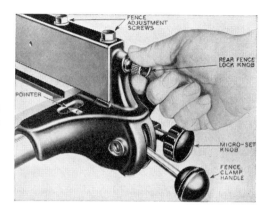

Fig. 6. Typical adjustments on a ripping fence.

both lengthwise and crosswise. The lengthwise movement past the saw is for crosscutting wide boards; the crosswise movement is simply for changing saws and for making room for thick grooving saws and dado heads. The table is mounted on roller bearings for the lengthwise movement.

Some tables are made in one solid piece and are, therefore, provided with throat plates which can be removed when changing saws. A throat plate is a soft metal casting which fits into an opening cut for it in the iron table. Each throat plate has a slot through which the saw blade projects. Several throat plates with slots of different widths are furnished. Quite often they are made in the shop, using a piece of hardwood such as birch or maple.

On the latest circular saws the saw blade and, therefore, the whole motor is tilted while the table is fixed in a horizontal position. On the universal saw, the whole yoke carrying the two motors is tilted (Fig. 2). While the current is on, only the motor carrying the saw above the table rotates; the other is automatically cut off. Circular saws with tilting saw blades are safer to operate than the ones with tilting tables, because the operator need not stand in an awkward position to hold the stock on the table. Another good safety device on modern saws is a brake which automatically stops the saw when the current is cut off.

A circular saw is equipped with three types of fences or gauges for ripping, crosscutting, and mitering.

The ripping fence is a rectangular casting, which may be fastened to the saw table on either side of the saw. It is used mostly on the stationary part or right side of the table. It is fastened parallel to the line of the saw for ordinary ripping, and may be tilted to any angle between 45 and 90 deg. It may be easily and quickly adjusted to rip any width up to 26 in., depending upon the size of the machine. The ripping fence usually can be set

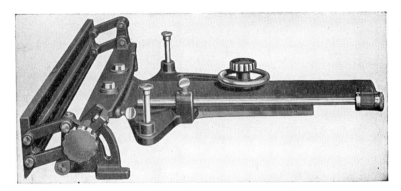

Fig. 7.   Tilting fence with micrometer adjustment.

according to a scale engraved in the table. It is generally fitted with a very accurate micrometer adjustment (Figs. 6 and 7).

The ripping fence is used for any lengthwise cutting such as ordinary ripping, grooving, rabbeting, or tapering.

The miter cutoff gauge (Fig. 8) is used for crosscutting or mitering wide boards, and is fastened near the end of the movable table. It is instantly located at the most common angles by means of taper pins which fit into corresponding holes drilled in the table.

When cutting a number of short pieces, the miter cutoff gauge generally is used in conjunction with the ripping fence. An iron block, called a clearance block, is screwed to the end of the ripping fence which is then fastened at the correct distance to the right of the saw. The piece to be cut is held with an edge against the cutoff gauge and the end butting against the iron block. When the table is pushed past the saw, the piece is cut off and left lying on the stationary part of the saw table, there being sufficient

Fig. 8.   Cutoff
gauge.

Fig. 9.   Cutting stock to length using clearance block. Saw guard removed while taking photo.

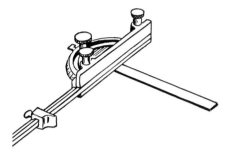

Fig. 10. Universal or miter gauge with stop rod and block.

Fig. 11. Cutting long pieces to length on circular saw. Saw guard removed while taking photo.

clearance between the saw and the ripping fence to prevent it from binding and being thrown backward by the saw (Fig. 9).

When longer pieces are to be cut, a square steel rod is clamped in a corresponding groove in the face of the gauge. It projects beyond the saw table to the left of the operator, and is furnished with an iron stop, which is set at the required distance to the left of the saw (Figs. 10 and 11). In this "setup," the ripping fence should be pushed out of the way so that the table around the saw is clear. The pieces cut off fall to the left of the saw and usually are removed by an assistant. Clearance blocks and stop rods also may be made of wood.

The miter cutoff gauge can be set to any angle from 30 to 135 deg. by means of a graduated scale marked on the table.

The universal gauge is a smaller cutoff gauge which runs in shallow grooves cut in the face of the table (Fig. 4). Two of these gauges, which can be set to any angle between 30 and 135 deg., are generally furnished with

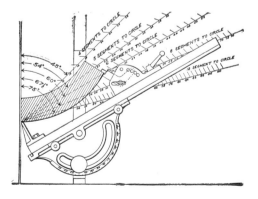

Fig. 12. Segment-gauge drawing.

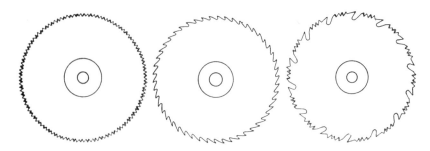

Fig. 13.   Crosscut saw, ripsaw, and miter saw.

the saw. They can be used on either side of the saw for mitering or cross-cutting. They can also be yoked together for crosscutting large pieces. Compound miters are cut by using these gauges while at the same time tilting the saw blade or the table to the correct angle. When not in use, the grooves are filled with steel strips so that the table presents a level, smooth surface.

A segment gauge, similar to the universal gauge, is made for the universal saw. A scale for determining the angle, length, and number of segments in any circle from 10 to 80 in. is engraved on the table (Fig. 12).

The cutting tools used on a circular saw are ripsaws, crosscut saws, miter saws, dado heads, straight and shaped molding cutters.

The teeth of circular ripsaws and crosscut saws are shaped very much like those of the corresponding handsaws. The miter saw has a series of about half a dozen crosscut teeth alternating with a ripsaw tooth all around its circumference. It makes a very fine, clean cut. When ordering any one of these saws, the following specifications should be given: kind of saw, as rip, crosscut, etc., diameter of saw, number of teeth, gauge or thickness, and diameter of arbor hole (Figs. 13 and 14).

Grooving saws are thick saws designed to cut grooves in wood.

A dado head consists of two saws or outside cutters, and a number of inside cutters of various thicknesses which may be placed between these. Grooves of from ¼ to 2 in. in width can be cut with a dado head. The outside cutters have a combination of rip and crosscut teeth, and cut equally well with or across the grain (Fig. 15). A dado sleeve and collars are furnished with the dado head. The use of an extension sleeve becomes necessary when wide dadoes must be cut.

A saw blade which is becoming increasingly popular in school and home workshops is the so-called cut-control safety blade. This type of blade has from eight to twelve teeth, depending upon the diameter of the blade. Each

POINT
BACK | FACE | 50°
10° BEVEL
15° BEVEL
GULLET
HOOK TO CENTER

10" CROSSCUT SAW (100 TEETH-SPRING SET)

Fig. 14. Teeth of standard circular saws.

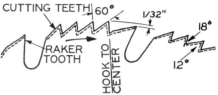

CUTTING TEETH | 60°
1/32"
18°
RAKER TOOTH
HOOK TO CENTER
12°

10" PLANER BLADE (HOLLOW-GROUND)

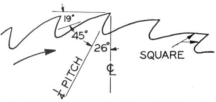

19°
45°
26°
SQUARE
PITCH
₵

10" RIP SAW (36 TEETH-SPRING SET)

COLLAR   DADO EXTENSION SLEEVE

THREADED INSIDE   LEFT-HAND THREADS

1½
1⅞   1⅝   ⅜

4
⅝
1½

Fig. 15. Parts of a dado head.

TWO ADDITIONAL COLLARS FURNISHED, ½" AND 1" THICK RESPECTIVELY.

OUTSIDE CUTTER   INSIDE CUTTER   DADO HEAD ASSEMBLED

Fig. 16. Section of a cut-control safety blade.

tooth stands only 0.02 of an inch above the noncutting periphery which forms the rest of the blade (Fig. 16). The two main advantages of this blade over the more conventional ripsaw blade are the elimination of "kickbacks" and reducing the danger of severe cuts. Kickbacks occur when a piece of wood is picked up by the saw teeth and thrown back toward the operator, often causing serious injury.

One of this blade's disadvantages is the difficulty of keeping it sharp by hand filing. When the 0.02-in. clearance has been filed away, the blade is likely to burn in the saw kerf, causing it to wobble and eventually lose its tension. When this happens it is best to send the blade to a reputable saw sharpening shop. Special sharpening jigs can be purchased or can be shop-made (see p. 154 ff.).

97. Procedure for Mounting a Dado Head. First, mount one of the saws, which resembles a combination saw, on the arbor, then mount one or more of the inside cutters, next the other saw, and finally the collar and nut which lock the whole assembly. The inside cutters are swaged;* therefore, place them so that their points will come in the gullets of the saws.

One saw or outside cutter makes a groove ⅛ in. wide. With the two saws side by side on the arbor, grooves ¼ in. wide are cut. Grooves up to ¾ in. wide may be made if you place inside cutters between the saws.

Mount the inside cutters so they are spaced on the saw arbor as evenly as possible. For example, when cutting a groove ½ in. wide, place the inside cutters at right angles to each other. When using three inside cutters, place them at approximate angles of 60 deg. Inside cutters which are "bunched" together are likely to cause the saw to run out of balance, creating excessive strain on the bearings.

Larger dado heads can cut grooves up to 2 in. wide. To make room for all the inside cutters necessary, screw an extension sleeve to the arbor (Fig.

---

* Swaging means to spread the cutting edge of a saw tooth so that it will cut a kerf that is wider than the thickness of the saw blade. Swaged saws are not set.

15). Dado heads of this type therefore have larger arbor holes than the ordinary saws used on the machine.

After you screw the sleeve on the arbor assemble the dado head in the same way as described in Steps 1 and 2.

If the groove to be cut is less in width than the full capacity of the dado head, fill up the extra space on the sleeve with steel collars. Three collars of different thicknesses usually are furnished. Place the regular saw collar and nut over the outside end of the sleeve, which is of the same diameter as the saw arbor.

When you mount a dado head, use special throat plates with wider slots. On saws with a sliding table, push the table as close to the dado head as possible and lock it. See that the dado head revolves freely before you turn on the power. You cannot use ordinary saw guards with a dado head.

Molding heads are circular in shape (Fig. 17). Molding heads should not be used on the larger circular saws where the distance between the center of the arbor and the top of the table is more than 3 in. The reason for this is that the centrifugal force is equal to the weight (M) times the radius (R) squared (MR^2). It follows therefore that the larger and heavier the molding head is, the greater is the centrifugal force and the greater the strain on the saw arbor which is usually only 1 in. in diameter.

Fig. 17. Round molding head.

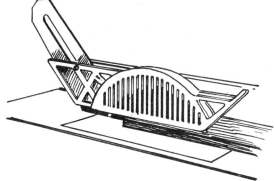

Fig. 18. Saw and splitter guard combined.

98. Safety Rules. The circular saw is one of the most dangerous wood-working machines and should never be operated by nervous or careless persons. For safety in operation, it is equipped with two guards, the saw guard, which covers the part of the blade that projects over the table, and the splitter guard, which looks like a curved sword and is bolted to the frame behind the saw blade. Its back is a little thicker than the saw blade and serves to keep the saw kerf open so that the wood being sawed does

Fig. 19. The anti-kickback dog shown to the left of the saw guard prevents the wood from being thrown back toward the operator.

not pinch the saw and cause a dangerous "kickback." The saw guard is made of metal, wire mesh, wood, or plastic. Sometimes the two guards are combined (Fig. 18).

A real foolproof guard that can be used under all conditions has unfortunately not yet been invented. It is often in the way and must be removed for measuring and for certain sawing operations. Therefore, many operators unless compelled to use the guard, get into the habit of using the saw without it.

Many guards also are provided with an anti-kickback dog which is an additional precaution against stock being thrown back toward the operator (Fig. 19).

When stock which is being sawed is thrown backward with great force and speed, it is called a kickback. This is one of the greatest dangers in operating a circular saw. It is caused: (1) when a saw has too little set; (2) when the splitter guard is not used; (3) when the clearance block (Fig. 9) is not used when crosscutting; (4) when a small piece of wood falls on an un-

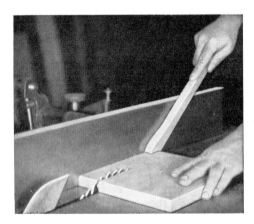

Fig. 20. Ripping stock to narrow widths with push stick. Saw guard removed while taking photo.

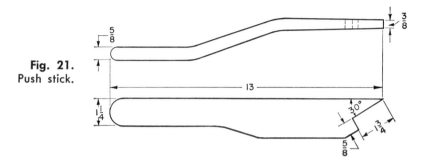

Fig. 21. Push stick.

guarded revolving saw or is picked up by its back teeth; or (5) when saw-ing badly warped stock.

Observe the following safety rules:

1. Keep the machine in perfect working order and the saw blades sharp and properly set. It is dangerous to work with dull blades.

2. Keep the floor around the machine clean and in good repair so as to avoid slipping or stumbling.

3. Keep your mind and eyes on the job and don't talk to anyone while operating the saw.

4. Use all guards and other safety devices whenever possible.

5. Use a push stick when ripping narrow pieces (Figs. 20 and 21), or saw halfway through from one side and then reverse the piece and saw the other half (Fig. 22).

6. Stand to the left of the saw to avoid being hurt by pieces that may be thrown back by the saw.

7. Adjust the saw so that it projects only ⅛–¼ in. above the stock being sawed.

8. Never reach over the saw to pick up pieces that have been sawed.

9. Stock must lie flat on the saw table and have one straight edge to be held firmly against a fence or guide. Never saw "freehand."

Fig. 22. Ripping narrow stock by cutting halfway from each end. Saw guard is likely to be in the way.

10. Make no adjustments while the machine is in motion.

11. Roll up your sleeves above the elbows or wear tight-fitting ones. Tuck your necktie inside your shirt, or better, do not wear any. Don't under any circumstances wear gloves.*

99. The band saw, like the circular saw, is one of the oldest and most indispensable woodworking machines. It is made in many sizes, from the large band mill with wheels 7 ft. or more in diameter to the little bench saw with 10-in. wheels. Band saws used mainly for sawing curves are called *scroll saws* (Figs. 23, 24, 25).

The most important parts of a band saw are the endless, flexible-steel saw blade from which it derives its name, two wheels on which this saw blade revolves, a heavy cast-iron frame, and a steel table. The wheels are fastened to shafts, which are mounted in roller bearings on the frame. These wheels are of the same size, and one is directly above the other. The upper one is supported on a curved arm of the casting called the "gooseneck." It can be

Fig. 23.   10-inch band saw.

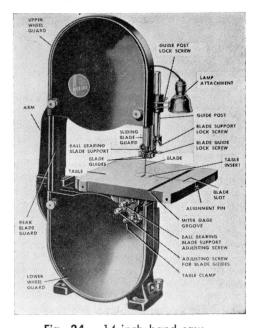

Fig. 24.   14-inch band saw.

---

* For a more complete discussion on circular saws and how to operate them, see: Hjorth, H., and Holtrop, William F., *Operation of Modern Woodworking Machines,* Chap. 1, pp. 1–39.

moved up or down for the purpose of giving tension to the saw and to accommodate saw blades which have become shorter through breakage and resoldering. It can also be tilted forward or backward so that the saw can be made to run on any part of the rim. This is called "tracking." The lower wheel is not adjustable.

The wheels usually are made of cast iron, and their rims are covered with rubber bands or tires which protect the teeth, cushion the saw, and prevent it from slipping. A tire made of a perforated metal band embedded in vulcanized rubber is used on the newer high-speed band saws having a special disk wheel with a demountable rim (Fig. 26). It need not be cemented or shellacked in place like the ordinary soft rubber tires; it wears much longer and is safer to use, because it cannot break or be thrown from the wheels (Fig. 26).

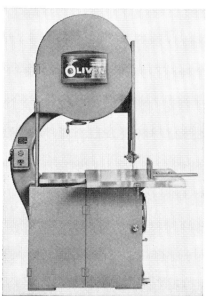

Fig. 25. Heavy-duty 36-in. band saw.

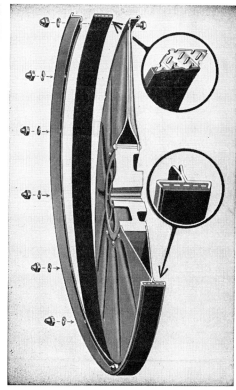

Fig. 26. High-speed band-saw tire and demountable rim.

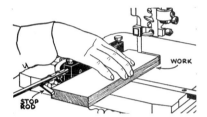

Fig. 27. Squaring longer pieces, using miter gauge and stop rod.

The table is fastened to the casting directly above the lower wheel. It can be tilted to an angle of 45 deg. to the right and 10 deg. to the left. It is slotted for the saw from the center to one edge and is furnished with a soft-metal or wood throat plate. A ripping fence is furnished with most band saws. Those of smaller size very often are grooved for a miter and crosscutting gauge (Fig. 27). The larger band saws have a two-piece table, the smaller or left part of which is fixed.

In order to keep the saw blade running straight and true and prevent it from being pushed off the wheels when sawing, two guides are used, one above the table and one below. A *guide* consists of two hardened steel jaws between which the blade runs, and a guide wheel which spins around when the back of the saw is forced against it (Figs. 28 and 29). The upper guide is fastened to the *guide post,* which is a steel bar that can be moved up or down as the thickness of the stock being sawed demands. It has a spring counterbalance, which makes it easier to push up and which prevents it from slipping down by its own weight.

The *guards* on a band saw are two metal doors enclosing the wheels, and a channel-shaped piece of steel which is fastened to the guidepost and slides up and down with it so that only the cutting part of the saw is exposed. A fixed guard covers the left part of the saw between the wheels.

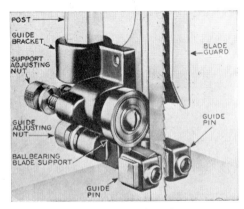

Fig. 28. Upper band saw guide.

Fig. 29. Sealed-for-life guide wheel.

Band saws are driven by individual motors connected by chains, gears, or couplings to the lower wheel shaft, or by the newer motor-on-arbor drive in which the lower shaft is the rotor of the motor. The speed of band saws varies considerably and is dependent upon the size of the wheels and the use for which the saw has been designed. The cutting speed in feet per minute may vary from 4000 to 11,000 or more for machines used in production work. To calculate the speed in feet per minute, find the circumference of the wheel in feet ($\pi \times D$) and multiply that by the revolutions per minute of the motor (r.p.m.).

Example: A 36-in. band saw makes 700 r.p.m. What is its cutting speed in feet per minute?*

Solution: $\pi \times D \times$ r.p.m. $^{22}\!/_7 \times ^{36}\!/_{12} \times 700 = 6600$ f.p.m.

100. Removing and Coiling a Band-Saw Blade. When a band-saw blade needs to be sharpened or is too narrow or too wide for the work to be done, it must be removed from the wheels and another one put in its place. Proceed as follows:

1. Pull out the little round pin from the slot in the table, open both the doors guarding the wheels, and lower the upper wheel by loosening the vertical adjustment screw.

2. The saw blade can now be slipped off the wheels and should then be coiled into three loops.

3. Hold the saw blade in the same position as it occupies on the wheels, but with the teeth pointing away from you. Place your hands in about the middle of the blade so that the loop above them is of the same size as the loop below them (Fig. 30).

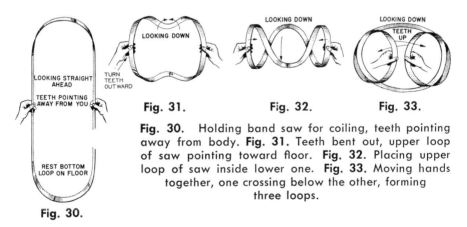

Fig. 31.   **Fig. 32.**   **Fig. 33.**

Fig. 30. Holding band saw for coiling, teeth pointing away from body. **Fig. 31.** Teeth bent out, upper loop of saw pointing toward floor. **Fig. 32.** Placing upper loop of saw inside lower one. **Fig. 33.** Moving hands together, one crossing below the other, forming three loops.

Fig. 30.

* For a more complete discussion on band saws and how to operate them, see: Hjorth, H., and Holtrop, William F., *Operation of Modern Woodworking Machines*, Chap. 2, pp. 40–60.

4. Press on the side of the saw with the thumbs so that the teeth turn out. This causes the upper loop to bend down toward the lower one (Fig. 31).

5. Place the upper loop inside the lower one and move both hands together until one crosses the other (Fig. 32). Then let go of the saw and it will coil up on the floor in three loops (Fig. 33).

6. When putting the new blade on the wheels, see that the teeth on the right side of the saw point downward. If they should point up, remove the saw from the wheels and turn it inside out. When you replace it on the wheels, you will find that the teeth point down.

7. Push the guides back and tighten the vertical adjustment screw. Rotate the wheels by hand and note on which part of the wheels the saw runs. If it does not run in the center of both wheels, tilt the upper wheel until it does. This is called "tracking the saw." It is important that the rear edge of the saw is plumb or perpendicular to the table (Fig. 34). If the rubber tires are worn in the center, tilt the upper wheel so that the saw blade runs either on the front or the rear part of the rims. Good band sawyers watch the wear on the tires and adjust the position of the blade back and forth so that this will be even.

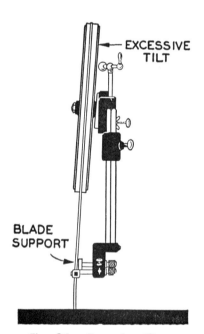

Fig. 34.   Excessive tilt.

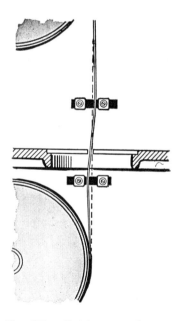

Fig. 35.   Guides out of line.

8. Move the two guides forward until the two jaws of each are in line with the gullets of the teeth. The points of the teeth must be outside the jaws, because they are set or bent to alternate sides.

9. Bring the jaws as close together as possible while still allowing the blade to run between them without friction. To do this accurately, place a piece of paper on each side of the saw blade while bringing the jaws together. Be sure the guides are in line (Fig. 35).

10. Finally, move the guide wheels forward until they are about 1/32 in. from the rear edge of the saw. When the saw runs without doing any work it should not touch the guide wheels, but when it is cutting, the stock is pressed against it and it should touch both guide wheels and cause them to spin around.*

101. Safety Rules. Although the band saw is considered one of the least dangerous woodworking machines, it is nevertheless important to observe the following rules of operation:

1. Check the adjustment of the band-saw blade by moving the wheels by hand before turning on the power. Are the guides correctly set? Does the saw track correctly?

2. See that no tools or scraps of wood are left on the table.

3. The floor around the machine also should be clear of scraps and in good condition.

4. Clamp the guidepost about 1/4 in. above the stock to be cut.

5. Use only a saw that is sharp and properly set. Work forced against it may cause it to break. Insufficient set causes it to bind and burn the wood.

6. Avoid backing the saw out of a long, curved cut. If it is necessary to back out the saw, first stop the machine, then spread the saw kerf with a small wooden wedge.

7. Do not allow anyone to stand to the right of the saw, because the blade may break and cause an injury.

8. Replace a worn throat plate, because chips of wood may fall through and be caught between the blade and the lower wheel causing the blade to break.

9. Do not wear loose or ragged clothing. Tuck in your necktie and roll up your sleeves.

10. Cut a curve of small radius with a blade of appropriate width.

11. If a band-saw blade should break while the machine is in operation, turn off the power immediately and step back. Let the machine come to a complete stop before removing the broken blade.

12. Do not allow fingers to come too close to the moving blade. Use a push stick for close work.

---

* For a more complete discussion on coiling and uncoiling a band-saw blade, see: Cunningham, B. M., and Holtrop, W. F., *Woodshop Tool Maintenance.*

13. Keep both hands in front of the blade; do not reach behind the blade for support or removal of stock.

14. When cutting long, heavy stock on the band saw, have someone assist by supporting the stock as it passes through the saw.

15. If cylindrical stock, such as dowels, is cut on the band saw hold it securely against the miter gauge.

102. The jig saw is a small scroll saw which is used for lighter and finer work than the band saw. Like most other machines, jig saws are made both in large and small sizes (Figs. 36, 37, 38). The bench saw is the most common.

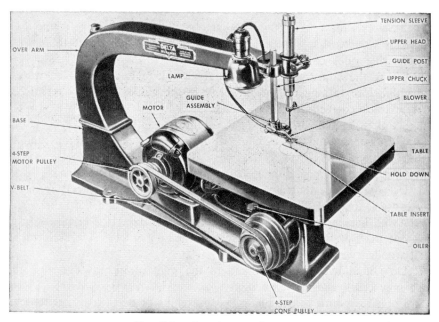

Fig. 36.   Bench-type jig saw.

The jig saw resembles the band saw in having a table which is fastened to the base, and an arm which extends over the table. It differs from the band saw in that the saw blade moves up and down in short strokes and that pierced work or interior cutting can be done on it.

The driving mechanism of the jig saw is the so-called pitman movement, which converts a rotary motion into a reciprocating one, or vice versa, as for example in the steam locomotive and the mowing machine. The pitman movement consists of a driving wheel with a crankpin off center, over which

Fig. 37. Heavy-duty power
jig saw.

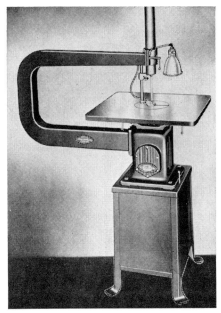

Fig. 38. Typical medium size
power jig saw mounted on steel
stand.

a bar or connecting rod fits. The other end of this bar, called the "cross-head," slides up and down between parallel guides called "gibs." The saw blade is held in a chuck on the other end of the crosshead (Fig. 39).

The upper chuck is fastened to the end of a bar which moves up or down inside a tube. This tube, called the "tension sleeve," is clamped to the arm above the table. It can be moved up or down so that saws of different lengths can be used. It also contains a tension spring which keeps the saw blades from buckling.

A guidepost is clamped to the end of the arm next to the tension sleeve. On its lower end it has a guide plate with slots of different widths and depths and a steel roller corresponding to the guide wheel on a band saw. In order to prevent the work from being lifted off the table on the upward stroke of the saw, a hold-down foot is fastened below the guide plate (Fig. 40).

Also fastened to the guidepost is a tube which blows a steady stream of air to clear away the sawdust obscuring the lines. The table can be tilted 45 deg. to each side and has a soft-metal throat plate.

The speed of the jig saw can be varied from 650 to 1750 r.p.m. by means

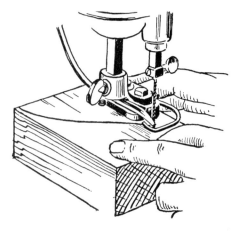

Fig. 40. Upper jaw, sleeve, hold-down foot, and air tube of jig saw.

Fig. 39. Guides, saw, table milled for throat plate, quadrant, and saw clamp.

Fig. 41. Jig-saw blades.

of two cone pulleys, one of them fastened directly to the rotor of the motor and the other to the pitman wheel.

The size of a jig saw is determined by the distance between the inside curve of the arm and the saw blade. On a 24-in. jig saw it is possible to handle work 48 in. wide, because the saw will cut 24 in. to center.

Jig-saw blades vary a great deal in size and fineness of the teeth (Fig. 41). For softwoods use saws with fairly large teeth (about 10 to the inch);

Fig. 42. Jig saw files.

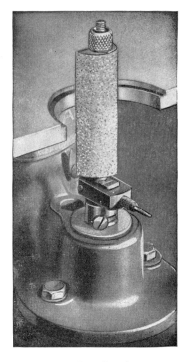

Fig. 43. Sanding attachment.

for hardwoods use saws with fine teeth. Saber blades are short, thick, and wide. They are fastened only in the lower chuck and are used for ripping and for sawing thicker stock. A special guide below the table is needed for saber saws. If a fence is clamped to the table, straight cuts may be made. As saber blades are not fastened to the upper chuck, the arm, extending over the table, may be removed to accommodate wider stock (Fig. 39).

Besides sawing, the jig saw also may be used for filing and sanding (Figs. 42 and 43). For sanding, run the saw at slow speed.*

103. The jointer or hand planer (Figs. 44, 45, and 46) is, next to the circular saw, the most necessary and useful machine in the woodworking shop. It takes the place of the hand plane and is particularly useful in straightening the surfaces of warped boards or planks, jointing edges of boards to be glued, rabbeting, squaring surfaces, and all straight planing in general.

The main parts of the jointer are a heavy cast-iron bed supported on two columns, two tables, a fence, and a cutterhead mounted on the bed. The cylindrical shape of the modern cutterhead is a great improvement in smoothness and safety of operation over the old, square cutterhead. On modern machines it runs in ball bearings bolted to the bed near its center. It has either two, three, four, or six thin steel knives. The size of the machine is given according to the length of the knives. These run from 4 in. on the small bench jointer (Fig. 45) to 36 in. on the large production machine.

---

* For a more complete discussion on jig saws and how to operate them, see: Hjorth, H., and Holtrop, William F., *Operation of Modern Woodworking Machines,* Chap. 3, pp. 61–69.

Fig. 44. Full-size jointer.

Instead of cutting long, narrow shavings like a hand plane, the jointer cuts wide and extremely short shavings. As each knife strikes the wood, it makes a small hollow across the entire width of the surface. As the wood is pushed along, a series of small ridges are therefore formed between these

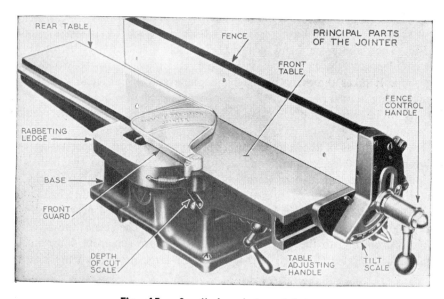

Fig. 45. Small, bench-type jointer.

Fig. 46. Floor model jointer.

Fig. 47. Table pulled away for easier removal and replacement of knives.

hollows. This is called "rotary cutting," the principle discovered by Samuel Bentham in 1791.

To minimize the ridges and hollows, the cutterhead must be perfectly balanced and the knives set so that they all project the same distance. Other factors are: greater speed, more knives in the cutterhead, and slower feeding of the stock.

With a motor-on-arbor drive, the cutterhead ordinarily revolves at a speed of 3600 r.p.m. For production work, however, this speed may be increased or even doubled by the use of a frequency changer. A frequency changer is an electrical device which increases the alternating-current impulses from the usual 60 cycles to 120 or more. Doubling the number of cycles doubles the speed of the motor.

Fig. 48. Rabbeting on jointer with rabbeting groove.

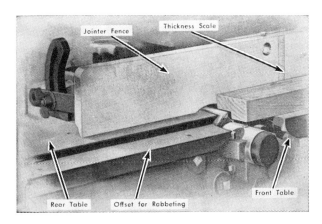

Fig. 49.   Rabbeting on a jointer,
using rabbeting arm.

Fig. 50.   Knife grinding attachment
in position.

The tables are from 1 to 2 in. wider than the knives, and can be lowered or raised on inclined ways by means of handwheels. For all ordinary work, the rear or outfeed table should be level with the knives at their highest point of revolution. Both tables have steel lips or throat plates next to the cutterhead. These lips are bolted to the table and may be renewed in case they become nicked or worn (Fig. 47). Some jointer tables have a recess on their outer edges for rabbeting (Fig. 48); others have a rabbeting arm bolted to the infeed table (Fig. 49). The tables may be pulled away from the cylinder for the purpose of changing or sharpening the knives. A knife-grinding and setting attachment (Fig. 50) consists of a small motor-driven emery wheel, which can be moved back and forth over the knives. It is bolted to the table and, therefore, eliminates the work of removing knives from the cutterhead every time they need sharpening.

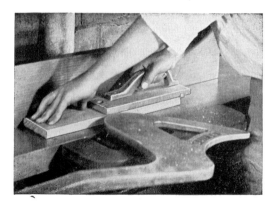

Fig. 51.   Planing face of
board using pusher.

A fence, somewhat similar to the ripping fence of a circular saw, is clamped to the outfeed table and may be moved across its entire width. It may also be tilted to any angle between 45 and 90 deg.

Several types of guards are being used for covering the part of the knives not in contact with the wood being planed. The most common one is made of aluminum and is held against the fence with a spring. When a piece of stock is planed, it pushes the guard outward, but the spring holds it against the stock so that it covers the part of the knives in front of the operator. As the stock leaves the infeed table, the guard slips back against the fence (Fig. 51).

104. Adjusting the Outfeed Table. 1. The outfeed or rear table must be at exactly the same height as the edge of the knives at their highest point of revolution. The distance the infeed or front table is below the outfeed table equals the depth of the cut made when planing a piece of wood. Most jointers have a graduated scale indicating depth of cut.

2. If the outfeed table is too high, more is planed off at the beginning of the cut and little or nothing at the end (Fig. 52). The experienced operator will also notice that the front end of the wood bumps against the lip of the outfeed table.

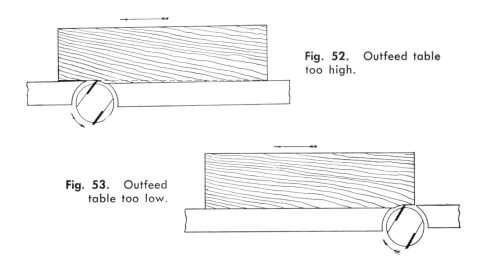

Fig. 52. Outfeed table too high.

Fig. 53. Outfeed table too low.

3. If the outfeed table is too low, the wood will drop down as it leaves the infeed table and the knives will cut deeper on the last inch or two (Fig. 53). This depression can be felt very plainly when running the hand over the planed surface.

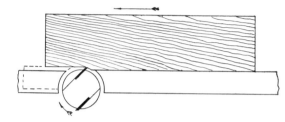

Fig. 54. Adjusting out-feed table to height. Stock part way over outfeed table.

4. The outfeed table can be set to the correct height as follows: Start the machine and run the edge of a piece of wood over the cutterhead until it projects a few inches over the outfeed table. Then stop the machine. If the table is too low, there will be a space between the table and the wood. If it is too high, lower it until there is a space between the table and the stock (Fig. 54). Then bring the table up slowly until it just touches the wood. Check the adjustment by planing the edge of a piece of stock.

5. Once the table has been adjusted, it may be a good plan to remove the handwheel.*

105. Safety Rules.   Although not nearly as dangerous as the circular saw, accidents, mostly of a minor nature, do happen on the jointer when it is operated in a careless manner. It, therefore, is well to learn the following safety rules thoroughly:

1. Give the machine your undivided attention; don't look around, and don't talk to anybody.

2. See that the knives are sharp and correctly set so that a smooth cut is produced.

3. Use only knives of equal weight to prevent vibration.

4. Do not plane stock shorter than 10 in., narrower than 1 in., or thinner than ½ in.

5. Use a push block for face planing, especially on short and thin pieces of stock (Fig. 55).

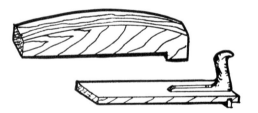

Fig. 55. Two designs for pushers.

---

* For a more detailed discussion of jointers and their operation, see: Hjorth, H., and Holtrop, William F., *Operation of Modern Woodworking Machines,* Chap. 4, pp. 70–80.

6. Do not hold the hands too near the knives or on the ends of the stock, because they might easily be jarred loose and come in contact with the knives.

7. Dull knives or too heavy a cut may cause a kickback, that is, the wood under your hand may be thrown back and your hand drop down on the knives.

8. Do not adjust the fence when the machine is in motion.

9. Use the guard at all times except when rabbeting and stop chamfering.

10. Wear no loose or ragged clothing and never any gloves. Tuck in your necktie and roll up your sleeves if loose fitting.

11. Keep the floor around the machine clean and in good condition.

12. Examine the stock carefully for knots, splits, or nails before running it over the jointer.

13. Do not push any stock over the knives until the machine is running at full speed.

106. The planer or surfacer (Figs. 56 and 57) is a machine which planes boards or planks to an even thickness. Double surfacers have two cutterheads, and plane both surfaces of a board at the same time, while single surfacers have only one cutter head and can plane only one surface at a time. Planers are made in widths from 12 to 50 in., and usually can take stock from 6 to 8 in. in thickness.

A single surfacer consists of the following main parts: a casting, between the sides of which a heavy table or bed can be raised or lowered, a cutter-

Fig. 56. Heavy-duty, 24-in. single surface planer.

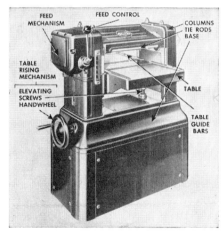

Fig. 57. Medium size, single surface planer.

Fig. 58. Frame of planer showing wedges.

head mounted over the table, four feed rolls driven by gears, belts, or chains, a chip breaker, and a pressure bar.

Briefly, the action of a planer is as follows:

1. The table is moved up or down, either by two pairs of wedges which slide upon one another (Fig. 58) or by two heavy screws which move in unison (Fig. 59). The wedge action is the better and more accurate and is used mainly on big production machines. On smaller planers the lifting mechanism is activated by a handwheel; on larger ones by a special motor hoist. A graduated scale on the front of the frame indicates the thickness of the stock when planed. One complete revolution of the handwheel usually raises or lowers the table ⅟₁₆ in. The bed should be set to about ⅟₁₆ in. less than the thickness of the stock to be planed.

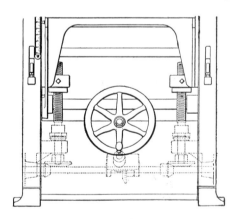

Fig. 59. Raising screws for planer table.

One surface of a warped board should first be planed straight, or out of "wind," on the jointer before planing it to thickness, as it otherwise will continue to be in "wind." The planed side should be placed "down"; i.e., in contact with the bed.

When planing a rough board, always place the smoothest side down, run it through the planer, and then reverse the surfaces.

2. Start the machine, set the feed to the speed desired, ordinarily from 20 to 130 ft. per minute, and then start the feed rolls. Some planers have a separate motor which drives the feeding mechanism, others have a belt drive from the cutterhead shaft. When belt-driven, a lever usually tightens or loosens the belt, thereby starting or stopping the feed. When motor driven, the feeding mechanism is also started or stopped independently of the cutterhead. On newer machines, a safety device stops the feed rolls automatically when too heavy a cut is taken. The four feed rolls are usually connected by gears, which are completely enclosed.

3. Push the board or plank into the machine. It is first gripped by the sectional feed roll on its upper side and a smooth steel roll mounted on the bed directly below this.

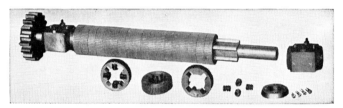

Fig. 60. Sectional feed roll.

The sectional feed roll (Fig. 60) consists of a cylinder, on which a series of wheels with corrugated edges are mounted. They yield as much as ⅜ in. independently of each other. This is to allow for unevenness in the thickness of the stock being planed. This sectional feed roll is held down on the stock by means of heavy weights or springs. On older or smaller machines the upper front feed roll is one solid corrugated cylinder.

4. The feed rolls now carry the stock along without further pushing. It next comes in contact with the chip breaker, which is a heavy sectional bar, also held down on the stock by means of an adjustable weight. It is placed immediately before the cutterhead, and can be swung out of the way without coming in contact with the knives. It holds the stock firmly to the bed and prevents chips from tearing its surface (Figs. 61 and 62).

5. The cutterhead is of the same type as the ones used on jointers. It is driven either by a motor on arbor, or a motor coupled or belted to the shaft. It revolves in the opposite direction to the movement of the stock at a speed of from 3600 to 5000 r.p.m. on newer machines. The knives can be sharpened with a grinding attachment similar to that described for jointer knives.

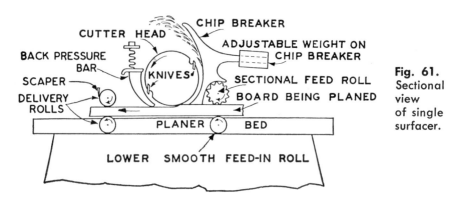

CHIP BREAKER
CUTTER HEAD
ADJUSTABLE WEIGHT ON
BACK PRESSURE   CHIP BREAKER
BAR
SCAPER   KNIVES   SECTIONAL FEED ROLL
DELIVERY   BOARD BEING PLANED
ROLLS
PLANER   BED

LOWER   SMOOTH   FEED-IN ROLL

Fig. 61.
Sectional
view
of single
surfacer.

6. After passing the cutterhead, which planes the upper surface of the board or plank, it comes in contact with the back pressure bar, which, like the chip breaker, serves to hold the stock down tightly to the bed so as to prevent chattering. This bar is held down by a spring, the pressure of which can be regulated by two screws (Fig. 61).

7. Directly behind the back pressure bar are the delivery rolls, which are smooth steel rolls carrying the stock away from the cylinder. One is mounted in the bed below the stock and the other one above the stock. The upper one sometimes has a scraper which keeps it free from shavings (Fig. 61).

The person operating a planer should stand a little to one side to avoid the danger of being hurt by chips, which occasionally may be thrown back with great force. For the same reason, pieces shorter than the distance between the feed and delivery rolls should not be planed on the surfacer.

It is often necessary to run stock several times through the machine to reduce it to the desired thickness. When several pieces are to be planed to the same thickness, run the thickest ones through first, then raise the table, and run them all through with the same setting. Raise the table again, if necessary, and repeat.*

Fig. 62.
Sectional chip
breaker.

* For a more detailed discussion on planers and how to operate them, see: Hjorth, H., and Holtrop, William F., *Operation of Modern Woodworking Machines*, Chap. 5, pp. 81–89.

107. Safety Rules. The single surfacer or planer is one of the safest woodworking machines to operate, because the cutting knives, gears, and other moving parts are enclosed, and the stock is power fed. The following rules, however, should be observed:

1. Do not plane warped or twisted boards until one side has been straightened on the jointer and will lie flat on a level surface.

2. The shortest stock that you may plane must be at least 2 in. longer than the distance between the rolls in the bed (usually not less than 14 in. long).

3. When the feed rolls take hold of a board, let go of it. Always keep your hands at a safe distance from the feed rolls.

4. On short boards, never place your fingers on the edge or underside of the board.

5. Long boards may be supported on wooden rolls, both in the front and the rear of the planer.

6. It is best to stand to one side when the feed rolls have taken hold so as to avoid being hit with bits of wood which sometimes are thrown back with considerable force.

7. Never bend down to look into a planer while it is running. The wood may be thrown out with great force.

8. Never plane stock of varying thicknesses at the same time. The thinner stock may be thrown back with great force.

9. Do not wear gloves, or loose or ragged clothing.

10. If possible, have a helper who will take the finished stock away from the machine.

11. See that the knives are sharp and the machine in perfect running order.

12. Lubricate the machine as directed by the manufacturer.

108. A swing cutoff saw is a type of circular saw used only in large shops for cutting stock to length. The older type is suspended from the ceiling, the newer one from a cast-iron column (Fig. 63). The swing cutoff saw has a movable arm, on the lower end of which the saw blade is mounted. The upper end of the arm is hung on a steel shaft, which in turn is supported on hangers from the ceiling, or on a column.

A long iron table with a hardwood or steel top is placed below the saw. The stock to be cut to length is placed on the table and is held against a fence while the swinging arm is pulled toward the operator and across the stock. The saw blade, which revolves counterclockwise, cuts just below the surface of the table. As soon as the cut is completed and the operator releases the handle, the arm automatically swings back to its first position, because it is counter-balanced by weights or springs.

The table is equipped with rollers, a graduated scale, and iron stops to facilitate the handling of the lumber and cutting it to accurate lengths.

Fig. 63.   Compact, self-contained cutoff saw.

Modern machines, both the suspended and column types, have motor-on-arbor drives. Dadoing may also be done on the swing cutoff saw.

109. The radial saw (Fig. 64) may be used as a swing cutoff saw, but it is really a variety saw, because of the many adjustments possible. The cutting unit, mounted on the end of the arm, can be turned to any angle so that ripping, crosscutting, plain and compound mitering, grooving, and dadoing can be performed on this machine. In addition, a special attachment permits the use of router bits of various sizes.*

---

* For a more detailed discussion on radial saws, see: Hjorth, H., and Holtrop, William F., *Operation of Modern Woodworking Machines,* Chap. 12, pp. 164–174.

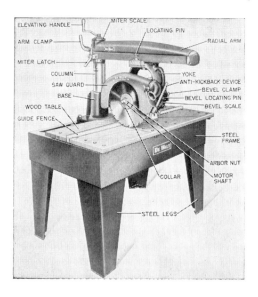

Fig. 64.   Radial saw.

110. The power handsaw is a portable circular saw with which all ordinary sawing operations can be performed. It is especially useful in carpentry work and other building construction.

One type (Fig. 65) has a flat base which rests firmly on the work, so that ripping, beveling, and crosscutting can be done accurately with guides. This saw may also be converted into a radial saw, because a radial arm and saw table may be obtained for it. Special saw blades for cutting brick, tile, or sheet metal also can be used.

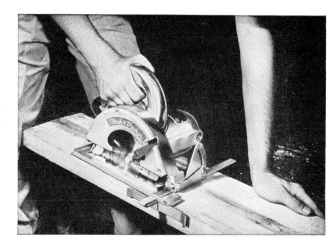

Fig. 65.
Power handsaw.

111. Mortising machines are made in three types, each operating on a different mechanical principle. The most common of these is the hollow-chisel mortiser; the others are the chain-saw mortiser and the oscillating-bit mortiser.

The hollow-chisel mortiser has an auger bit which revolves inside a square hollow chisel. It is used for all-round work and makes a mortise with square sides, ends, and bottom (Fig. 67; see also Fig. 82, p. 226). The chain-saw mortiser has an endless chain with saw-shaped teeth, which revolves around an oblong guide bar (Fig. 66). It is the fastest mortising machine and is used principally for door- and window-sash work. It makes a mortise with a rounded bottom (Fig. 67). The oscillating-bit mortiser cuts mortises with a router bit. Because it makes relatively small and

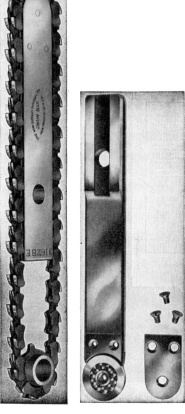

Fig. 66. Chain, chain bar, and sprocket wheel.

Fig. 68. Router bit and mortise.

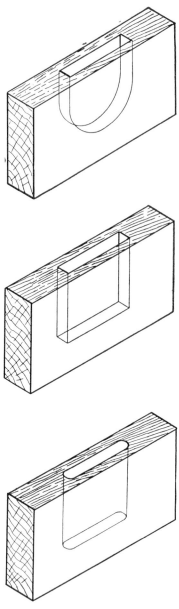

Fig. 67. Shape of mortises produced by mortising machines. Upper: chain-saw mortiser; center: hollow chisel mortiser; lower: oscillating-bit mortiser.

shallow mortises, it is used principally for chair making and other curved work. It makes a mortise with rounded sides (Fig. 68; see also Fig. 82, p. 226).

The hollow-chisel mortiser (Fig. 69) has a cast-iron column, on which a horizontal table is mounted about midway, and the mortising head or ram at its extreme upper end.

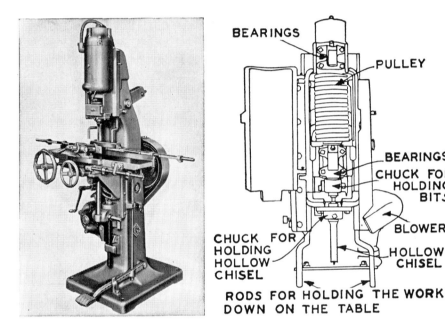

Fig. 69. Hollow-chisel mortiser.　　Fig. 70. Mortising head.

The mortising head or ram in belt-driven machines (Fig. 70) carries the bit spindle, which is mounted in two self-oiling bearings. A long pulley, 4 by 8 in., is fastened to this spindle between the two bearings. The lower end of the spindle carries a chuck, in which the ends of the bits are held by means of a setscrew. The bits and the bushings have a flattened side, which should butt up against the end of the screw.

Directly below this chuck is a similar chuck mounted on the mortising head independently of the spindle. This lower chuck holds the square hollow chisels, inside of which the bits revolve. When putting a bit in the machine, fasten the hollow chisel first, and then insert the bit from below and fasten it in the spindle chuck. A little clearance should be allowed at the end of the chisel so that the bit revolves freely, without overheating.

In a newer type, the mortising head consists of a ball-bearing self-contained motor (Fig. 69). The end of the armature carries the bit chuck, while the chuck for the hollow chisels is held in the motor casting.

The mortising head is moved downward by means of a foot lever. When this is released, a spring causes it to return to its first position. Some mortising machines are equipped with an adjustable power feed to give from 15 to 50 strokes per minute. The length of the stroke is also adjustable. A blower keeps the work free from shavings and cools the chisel and bit.

The table can be moved up or down on the column to allow for work of different dimensions. It has a crosswise movement for centering the stock to be mortised directly under the chisel, and a clamp for holding it firmly in place. It also has a sidewise movement for making successive cuts to complete a mortise. For example, if a ½-in. mortise 3 in. long has to be made, the mortising head must be moved down 7 or 8 times, while the table is moved a little sideways between each cut or stroke.

When a number of pieces have to be mortised alike, the sidewise movement of the table may be controlled by iron rods and stops. The table is also adjustable for oblique mortising. Two bent iron bars fastened to the column can be adjusted so that they hold the work firmly against the table, thus preventing the tendency to climb up when the chisel is withdrawn.

Mortising machines are driven either by belts or by an individual motor mounted on a bracket and belted to the spindle pulley, or by a ball-bearing motor on arbor. This latter type eliminates all pulleys and belts. The speed of the spindle should be about 3600 r.p.m.

The hollow chisel is generally square and is made in sizes from ¼ to 2½ in. For ordinary work, though, ¾ in. is the largest size used. The length of the chisel varies with its size. Its lower end is reamed out and sharpened; its upper end is round and held in a split bushing having one flat side for the setscrew (Fig. 71). One or two oblong holes are made in the sides of the chisel, through which the shavings drop (Fig. 72).

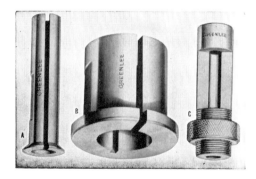

Fig. 71. Hollow chisel and bit bushings. A, Split-bit bushing; B, split-chisel bushing; C, adjustable bit bushing.

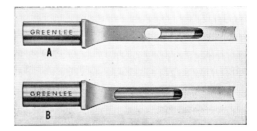

Fig. 72. Hollow chisels.
A, Hard-wear hollow chisel;
B, regular hollow chisel.

Hollow-chisel bits are similar to auger bits, but have no screw in the center. The nibs are wider than the diameter of the bit, so that the hole bored will be almost as large as the chisel itself (Fig. 73). The round shank of the bit is held in a split bushing. Bushings for both chisel and bits vary in the size of inside diameters according to the size of the chisels and bits. The bit should be adjusted so that the wide nibs just clear the cutting edges of the chisel, as any friction will otherwise tend to overheat both chisel and bit, causing them to turn blue and lose their temper.

Hollow-chisel mortisers can be used as boring machines by using machine boring bits.*

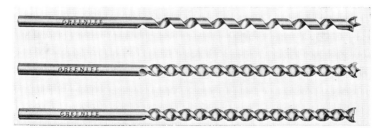

Fig. 73. Examples of single twist, hard-wear, and regular hollow-chisel bits.

Boring machines are used a great deal in woodworking shops, especially those in which furniture, radio and TV cabinets are manufactured. Boring machines may have either vertical or horizontal spindles, and may have either one or several spindles.

112. The single-spindle borer looks very much like a hollow-chisel mortiser (Fig. 74). It has a cast-iron column, a table, and a boring head, which in the modern machine is an electric motor. The table is wider than that on

---

* For a more detailed discussion on hollow-chisel mortisers and how to operate them, see: Hjorth, H., and Holtrop, William F., *Operation of Modern Woodworking Machines,* Chap. 6, pp. 90–95.

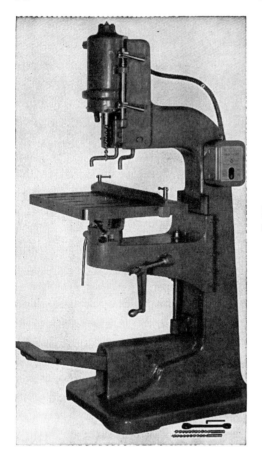

Fig. 74. Electric single-spindle borer.

the mortiser. It is adjustable vertically but not horizontally and sideways. It can, however, be swung around and tilted to any angle. It has a movable back fence which can be clamped in any position on the table. A number of holes and slots are drilled in the table for fastening stops and jigs of various kinds.

The boring head is moved downward by depressing a foot pedal. A coil spring returns it automatically to its first position. Hold-down bars prevent the stock from climbing up while boring. The length of the stroke is also adjustable. Large boring machines are equipped with a power-feed mechanism which can deliver 16, 25, or 37 strokes per minute.

Various types of machine boring bits are shown in Figure 75. The first three are auger bits; 4 is a center bit used for boring shallow holes of large diameter; 5 is a twist bit, and 6 is a spur bit, which is especially useful for boring in cross-grained woods. Both 7 and 8 are router bits; 9 is a counter-

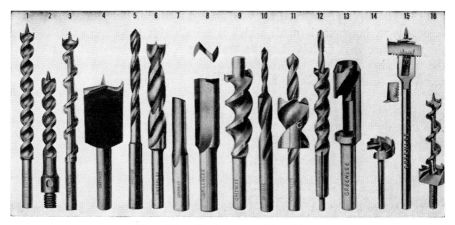

Fig. 75. Various machine bits.

boring bit for enlarging holes, and 10, 11, and 12 are countersink bits, which bore and countersink a hole in the same operation. Number 13 is a plug cutter.

The horizontal double-spindle boring machine (Fig. 76) is particularly useful when making dowel joints in light construction work (see Chapter 6, Part 2, p. 207 ff.). By changing the machine into a single borer, it quickly and accurately bores holes in edge stock prior to gluing separate boards into a single unit. Glued edges, so reinforced with dowels, are made a great deal stronger by such construction.

On this machine the stock to be bored is supported on an adjustable table where it is held in position with a hand operated hold-down. After making the necessary adjustments as to depth and position of holes, the boring unit with either one or two spindles is brought forward by pressing down on the foot pedal. The machine is readily adapted to varying sizes of bits.

Fig. 76. Horizontal double-spindle borer.

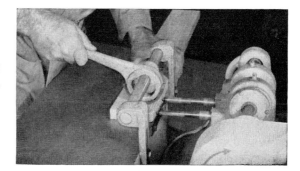

113. The drill press formerly was used only for drilling holes in metal. A new type, however, is made which is suitable for the small woodworking shop, because it is such a versatile tool (Fig. 77). Besides drilling in metal, the following woodworking operations can be performed on it: boring, mortising, routing, shaping, planing, sanding, and grinding.

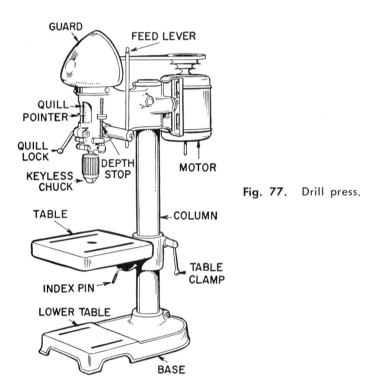

Fig. 77.   Drill press.

The principal parts of this type of drill press are a polished steel column, which is screwed into a cast-iron base, a table, which can be clamped to the column at any point, and a motor-driven head.

The head contains a boring spindle which revolves inside a sleeve called the "quill." The upper end of the spindle has a cone pulley, which is driven by a V-shaped belt from a corresponding pulley on a motor bolted to the rear side of the head casting. The cone pulleys give the drill press a speed range from 600 to 5000 r.p.m. Various types of spindles are furnished with the drill press (Fig. 78).

The table is of cast iron with a planed upper surface. It is slotted so that work can be clamped to it, and it has a central hole in which a pivot pin,

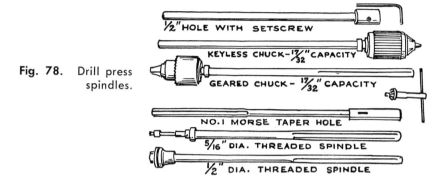

Fig. 78. Drill press spindles.

used in routing operations, is fitted. The table can be tilted to any angle, and it can be swung all around the column.

The base also is slotted, and its upper surface is planed, so that it can be used as a table when long stock has to be bored.

The size of a drill press is given as twice the distance from the center of the table to the column. If this distance is 10 in., you have a 20-in. drill press; or, in other words, stock 20 in. wide can be bored through the center.

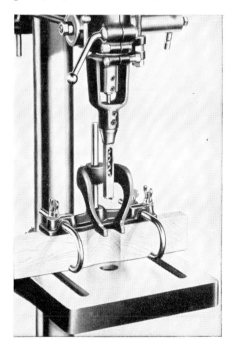

Fig. 79. Mortising attachment mounted on drill press.

Fig. 80. Drilling holes in metal.

For mortising, a special fitting, which holds the hollow chisel, is screwed onto the quill, while the bit is held in the spindle chuck. A special fence and hold-down bars are also provided (Fig. 79).

When drilling holes in metal the work should not be held in the hand alone. The lips of the drill may seize the work at any time, especially when breaking through the stock. If the piece is whirled out of the operator's hand, he may be injured. In any case, the drill will be broken when the work strikes the column.

The work must be held steady while drilling. Any tilting, twisting, or shifting results not only in a rough hole, but also increases drill breakage. For flat work, lay the piece to be drilled on a wooden base (Fig. 80) and hold it firmly against the column. If the piece is of irregular shape and cannot be laid flat on the table, it should be securely blocked and clamped.

For shaping, a special shaper spindle is clamped in a ½-in. chuck. Three-lip shaper cutters fit over the end of the spindle (Fig. 81).

Fig. 81.   Shaper spindle and three-lip cutters for drill press.

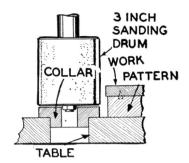

Fig. 83.   Sanding after pattern.

Fig. 82.   Grinding jointer knife on drill press.

Knife grinding can be done with a cup-shaped wheel as shown in Figure 82, and edge sanding can be done with spindles up to 3 in. in diameter (Fig. 83).

Routing is done very easily on the drill press. The bit may be fastened in a spindle having a ½-in. hole. It is centered in a bushing and held in place with a setscrew (Fig. 84). It also may be held in a keyless chuck having three jaws.

Many routing operations may be performed on the drill press. The bit should revolve at its highest speed, about 5000 r.p.m.

Carving may be done by substituting carving bits for router bits.*

Fig. 84.   Routing on drill press.

114. The shaper is one of the most useful woodworking machines. The following operations can be performed on it: rabbeting, grooving, fluting, beading, sash sticking, tenoning, panel raising, and shaping of moldings both straight and curved. Like other woodworking machines, shapers are made in many different sizes and shapes, from the large, single-spindle production machine (Fig. 85) to the small bench shaper (Fig. 86).

The principal parts of a shaper are a cast-iron base and a table through which the vertical shaper spindle projects. On the larger machines the table is stationary, and the spindle, which is mounted in a casting called a "yoke," can be moved up or down by means of a handwheel (Fig. 87). On some of the smaller bench machines the table can be moved vertically while the spindle remains at a fixed height.

The spindle is a steel forging and revolves in two roller bearings. On modern machines it is run at a speed of from 5000 to 10,000 r.p.m. and is, therefore, in most cases belt-driven from a motor bolted directly to the base. On account of its high speed, the bearings on larger machines are oiled by a force pump.

The spindle top is a turned steel bar which is screwed to the threaded

---

* For a more detailed discussion on the drill press and how to operate it, see: Hjorth, H., and Holtrop, William F., *Operation of Modern Woodworking Machines*, Chap. 9, pp. 119–128.

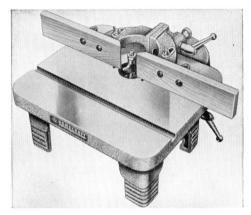

Fig. 86.   Small bench-type shaper.

Fig. 85.   Production shaper.
Note rubber mat on floor.

upper end of the spindle. Spindle tops vary both in length and diameter according to the work to be done and the size of the machine used.

Two identical flat shaper knives are used on most large machines and many small ones. They have beveled edges and are held between two round, slotted collars, which are slipped over the spindle top (Fig. 88). One or more plain, round collars are used both above and below the slotted collars, and a nut tightens up the whole assembly. While tightening the nut, the spindle is held stationary with a pin which passes through it or it can be fastened with a clamp. It is very important that the knives are exactly of the same width and that the nut is tight, otherwise one of them might work loose and injure someone. To prevent this, knives with corrugated edges and collars with corresponding screws may be used (Fig. 89). The safest type of shaper cutter is the three-lip or wing cutter which slips over the spindle top and cannot get loose (Fig. 81).

Smaller shapers usually have a fence that can be clamped to the table, as well as a sliding fence resembling the universal gauge of a circular saw. The fence clamped to the table is used for shaping straight edges and the sliding fence for shaping end wood (Figs. 86 and 90). Curved work is held against a shaper collar of the right diameter. No other fence or guide except a starting pin is used. Two rings fit in the central hole in the table around the spindle, one inside the other. Some rings have a raised edge against

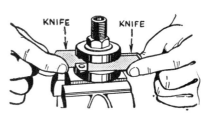

Fig. 88. Flat or open-face knives inserted between collars.

Fig. 87. Yoke with belt-driven spindle.

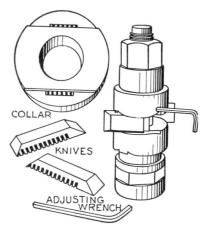

Fig. 89. Shaper knives and collars with screws. Right: assembly of collars and cutters on spindle top.

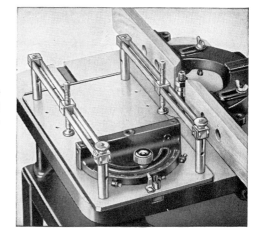

Fig. 90. Sliding fence equipped with clamping device.

which curved work may be guided. Frictionless shaper collars prevent the burning of the edge of the wood, because they do not revolve (Fig. 91). Although the outside edge of shaper collars is highly polished, considerable friction is generated. Note: the spindle always revolves against the wood.

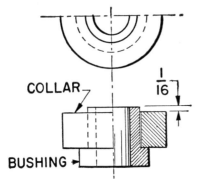

Fig. 91. Frictionless shaper collar.

Fig. 92. Four-knife, round, slip-on, and screw-on cutterheads.

Shaper cutters, either plain or milled, may also be fastened to square or round cutterheads, which can be slipped over the spindle (Figs. 92 and 93). Only a flat bevel needs to be ground on milled cutters. If this bevel is ground at the same angle, the cutters will always be shaped exactly alike. Shaper cutters resembling grooving saws are used for door sticking, tenoning, and

Fig. 93. Shaper head with milled knives.

Fig. 94. Solid shaper cutters for door and window sash, and work turned out on shaper.

panel raising (Fig. 94). Various types of guards, jigs, and hold-down springs are made for the shaper and should be used whenever possible (Figs. 95 and 96).*

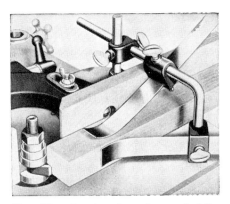

Fig. 95. Steel spring clamps holding the stock firmly against the fence.

Fig. 96. Close-up of shaper head, spindle, fence, ring guard, and holding device.

115. Safety Rules. As stated before, the shaper is, on account of its high speed, a very dangerous machine to operate, especially when flat or open-face knives are used. It is important, therefore, to take every precaution to prevent the hands from coming in contact with the cutters.

1. Use a fence or jig whenever possible.

2. Use a guard, hold-down, or pressure bar when possible.

3. The shaper knives must rotate toward the work being fed.

4. Do not "back up" any work, because it may be thrown out of your hands. Stop the machine and start over again.

5. Remove all tools and materials from the table before starting the machine.

6. See that the knives are of exactly the same weight and width.

7. See that the spindle is free before turning on the power.

8. Make a final checkup on all bolts, screws, or clamps used in the setup.

9. Do not wear loose or ragged clothing. Tuck in your necktie, and roll up loose sleeves.

10. Do not take your attention off the work and the machine for one instant.

11. Do not attempt to shape small pieces of wood.

---

* For a more detailed discussion on shapers and how to operate them, see: Hjorth, H., and Holtrop, William F., *Operation of Modern Woodworking Machines,* Chap. 7, pp. 96–109.

116. The router is one of the newest and most indispensable machines in the furniture industry, because so many operations can be performed on it. The router is used for making fine lines and grooves for veining and inlaying; it may be used for light shaping cuts, for shallow boring and mortising, and for dovetailing, fluting, grooving, etc. For pierced work it completely eliminates the jig saw, because it produces finished, shaped edges at one cut. Furthermore, rope moldings, spiral turnings, rosettes, and other decorative work can be produced on the larger machines.

The production router has a substantial cast-iron frame, whose upper part is an arm extending over the table. On some machines the router is moved down to the table, on others the table is moved up to the router. The raising or lowering is done by a treadle, and the length of the stroke is adjustable. The table can be tilted and is equipped with a fence and a steel guide pin, which is directly below the spindle.

The spindle in Figure 97 is mounted in the outer end of the arm and is belted to a motor in the inner part of the arm, which drives it at a speed of from 10,000 to 20,000 r.p.m. Other router motors obtain their high speed directly through a frequency changer.

Fig. 97. High speed, heavy-duty router.

The end of the spindle has a chuck which holds different kinds of router, veining, and carving bits (Fig. 98). A shaper attachment (Fig. 99) may also be held in the chuck.

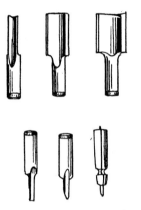

Fig. 98. Router and veining bits.

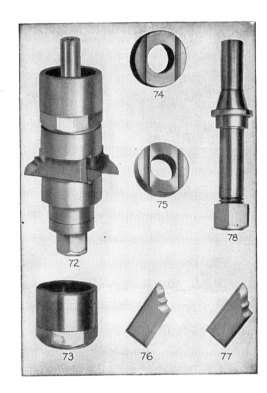

Fig. 99. Shaper attachment for router. 72, Assembly of attachment. 73, Nut for spindle. 74, 75, Collars. 76, 77, Knives. 78, Spindle.

The guide pin in the table is used when routing after a template (Fig. 100). The pattern or template is nailed to the stock to be routed. It is then placed over the pin, which must be of the same diameter as the bit in use, and the stock is brought in contact with the revolving router bit. As the template is moved over the pin, the outlines of the design are followed and reproduced exactly in the stock.

Special bits and guides are used for dovetailing (Fig. 101).

A portable router (Figs. 102 and 103) is simply a high-speed motor, which is held in the hand while it cuts. The motor screws into an aluminum base which is equipped with guides for routing or veining along straight and curved edges. When veining lines along an irregular template, as shown in Figure 104, a follower must be used over the bit. If such a follower, or guide, is not used, there is a possibility of cutting into the template, thus ruining the entire job. A guide for this work is shown in Figure 105. Some portable

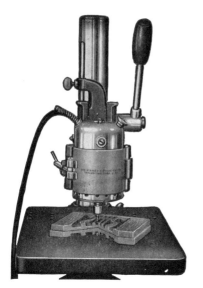

Fig. 100. Routing after pattern, using guide pin in table.

Fig. 101. Router mounted on dovetail attachment.

Fig. 102. Portable router with guide attached.

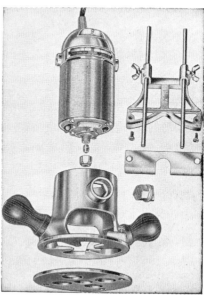

Fig. 103. Parts of small portable router.

Fig. 104. Vein-line routing on flat work.

Fig. 105. Guide for router and veining bits.

routers can be used either for shaping or routing. Those with turbine motors, driven by air pressure, make as much as 50,000 r.p.m. (Fig. 106).*

Fig. 106. Portable air-turbine router. Upper left, motor; upper right, hand router; lower illustrations, three types of pattern followers.

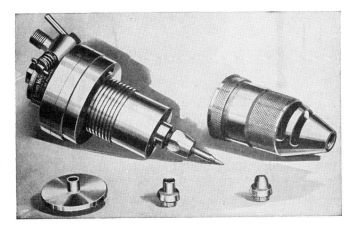

117. Sanding machines have been developed during the past 70 or 80 years. These machines are not only made in many different sizes, but also in many different forms that do not resemble each other either in construction or mode of operation. The most common types are the belt sander,

---

* For a more complete discussion on routers and how to operate them, see: Hjorth, H., and Holtrop, William F., *Operation of Modern Woodworking Machines*, Chap. 8, pp. 110–118.

the disk sander, the spindle sander, the drum sander, and a variety of portable sanders.

118. A belt sander (Fig. 107) generally has two cast-iron columns, each of which carries a large pulley and a table placed between these. They are used principally to sand flatwork and straight moldings. The sanding operation is performed by pressing an endless, abrasive belt against the work. The dust either is collected in a bag or is exhausted. A motor driving the

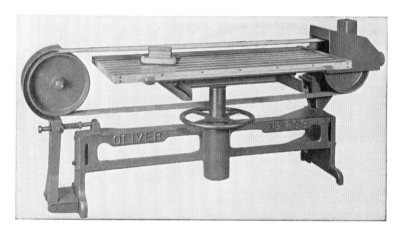

Fig. 107.   Hand-block belt sander with dust hood guard.

pulley is mounted on one of the posts. This post is, therefore, called the "power stand." The other post is called the "idler stand." On some machines the two pulleys, including the motor, are adjustable vertically as much as 48 in., and are moved in unison by means of a screw, bevel gears, connecting shaft, and handwheel. On others the table has a vertical movement. A weight or a horizontal adjustment tightens the belt. The pulleys on the machine illustrated run in ball bearings, are rubber faced, measure 24 in. in diameter, have a 10-in. face, and a speed of 600 r.p.m.

The table is built of wooden strips set 1 in. apart and bolted to an iron frame. It has a horizontal movement of 36 in.

The work to be sanded is placed on the table, and the pulleys carrying the sanding belt or the table are adjusted to the right height. The belt is made of canvas to which the abrasive has been applied. It is known as garnet cloth and is sold by the roll or in ready-made belts.

Fig. 108. Pneumatic sanding pad.

A cloth-covered wooden block with rounded edges and a handle, or a pneumatic sanding pad (Fig. 108) which can be inflated to conform to flat, convex, or concave work, should be used to press the belt down to the work being sanded.

Other belt sanders, called automatic-stroke sanders, have a motor-driven sanding block which slides back and forth on a steel bar and exerts a uniform pressure on the work being sanded (Fig. 109).

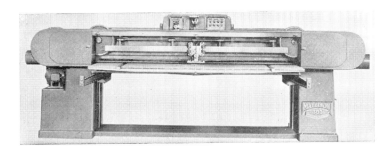

Fig. 109. Automatic stroke sander.

The hand-lever-stroke belt sander also has a sanding block which slides on a metal bar, but it is pushed back and forth and pressed against the sanding belt by hand.

Smaller belt sanders are called *variety sanders* (Fig. 110). They have a table with a back plate between the pulleys. The machine illustrated can be operated either in a vertical or a horizontal position and it can be used both for flat and curved work (Fig. 111).

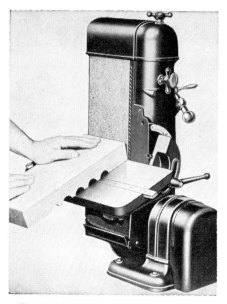

Fig. 110.   Variety belt sander in
a vertical position.

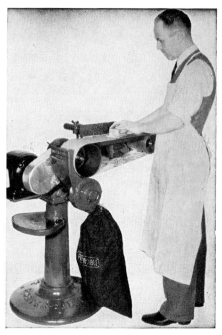

Fig. 111.   Variety sander in
horizontal position.

Belt sanders are also made in portable types (Figs. 112 and 113). They are similar in construction to the variety sander having a flat shoe, corresponding to the table, between the pulleys. They are used mostly for sanding flat work.

Fig. 112.   Portable belt sander
in use.

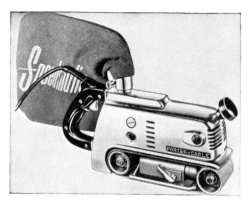

Fig. 113.   Portable belt
sander.

119. The disk sander (Fig. 114) is simply a wooden or metal disk mounted on a shaft which runs in ball bearings. The larger machines are fastened to a cast-iron column; the smaller ones are bench machines. Disk sanders have a guard on the top side of the disk and a table which can be tilted 45 deg. The table is slotted lengthwise for an angle gauge resembling a universal gauge on a circular saw. Most machines also have a metal jig for sanding circular disks. A special mastic cement is used for gluing the sanding sheets to metal disks, although a casein glue may be used.

Fig. 114. Pedestal-type disk sander, with adjustable table.

A fairly good disk sander may be made for the lathe by fastening a piece of 1¾-in. stock to a faceplate, and turning it to as large a diameter as the lathe will swing. An auxiliary table can be clamped to the lathe bed (Fig. 115).

A small band saw may be used as a belt sander when the saw blade is replaced with a narrow sanding belt. The guides should be removed and a backing, made of wood or metal, clamped to the saw table behind the belt (Fig. 116).

Fig. 116.   Narrow sanding belt
mounted on band saw.

Fig. 115.   Lathe disk sander.

120. The spindle sander is composed of a vertical spindle projecting through a horizontal table, which is supported on a cast-iron column. Steel rolls of different diameters can be fastened to the end of the spindle, which revolves at a speed of about 1700 r.p.m. and has an oscillating up-and-down movement. The table may be tilted to various angles. It may be driven by belts or by a self-contained ball-bearing motor (Fig. 117). Some spindle sanders are horizontal and have pneumatic spindles or spindles made of soft rubber. They are used for sanding irregular-shaped pieces such as chair parts (Fig. 118).

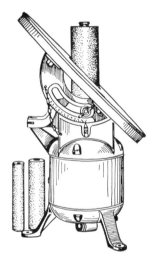

Fig. 118.   Sanding on pneumatic drum.

Fig. 117.   Spindle sander.

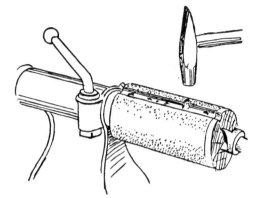

Fig. 119. Fastening sandpaper to spindle with staples.

Horizontal spindles may also be turned on the lathe and covered with sandpaper. The sandpaper may be fastened with staples in a groove about ¼ in. wide and ⅛ in. deep, cut, lengthwise in the cylinder (Fig. 119). Another way to fasten the sandpaper is to turn the cylinder in two halves, fold a piece of sandpaper around each half, and then screw them together (Fig. 120). See also Article 270.

Fig. 120. Split sanding spindle.

121. Drum sanders are large production machines which work on the same principle as planers. They have three or more drums covered with sandpaper of various degrees of fineness, and several rollers which carry the work through the machines (Fig. 121).

A floor sander is a portable type of drum sander (Fig. 122).

122. Orbital and Straight-Line Stroke Sanders. A small sander like the one shown in Figure 123 is useful particularly in finish sanding. It is called an orbital sander. Abrasive sheets of different grades can be attached to the shoe.

Fig. 121. Three-drum endless belt sander.

Another sander now on the market is air-driven. This sander has a straight-line stroke, which means that there is no side motion to the shoe. This type of sander is becoming increasingly popular among wood finishers (Fig. 124).*

* For a more complete discussion of sanding machines, see: Hjorth, H., and Holtrop, William F., *Operation of Modern Woodworking Machines,* Chap. 10, pp. 129–140.

Fig. 123. Small orbital sander.

Fig. 122. Drum-type floor sander.

Fig. 124. Straight-line stroke, air-driven sander.

123. Multi-Purpose Tools and Machines. During recent years there has come about an ever increasing desire on the part of many people to make things themselves. Homeowners make improvements and repairs in order to save money; others work with tools purely as a leisure time activity.

To complete various pieces of furniture, built-ins, and small additions to the home, a number of power tools is highly desirable. However, many people have neither adequate space nor sufficient money to put a number of single-purpose machines into their home workshop.

Keeping in mind these two factors, space and cost, some manufacturers of woodworking equipment have developed machines which accomplish, as a single unit, the work previously done by a number of separate machines. Three such machines are presented here. No attempt is made to show the superiority of one machine over the other.

The *Shopsmith,** a multipurpose power tool (Fig. 125), was introduced

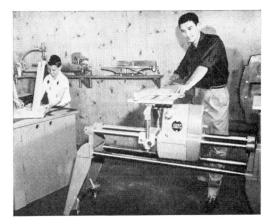

Fig. 125. Typical arrangement of "Shopsmith" home workshop.

---

* Manufactured by: Magna Power Tool Corporation, Menlo Park, Calif.

to the public in 1947. In its basic form it can be used as a circular saw, disk sander, horizontal drill press, vertical drill press, and lathe. In addition to these basic operations of sawing, sanding, drilling, and wood turning, additional accessories make it possible to use the machine as a band saw, jointer, belt sander, jig saw, shaper, router, and as a finishing unit.

Figure 125 shows how the major *Shopsmith* accessories can be stored conveniently. Twin-tube mounting permits the accessories to be stored on the wall when not in use. This shop-on-the-wall feature gives more floor space in the actual working area. Workbench and machine can be rolled back against the wall for storage.

Fig. 126. "Shopsmith" speed dial.

The speed dial (Fig. 126) on *Shopsmith* insures the correct speed for each job. Dialing the required operation without changing pulleys and belts automatically sets the correct speed. The variable selections of speed range from a slow 700 r.p.m. for the jig saw to a high 5200 r.p.m. for the shaper.

Shopsmith can be used for ripping and crosscutting (Fig. 127). When crosscutting long pieces an extension table can be placed in the so-called headrest mount, located at one end of the machine (Fig. 127). The use of this extension table provides for a maximum table size of 18⅜ in. by 56 in. Angular cuts can be made either by tilting the table or by setting the miter gauge at the required angle. By removing the sawblade and replacing it with a sanding disk, *Shopsmith* is changed into a disk sander (Fig. 128). Sanding can be done either by moving the work against the disk or by moving the disk forward with the use of the quill feed.

With the parallel ways raised and locked in a vertical position, *Shopsmith*

Fig. 127.
Crosscutting on
"Shopsmith."

becomes a 16½-in. vertical drill press (Fig. 129). The quill is fed to the exact depth of the hole with the use of the depth-control dial. Locked miter gauge and fence serve as a ready-made jig for repeat drilling operations, while the speed dial on the headstock provides the exact speed needed for operations from heavy-duty drilling to high-speed routing. On *Shopsmith* the distance from chuck to table is 26 in.; from chuck to floor, 58 in. It will drill to the center of a 16½-in. circle. When boring holes for dowel joints, it may be more convenient to use the machine in a horizontal position.

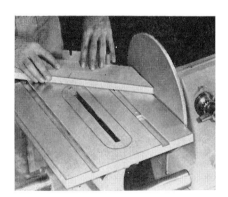

Fig. 128. "Shopsmith" set up
as disk sander.

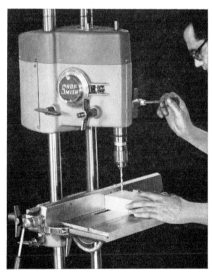

Fig. 129. "Shopsmith" set up as
a drill press.

Fig. 130. "Shopsmith" with 4-in. jointer and table saw.

The ideal workshop combination is a properly guarded jointer and table saw operating simultaneously (Fig. 130). The 4-in. jointer utilizes power from the lower auxiliary spindle on *Shopsmith*. The three jointer knives are precision-ground and tapered to seat against matching retaining wedges. The one-piece, cast-iron fence can be set at any angle up to 45 deg. each way and has adjustable stops. The safety guard shown on the jointer is spring controlled and can be used on either side of the fence for jointing or rabbeting. A saw guard is placed in its proper position over the saw blade.

The setup shown in Figure 131 for simultaneous operation of belt and disk sander often proves useful. Two different types of sanding operations can be performed and two types of abrasives can be used. The belt sander utilizes the power of the ¾ h.p. motor. The 6-in. belt sander has automatic

Fig. 131. Setup for simultaneous use of belt and disk sander.

Fig. 132. Faceplate turning on "Shopsmith."

belt tensioning and operates in a horizontal or vertical position. The 6-in. by 9-in. sander table can be used across the belt or can be mounted on either side as a fence for surface or edge sanding.

The lathe operation known as faceplate turning is shown in Figure 132. The headstock has been moved to the end of the ways to permit the operator to face the work with greater convenience and ease of operation. The tool rest slides parallel to the work, and swings in a 360 deg. arc. It can be raised and lowered by means of a rack-and-pinion height control. Spindle turning also can be done on the *Shopsmith*. To support the stock a special tailstock is placed into the openings as shown in Figure 132.

Fig. 133. 18-in. jig saw mounted on end of "Shopsmith."

Fig. 134. 11-in. band saw mounted in position on "Shopsmith."

With the 18-in. jig saw mounted on the end of *Shopsmith,* as shown in Figure 133, the rotary motion of the spindle is converted into an up-and-down movement. This up-and-down motion is carried to a straight blade that cuts on the down stroke. Because the jig saw can cut a curve of small radius, with an extremely fine kerf, it especially is adapted to do intricate

Fig. 135. Paint sprayer with ¾ h.p. motor.

scroll and fretwork. A drum sander can be mounted on the front spindle for sanding edges after sawing. The jig saw has a built-in blower, adjustable blade guides, hold-down, and adjustable tension device for light or heavy blades. For use as a saber saw, the tubular arm can be pivoted to a position below the table surface.

The band saw (Fig. 134) is used mostly for sawing curved or irregular stock, but can be used equally well for straight line cutting and resawing. The 11-in. band saw mounts on the power-mount end of *Shopsmith,* and, like other accessories, is driven by a flexible coupling that connects to the upper auxiliary spindle of the headstock. It utilizes the ¾ h.p. motor and variable speed mechanism. A dual mounting with the drum sander on the front spindle allows for sanding edges after a saw cut has been made.

In addition to doing a variety of operations with the use of separate accessories, *Shopsmith* lends itself to do spray finishing (Fig. 135). The spraying unit consists of the following three parts: a compressor, equipped with a ¾ h.p. motor, hose of convenient length, and a spray gun which can be used for either internal-mix or external-mix spraying.

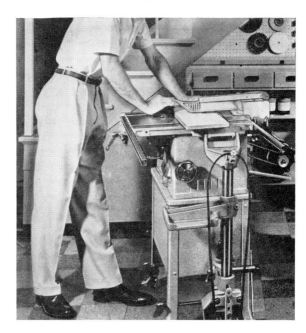

Fig. 136. "Deltashop" set in a basement home workshop.

The *Deltashop** is a multipurpose machine that is designed primarily around a 9-in. tilting arbor circular saw, 4-in. jointer, 11-in. drill press, and

* Manufactured by: Delta Power Tool Division, Rockwell Manufacturing Company, Pittsburgh, Pa.

Fig. 137. Cutting molding with cutterhead mounted on saw arbor.

8½-in. disk sander. Separate accessories make it possible to use it as a jig saw, shaper, router, mortiser, buffer, grinder, etc. Figure 136 shows this machine in a basement home workshop atmosphere. The 9-in. circular saw crosscuts and rips stock up to 2¾ in. in thickness. Angular cuts from 0–45 degrees can be made by tilting the saw blade.

By removing the saw blade and replacing it by the molding cutterhead, a variety of moldings can be made (Fig. 137). A special table insert with wide opening is provided for this operation.

The 4-in. jointer can be used in combination with the circular saw or

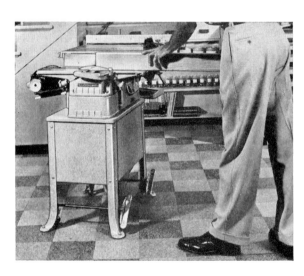

Fig. 138. Jointing on 4-in. jointer. Circular saw blade below saw table.

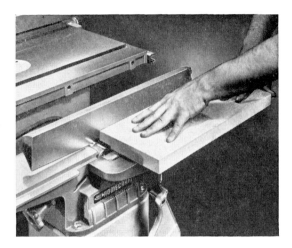

Fig. 139. "Deltashop" jointer used to cut rabbets.

with the drill press as shown in Figure 138. The jointer fence can be set at any angle up to 45 deg. The spring controlled swing guard completely covers the knives but may be removed when rabbeting (Fig. 139). The maximum depth for rabbeting is ¼ in.

The sturdy drill press lends itself to a variety of jobs ranging from slow-speed boring operations to high speed shaper operations. In Figure 140

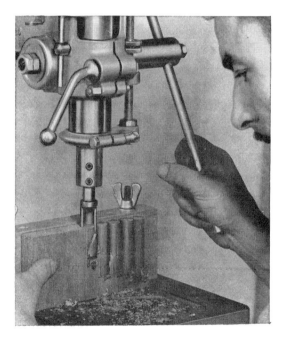

Fig. 140. Cutting plugs on "Deltashop" drill press.

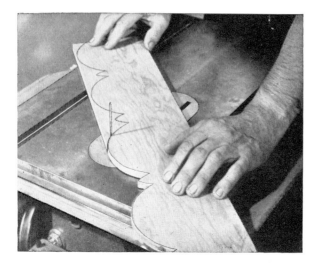

Fig. 141. Cutting curves with saber saw.

this unit of the machine is being used to cut a number of plugs. When not in use, the drill press can be swung out of the way (Fig. 138).

The *Deltashop* can be converted into a jig saw by means of the saber saw attachment. Since no over arm is used above the table, it allows for unlimited curve cutting (Fig. 141). The chuck can be opened wide enough to hold files and small sanding attachments (Fig. 142).

Figure 143 shows *Deltashop* with the 8½-in. disk sander placed in position. The sanding table can be tilted 45 deg. to the front or 35 deg. to the rear for bevel sanding operations. The opposite end of the shaft can be mounted with a grinding wheel to sharpen tools or household articles.

Fig. 142. File inserted in chuck to smooth edges of thin metal.

Fig. 143. Sanding on 8½-in. disk sander.

The *Power Shop** is a power tool that has the appearance of a typical radial saw, but performs, in addition to various sawing operations, a number of other machine woodworking operations. By making minor changes the machine can, among others, be used as a shaper, router, boring machine, saber saw, lathe, and disk sander.

Figure 144 shows the *Power Shop* as it might be used by the home crafts-

* Manufactured by: DeWalt Division, American Machine and Foundry Co., Lancaster, Pa.

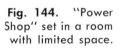

Fig. 144. "Power Shop" set in a room with limited space.

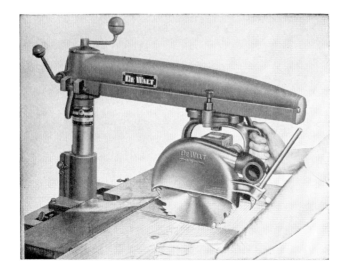

Fig. 145. Cross-cutting with "Power Shop."

man. The table supports the multipurpose saw and also serves as a workbench. Clip-boarded walls serve for ready storage of machine accessories.

Radial arm saws for the home workshop come in 8-, 9-, and 10-in. sizes. Proper safety guards are provided for saw blades and attachments.

This machine performs two basic types of cutting with the other operations closely related to these basic procedures. For such operations as crosscutting (square, angular, or compound cuts), and dadoing the blade is pulled

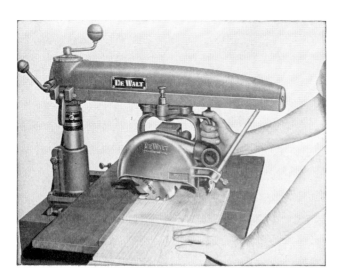

Fig. 46. Cutting dadoes.

Fig. 147. Using "Power Shop" as a shaper.

across the work. For ripping, rabbeting, and related operations the motor and blade are locked at a right angle position and the work is pushed through. By turning the blade around, ripping may be done from the other side of the saw.

In Figure 145 a board is cut at right angles with its edge. In Figure 146 the crosscut saw has been removed and the dado head is mounted on the motor shaft.

To use *Power Shop* as a shaper, a shaper head with the proper knives takes the place of the saw and is mounted on the shaft as shown in Figure 147. To shape, the motor unit and shaper head are changed to the position

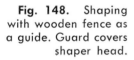

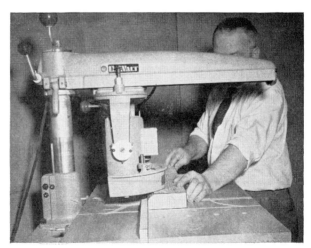

Fig. 148. Shaping with wooden fence as a guide. Guard covers shaper head.

Fig. 149. Planing with rotary planing attachment.

as shown in Figure 148. Notice how the guard covers the entire shaper head, fully protecting the operator.

In Figure 149 a rotary planing attachment has been mounted on the motor shaft. With this tool narrow boards can be planed to thickness in one pass; wide boards require two or more passes.

In Figure 150 *Power Shop* has been set up as a router. With a variety

Fig. 150. "Power Shop" set up as a router.

Fig. 151. Boring holes for dowel joint, with motor unit and bit in horizontal position.

of routing and veining bits, numerous routing jobs can be performed. The depth of cut is controlled by either raising or lowering the motor unit.

Power Shop is readily changed into a satisfactory boring machine. With the use of a simple supporting cradle as shown in Figure 151 a variety of boring jobs can be completed. Centers for holes are determined by raising or lowering the motor unit and by locking it into position at any point along the travel arm.

A special saber saw attachment changes the machine into a saber saw with

Fig. 152. Using special saber saw attachment.
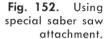

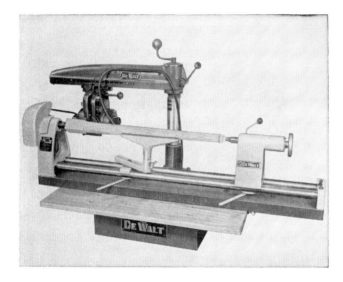

Fig. 153. "Power Shop" set up for spindle turning.

a maximum throat capacity of 27 in. (Fig. 152). Saw blades range from 7 to 20 teeth per inch, permitting a coarse or fine saw cut.

By mounting a lathe bed on the saw table, *Power Shop* can be used as a wood-turning lathe (Figs. 153 and 154). A step pulley on the headstock makes it possible to run the lathe at slow or fast speeds. When not in use as a lathe, the headstock can be used as a disk sander by placing a sanding disk on the threaded live center shaft.

Fig. 154. "Power Shop" set up for faceplate turning.

Fig. 155. Oscillating-bit mortiser with pneumatic clamps.

124. Compressed air is used a great deal in modern woodworking plants for air-turbine motors (page 109), for clamping stock to tables of different machines such as mortisers, borers, and shapers (Fig. 155), and for clamping stock to be glued (Fig. 156). This saves a great deal of time in tightening and loosening screw-operated clamps, because air pressure can be applied and released instantly, and at several points at the same time, merely by the pressure of a foot pedal. Furthermore, the operator always has both hands free.

Fig. 156. Air electric molding bander for flat work.

125. Sharpening machines are saw-filing machines, saw-setting machines, grindstones, emery grinders, and automatic knife grinders.

Of these, the first two are discussed in connection with the directions given for sharpening saws in Chapter 4.

The old-fashioned grindstone is a natural sandstone wheel which is mounted on a troughlike iron frame. It may be driven either by belt or by coupled motor drive. The arbor of the motor has a worm gear which engages a cogwheel on the shaft of the grindstone.

Water should drip continually on the stone while it is in use. When its surface becomes glazed or filled with small particles of steel, a truing device, consisting of a corrugated roller, can be clamped to the iron frame and forced against the revolving stone, making its cutting surface as sharp as ever. For grinding chisels and plane irons the grindstone is an excellent machine tool.

Emery grinders vary in design and construction all the way from the single hand-driven emery wheel to the ball-bearing, motor-driven, oilstone grinder shown in Figure 157. A machine of this type usually has two emery wheels, one coarse for rapid grinding and one fine for whetting. The wheels are often cup-shaped, being about 8 in. in diameter and having a 2 in. face.

Fig. 158. Grinding a plane iron on an oilstone grinder. Kerosene drops on inside of cup wheel and filters through to the surface.

Fig. 157. All-purpose oil stone grinder.

The oil drips on the inside of the cup wheels, saturating them, and a wiper prevents the oil from being thrown off the wheels. These wheels run at a speed of 300 r.p.m.

Besides these wheels the machine illustrated carries a dry emery wheel, an emery cone for grinding gouges, and a leather stropping wheel.

The latter three wheels run at a speed of 1800 r.p.m.

The machine has a table which can be tilted to different angles, and a tool holder for chisels, plane irons, and similar cutting tools (Fig. 158). The tool-holder which slides in a groove in the table has a screw-feed mechanism. Gears and wheels are fully guarded.

126. Automatic knife grinders are similar to oilstone grinders, but have a table which automatically slides back and forth at right angles to the cutting wheels (Figs. 159 and 160). With the new knife-grinding attachments on jointers and planers, these machines are not so indispensable for ordinary woodworking machinery.

The lathe is described in Chapter 9 on Wood Turning.

For further information on woodworking machines and machine operations consult the author's books *Modern Machine Woodworking* and *Operation of Modern Woodworking Machines,* both published by The Bruce Publishing Company, Milwaukee, Wisconsin.

Fig. 159.
Automatic knife
grinder.

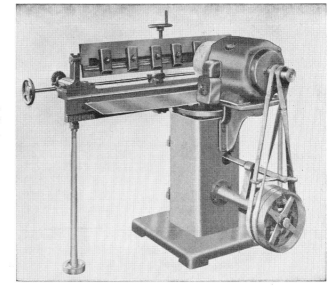

Fig. 160.
Automatic knife
grinder, with knife
in position.

REVIEW QUESTIONS, CHAPTER 3

Possible score 50 points

Your score . . . . . .

PART I. COMPLETION QUESTIONS.   Complete the following statements:

1. It is generally agreed that the most useful and indispensable woodworking machine is the . . . .
2. A universal saw has a . . . .
3. Saws with one arbor are called . . . .
4. On a direct-motor drive saw the saw arbor is the. . . . . of the motor.
5. A soft metal or wooden plate which has a slot through which the saw blade projects is called a . . . .
6. When cutting a number of short blocks on the circular saw, a . . . . is first fastened to the ripping fence.
7. . . . . occur when a piece of wood is picked up by the saw teeth and thrown back toward the operator.
8. When ripping short, narrow stock the operator should use a . . . .
9. The heavy, cast, curved arm of a band saw is called the . . . .
10. The method of adjusting a band saw blade properly on the upper wheel is called . . . .
11. Band saw blades are generally folded in three and . . . . loops.
12. The driving mechanism of a jig saw is called . . . .
13. Short, thick, and wide blades used on the power jig saw are called . . . .

14. On a jointer, the infeed table is moved up or down whereas the outfeed table usually remains ....
15. The planer or surfacer is a machine which planes boards or planks primarily to ....
16. Chip breakers on planers are either made as single units or in ....
17. The machine which cuts mortises by way of an auger bit and hollow chisel is called a ....
18. The horizontal double-spindle boring machine is particularly useful when making ....
19. Of all woodworking machines, the .... is considered the most dangerous one.
20. The safest type of shaper cutter is the so-called ....

PART II. TRUE-FALSE QUESTIONS. Indicate, by encircling T or F, whether the following statements are true or false:

21. The portable router is one of the oldest machines used in general woodworking.   T   F
22. A large belt sander generally has two cast-iron columns each of which carries a large pulley and a table placed between them.   T   F
23. The supporting table of a disk sander is always stationary.   T   F
24. A wood-turning lathe is readily made into a disk sander.   T   F
25. Straight-line stroke sanders are particularly useful in finishing work.   T   F
26. Multipurpose machines are of recent development.   T   F
27. "Shopsmith" cannot be made into a band saw.   T   F
28. The "Deltashop" can be converted into a jig saw by means of the saber saw attachment.   T   F
29. "Power shop" has the appearance of a typical circular saw.   T   F
30. Compressed air has little or no application in the furniture industry. T   F

PART III. MULTIPLE-CHOICE QUESTIONS. Select, by encircling the correct letter, the answer which completes each statement:

31. One of the following cannot be performed on the circular saw:
    A. Cutting holes
    B. Ripping
    C. Dadoing
    D. Grooving
32. Which of the following four saws protects the operator from kick-back?
    A. Dado saw
    B. Ripsaw
    C. Cut-control saw
    D. Hollow-ground saw
33. When the jointer cuts deeper on the last inch or two on the edge of a board, it is caused by:
    A. Outfeed table too high
    B. Infeed table too high
    C. Outfeed table too low
    D. Both tables too high

34. The part of the planer that feeds stock into the machine is:
    A. Lower infeed roll
    B. Chip breaker
    C. Pressure bar
    D. Corrugated feed roll
35. One of the following companies manufactures a multipurpose woodworking machine:
    A. Rockwell Mfg. Co.
    B. Oliver Machine Co.
    C. Stanley Tools
    D. S. A. Woods Machine Co.

PART IV. MATCHING QUESTIONS.   Match the terms to the left with the descriptions to the right by placing the correct letter in the parentheses:

36. (   ) "Power Shop"
37. (   ), Splitter guard
38. (   ) Stop rod
39. (   ) Raker teeth
40. (   ) Inside cutters
41. (   ) Anti-kickback dog
42. (   ) Steel jaws
43. (   ) Rotary cutting
44. (   ) Barefaced tenon
45. (   ) Ram

A. A part of the circular saw.
B. Parts of an assembled dado head.
C. A tenon with one shoulder and one cheek cut.
D. The cutting principle discovered by Samuel Bentham in 1791.
E. Manufactured by De Walt, Inc.
F. Teeth on a hollow-ground planer blade, shaped as rip teeth.
G. A device on the miter gauge used to cut pieces to even length.
H. Driving mechanism of a mortising machine.
 I. Part of a saw guard that prevents stock from being thrown back.
J. Parts of a band-saw guide.
K. Oliver Machine Co.
L. A sliding fence equipped with a clamping device.

PART V. PROBLEMS.   Calculate the answers to the following problems:

46. What is the length of a 6-in. endless belt, when the diameter of the pulley is 14 in. and the distance between pulley centers is 96 in.? How much belting material would be required to splice a belt for a machine of that size? The splice is made at a 45-degree angle with 1 in. allowed for overlaps.
47. If the diameters of the wheels of two band saws are 24 and 36 in. and the distances between wheel centers are 48 and 72 in. respectively, how much blade stock is required for each machine to prepare a new blade?
48. If a 36-in. band saw makes 600 r.p.m., what is its cutting speed in feet per minute?

CHAPTER

4

The Sharpening of Tools*

The ability to sharpen tools properly is the first requisite of anyone aspiring to become a woodworker. It always pays *to take the time to sharpen tools, both from the standpoint of performance, as well as actual time saved in the execution of the work.*

A. Hand Tools

128. Sharpening a Saw. The process of sharpening a saw may be divided into three operations: (1) jointing and shaping the teeth, (2) setting, and (3) filing. *Jointing* is necessary only when the teeth of a saw have been worn uneven by hard use, or damaged through carelessness or accident.

1. To joint a saw, clamp it in a saw vise, and run a flat file over the teeth until every tooth is touched by the file (Fig. 1). The points of some of the teeth will now be quite flat, while others will barely be touched by the file. The best results are obtained if the file is fastened in a holder made especially for the purpose.

Fig. 1. Jointing a hand crosscut saw.

---

* For a more complete discussion of sharpening hand and machine tools, see: Cunningham, B. M., and Holtrop, W. F., "Woodshop Tool Maintenance." Ch. A. Bennett Co., 1956.

2. When the teeth are of uniform height, they are filed until they are of the same size and shape. Use a 6- or 7-in. slim-taper, triangular file, and begin in the gullet next to the handle. File down into the blade, until the tooth to the right is up to a point, and half of the flat point of the tooth to the left has been removed. Start the file in the next gullet to the left, and continue until all the teeth have been filed. The file is held level and at right angles to the blade of the saw, whether the saw is of the rip or crosscut type. Make no attempt to bevel the teeth of a crosscut saw at this stage. As shaping the teeth requires experience and skill, the learner should practice on an old saw with a new one as a model in front of him.

Setting a Saw. When the teeth of a saw are all even as in a new saw, they must be bent slightly outward (Fig. 2) so that the saw kerf will be wide enough to prevent the saw from binding in the wood. This operation is called "setting," and requires a special tool called a "saw set" (Fig. 3). All saws need to be set.

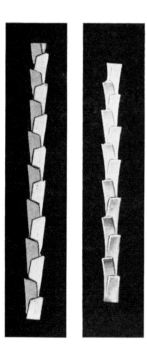

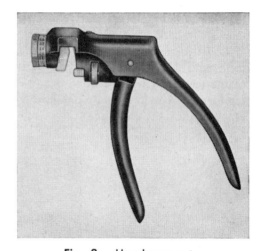

Fig. 3.   Hand saw set.

Fig. 2.   Crosscut and ripsaw teeth properly set.

3. The saw set is adjusted so that the amount of set given the teeth corresponds to the number stamped on the lower edge of the saw blade near the handle or to the number of points per inch (p. 27). Some saw

sets have a metal disk or anvil varying in thickness on the edge of which several numbers indicating points to the inch are stamped. When the disk is turned until the desired number is opposite the plunger pin the teeth will be bent to the correct angle.

4. Fasten the saw in the vise, and, starting at one end, bend every other tooth in the same direction it was bent before. The teeth should be bent about two thirds from the point to the gullet. Reverse the saw, and set the other half of the teeth in the same way (Fig. 4). A saw usually can be filed several times between each setting. Figure 5 shows a mechanical saw

Fig. 5. Mechanical saw set.

Fig. 4. Setting a hand ripsaw.

set. This machine sets handsaw teeth fast and accurately by means of a small trip hammer. As each tooth is set, a feed pawl moves the saw to the next one. After completing the set in one row of teeth, the saw is moved upside down, and the second row of teeth is set. The machine illustrated here sets teeth ranging from 4½ to 16 points per inch.

Filing a Ripsaw. The teeth of a ripsaw are shaped like a series of small chisels, and should be filed straight across (Fig. 6).

Fig. 6. Ripsaw teeth.

5. After the saw has been set, place it in a saw vise so that the gullets of the teeth are about ⅛ in. above the jaws of the vise. If a saw vise is not available, the saw may be placed between two pieces of wood in an ordinary bench vise (Fig. 7).

6. With the handle of the saw placed to the right, begin filing from the point or narrow end of the saw. Start in the first gullet to the left of the first tooth set toward you.

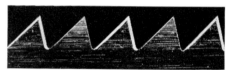

Fig. 8.   Crosscut saw teeth.

Fig. 7.   Filing a ripsaw.

7. Hold the file level and at right angles to the saw blade, and push it straight across the teeth.

8. Repeat the process in every other gullet, until half of the teeth have been filed. Then reverse the saw, placing the handle at the left, and file the other half.

Filing a Crosscut Saw.   The teeth of a crosscut saw (Fig. 8) are filed to a knife point. The process is the same as described for filing a ripsaw.

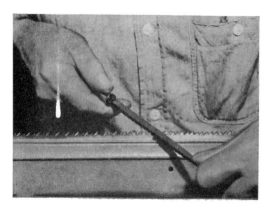

Fig. 9.   Filing a crosscut saw.

The file is almost level, but at an angle of about 60 deg. to the blade of the saw. In this way a bevel is filed on the front side of one tooth, while at the same time a corresponding bevel is filed on the rear side of the adjoining tooth (Figs. 8 and 9). The front of each tooth makes an angle of 15 degrees with a line perpendicular to the tooth line.

129. Procedure for Sharpening a Plane Iron. When a plane iron, gouge, chisel, or spokeshave blade has been nicked, or has been whetted on the oilstone so often that its bevel has become short, it is necessary to grind it on a grindstone or emery wheel. Ordinarily, a cutting iron may be whetted a few times before it is necessary to regrind it.

1. Remove the cap from the cutter iron, and grind the bevel on an oilstone grinder or emery wheel (Fig. 158, p. 134) until it is true, straight, and at right angles to the side of the iron. Move the iron back and forth across the face of the stone while grinding, and use plenty of water to prevent burning.

2. It is important that the bevel is ground flat or slightly concave, and that the iron is not burned while grinding. Burning means that the edge or part of it turns a blue-black color. When this happens, the temper of the steel is drawn or lost, and the edge will not stay sharp.

3. The length of the bevel should be about twice the thickness of the tool. This gives a grinding angle of 25 to 30 deg. The tool with the holder is moved from side to side across the face of the stone. The stone should always revolve toward the tool, because it cuts faster that way and forms a smaller wire edge. Kerosene is used as a cooling liquid on oilstone grinders. On cup wheels the kerosene drops on the inside of the wheel through a small pipe (Fig. 158, p. 134), and filters through to the surface of the stone.

4. It is extremely difficult to grind tools on a dry emery wheel without burning them, even though dipping them frequently in cold water. The tools should be tested for squareness of bevel with sides when they have been ground (Fig. 10).

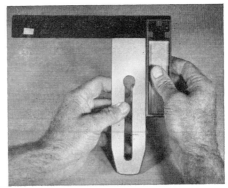

Fig. 10. Checking squareness of plane iron.

5. The wire edge formed during the grinding process is now removed by *whetting* the iron on an oilstone. Machine oil thinned with kerosene is used as a lubricant. Never use water on an oilstone, because it allows small particles of steel to be embedded in its surface (glazing).

6. Place the bevel flat on the oilstone, raise the iron a little, and move it back and forth or with a circular motion, pressing on it with the left hand (Fig. 11). Use the whole surface of the stone to wear it down evenly.

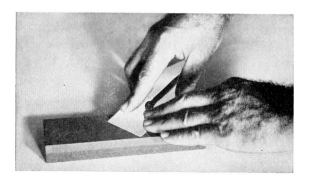

Fig. 11. Whetting plane iron, bevel side down.

7. Reverse the iron, and place it flat on the oilstone, beveled side up. Press on it with the left hand, and move it back and forth a few times (Fig. 12). Be careful to hold it absolutely flat.

8. Repeat the process until the wire edge has been removed (Fig. 13). This usually drops off on the oilstone and appears as a silvery thread.

9. Finish the whetting by drawing the iron a few times over a piece of leather belting which has been glued to a wooden block with the smooth side of the belting up. A smooth hardwood block without the leather will also serve. Test the sharpness of the iron on the thumb (Fig. 14).

Most of a wire edge can also be removed on a so-called grinder-hone (Fig. 15). Complete honing on a hard Arkansas stone.

Chisels and spokeshaves are sharpened in the same way.

A worn-down oilstone can easily and quickly be leveled off by rubbing

Fig. 12. Whetting plane iron, flat side down,

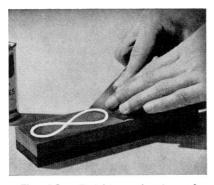

Fig. 13. Finishing whetting of plane iron.

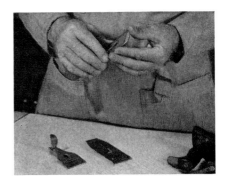

Fig. 14. Testing plane iron for sharpness.

it on a iron surface, using kerosene and powdered emery as an abrasive. It may also be rubbed down on a piece of level concrete with sand and water, or on a piece of coarse garnet paper.

130. Procedure for Sharpening Gouges. 1. Outside bevel gouges are ground on the outside only. Grasp the handle with the right hand, and hold the blade to the surface of the stone with the left hand. Move the gouge across the face of the stone with a rolling motion.

2. Inside bevel gouges are ground on a conical grinding wheel.

3. Both types of gouges are whetted on an oilstone having a wedge-shaped cross section and rounded edges (Fig. 16). Such a stone is called a "slip stone" (see Sharpening of Wood-Turner's Gouge, Art. 134).

Fig. 15. Removing wire edge on so-called grinder-hone.

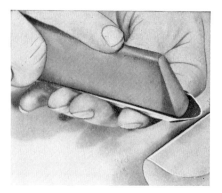

Fig. 16.   Whetting inside
of gouge.

Fig. 17.   Filing edge of cabinet
scraper.

131. Procedure for Sharpening and Adjusting a Cabinet Scraper.   1. File the edge of a cabinet scraper to an angle of 60–70 deg.; next whet it exactly as you would a plane iron (Art. 129). It is necessary to re-sharpen the cabinet scraper every time it becomes dull (Fig. 17).

2. Place the scraper in a vise, and bend the edge with a burnisher. Start the burnisher in contact with the whole bevel, and move it across the blade, pressing lightly. Elevate the handle of the burnisher gradually in the succeeding strokes until it forms an angle of about 15 deg. with the horizontal, and increase the pressure (Fig. 18).

Fig. 18.   Turning cabinet scraper
edge.

Fig. 19.   Using a sharp cabinet
scraper.

An excellent burnisher can be made from an old triangular file by grinding away the teeth on a grindstone.

3. To adjust the blade in a cabinet scraper, loosen the three thumbscrews in the holder, place it on a flat wooden surface, and insert the blade from the bottom so that the bevel is toward the adjusting thumb screw in the center.

4. Tighten the two thumbscrews which clamp the blade to the holder, and turn the adjusting screw until it bears loosely against the blade. Turn it a fraction of a revolution at a time, until the scraper cuts a shaving of the desired thickness (Fig. 19).

132. Procedure for Sharpening a Hand Scraper. 1. Fasten the scraper blade in the vise with one of the long edges up.

2. Grasp a flat mill file with both hands, one at each end. Hold the file level and at right angles to the blade, and move it back and forth over

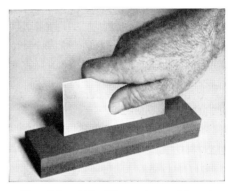

Fig. 21. Whetting edge of hand scraper.

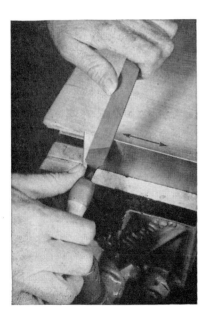

Fig. 20. Drawfiling hand scraper.

the edge, longitudinally (Fig. 20). This method of using a file is called "drawfiling." Test the edge for flatness.

3. When the two long edges have been drawfiled, the burr formed by the filing must be removed on the oilstone. Hold the scraper perpendicular to the face of the stone, and whet the edge (Fig. 21). Then place one side flat on the face of the stone moving it back and forth (Fig. 22), then on the other side, and then again the edge until the burr has disappeared.

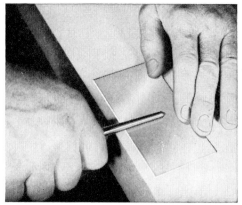

Fig. 23.   Flattening edge of
hand scraper.

Fig. 22.   Whetting side of scraper.

4. Place the scraper flat on the bench near the edge and rub a burnisher over the sides in order to draw the metal slightly over the edges as in Figures 23 and 24.

5. The edges may now be turned in one of three different ways: (*a*) Place the scraper in a vise and turn the edges by rubbing a burnisher over them,

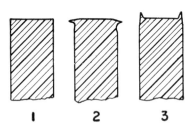

Fig. 24.   Enlarged sections of hand scraper. 1. Sharpened on oilstone; 2. edges turned with burnisher; 3. edges flattened for resharpening.

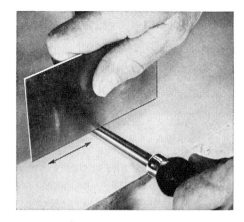

Fig. 25.   Burnishing edge of hand scraper.

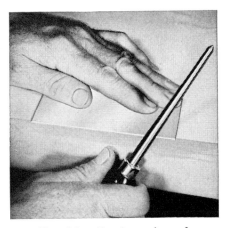 

Fig. 26. Turning edge of hand scraper.

Fig. 27. Smoothing with a hand scraper.

tilting it slightly to alternate sides. (*b*) Hold a triangular burnisher flat on the workbench and rub the scraper across it, tilting it slightly to alternate sides (Fig. 25). (*c*) Hold the scraper flat on the bench, so that its edge projects a little over the edge of the bench, and draw the burnisher slightly upward and toward you (Fig. 26). To produce an extra fine edge on a scraper, a drop of oil should be rubbed on the burnisher.

6. To resharpen a hand scraper, place it flat on the bench top, and flatten the turned-up edge carefully with the burnisher as in Figure 23. Then repeat the process described in the preceding paragraph.

A hand scraper may be resharpened with the burnisher several times before it needs to be drawfiled.

When properly sharpened a hand scraper should make thin shavings as shown in Figure 27.

133. Procedure for Sharpening an Auger Bit. 1. To sharpen the spurs, hold the bit against the side of the workbench so that the screw points upward. File the spurs on the *inside* only, with an auger-bit file, until the cutting edge is sharp (Fig. 28).

2. To sharpen the lips, rest the screw of the bit on the bench, and file the lips on the *upper* side only (Fig. 29). Remove an equal amount of material from both lips.

3. To straighten an auger bit that has been bent, roll it on a flat surface to determine where it has been bent. Strike light blows on the high side with a mallet until the bend has disappeared.

Fig. 28.   Filing spurs on auger bit.

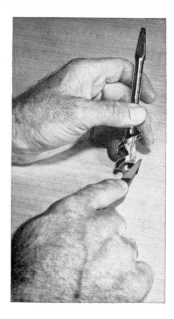

Fig. 29.   Filing lips on auger bit.

Sharpening Turning Tools

134. The gouge (Fig. 30), which is similar to an ordinary outside bevel gouge, is ground on a sandstone or an emery wheel.

1. The end of the gouge is ground to a semicircular shape, and the bevel should extend well around to the sides so as to leave no sharp corners as on the ordinary gouge. The bevel should be about twice as long as the gouge is thick.

2. Grasp the handle with the right hand, and hold the blade to the surface of the stone with the left hand. Move the gouge across the face of the stone with a rolling motion.

3. When the grinding has been completed, the gouge is whetted on an oilstone. The bevel is brought in contact with the stone, and the gouge moved back and forth, at the same time rolling it from one side to the other.

4. The wire edge, which is bent toward the inside by this process, is removed by rubbing the rounded edge of a slip stone back and forth over it (Fig. 31). Care should be taken to keep the whole edge of the slip stone in contact with the inside of the gouge during this operation.

135. The square-nose chisel is like an ordinary chisel, except that it is longer (Fig. 30). In fact, a common chisel, which is fairly heavy and has a long blade, may be used in its place. It is sharpened exactly in the same manner as a common chisel (Art. 129) except that the bevel should be shorter.

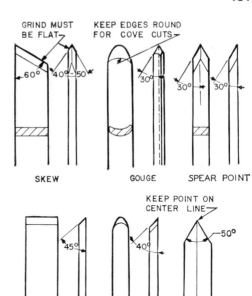

Fig. 30. Grinding angles for wood-turning tools.

136. The skew chisel (Fig. 30) is ground so that two bevels are formed instead of one. The cutting edge should be at an angle of about 60 deg. with the side of the chisel. While grinding, grasp the handle firmly with the right hand, press down on the blade with the left, and hold the chisel at such an angle that the cutting edge is parallel to the axis of the grindstone or emery wheel (Fig. 32).

Fig. 31. Whetting inside of gouge with slip stone.

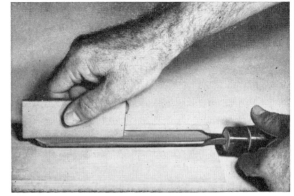

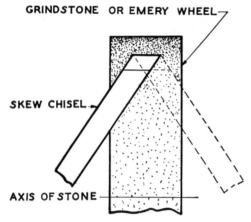

GRINDSTONE OR EMERY WHEEL

SKEW CHISEL

AXIS OF STONE

Fig. 32. Position of a skew chisel on a grindstone.

Whet the chisel on the oilstone, and test for sharpness on the thumb nail.

137. The parting or cutoff tool (Fig. 30) has two bevels, which should be of equal length and meet in the ridge running through the center of the blade. If they do not meet at this point, which is the thickest point on the chisel, it will not cut itself free, but will bind and stick in the wood. The bevels should be ground straight and true. The wire edge is removed on the oilstone.

138. The round-nose chisel (Fig. 30) is ground very much like a gouge. As it has only one bevel, the opposite side is held flat on the oilstone in the same manner as a square-nose chisel.

139. The diamond-point or spear-point chisel (Fig. 30) is like a round-nose chisel except that it is pointed instead of rounded. It has two bevels, both on the same side of the chisel. While grinding, it should be held on the stone at an angle, so that its edge is parallel to the axis of the stone. It is whetted in the same manner as a square-nose and a round-nose chisel.

140. The right or left skew chisel or turning chisel is shaped like an ordinary skew chisel, but has only one bevel. It is sharpened like a spear-point chisel (Fig. 30).

141. Procedure for Cleaning a Rasp or a File. The old accepted method of cleaning files is to use fire, as follows:

1. When a rasp or file has been gummed up with particles of wood wedged between its teeth, it may be cleaned by dipping it in alcohol and setting fire to it. Hold the file by the handle, dip it into a bottle, or pour a little alcohol over it carefully. *Cork the bottle,* hold the wet file horizontally, light a match, and apply it to the file. The alcohol will burn with a small blue flame for about half a minute, and then die out.

Fig. 33. Cleaning a file.

Solid alcohol may be used instead of liquid alcohol. Hold the file in the flame for short periods at a time.

2. Brush the file with a file card (Fig. 33). This usually removes all traces of wood from the file. If the file is not clean after it has been brushed, a second application of alcohol is necessary.

In most cases, however, it is readily possible to clean files in a very satisfactory way by soaking them in hot water for an hour and then brushing them with a steel brush. The soaking swells the wood which is stuck between the teeth of the file and loosens it so that it may be readily removed with a brush. It is necessary, however, that files dry quickly to prevent rusting.

B. Machine Tools

It is even more important to sharpen machine tools than hand tools, because a dull tool driven by the force of a motor endangers the safety of the operator, is difficult to work with, and does not produce clean and accurate work.

142. Jointing Circular Saws. To joint a circular saw, lower it until its teeth barely project above the saw table. They should project just enough to score a piece of wood held flat on the table.

1. Start the saw, and pass an emery stone over the table above it. A lot of sparks will now fly. When they diminish, stop the saw and examine every tooth. If some of the teeth have not been touched by the stone, raise the saw slightly and continue jointing until every tooth has a bright point. The saw is then perfectly round (Fig. 34).

2. Jointing is usually not done every time a saw needs sharpening, but as the job takes only a short time and the bright points help in filing a saw correctly, it is recommended to joint it often.

Fig. 34. Jointing a circular saw.

3. As the arbor hole is slightly larger than the arbor, the saw will not run perfectly true unless replaced in the same position. Make it a habit to replace saws on the arbor with the manufacturer's name up.

143. Gumming a Circular Ripsaw. 1. After repeated filings, the gullets between the teeth become too shallow and clog up easily with sawdust. They must, therefore, be ground or filed down to their original depth. This operation is called "gumming" and is usually done with a thin emery wheel, mounted on a regular grinding machine, or in a lathe.

2. This grinding wheel should be about ¼ in. thick by about 8 in. in diameter. It should have a rather hard, medium grain. If it is to be used in a lathe, it is mounted on a mandrel having the same taper as the lathe center. Its other end has a small hole and runs on the dead center. The

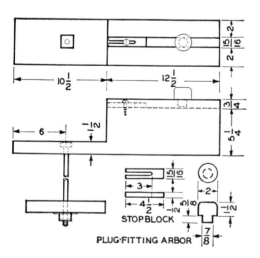

Fig. 35. Jig for gumming circular saws.

edge of the emery wheel is then shaped with an emery-wheel dresser to fit the shape of the gullets in the saw.

3. A wooden jig, as shown in Figure 35 is made to clamp to the lathe bed. The thick part is made equal to half the swing of the lathe. Its upper edge is grooved through the center and fitted with a stop block. The width of the groove is equal to the diameter of the arbor hole. A turned plug fits into the arbor hole. It slides in the groove until it butts up against the stop block. In this way all the gullets are ground to the same depth and angle.

4. Before adjusting the jig, the correct angle must be found. To do this, draw a circle halfway between the edge and the center of the saw. Then draw a tangent to this circle from any one of the tooth points (Fig. 36). This line gives the correct angle at which the front of the teeth must be ground. It is called the "rake." The lines may be drawn on the circular saw with a red pencil, chalk, or a fountain pen.

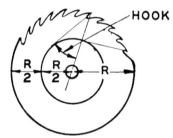

Fig. 36. Laying out the rake on a circular ripsaw.

Fig. 37. Setup on lathe for gumming a circular saw.

5. The jig is now clamped to the lathe and the stop block is adjusted. Put a drop of oil on the dead center before starting the lathe (Fig. 37). Run it at a medium speed and be careful not to burn the saw. Crosscut saws are generally filed, but may be gummed with a very thin emery wheel.

144. Setting Circular Saws. 1. The next step in sharpening circular saws is to set or bend the teeth. Small saw blades are set with an ordinary saw set like those used for handsaws. Larger saw blades, from 10 to 16 in., are set by striking the teeth with a hammer.

2. A setting device consists of a beveled anvil fixed to a cast-iron base. At the other end is a movable pin over which the saw is placed. A cone-shaped casting fits over this pin and into the arbor hole of the saw, so that it will be accurately centered (Fig. 38).

Fig. 38.   Circular-saw set.

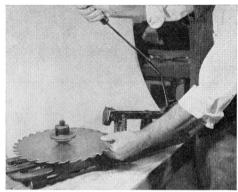

Fig. 39.   Saw setting machine.

3. The pin is then adjusted so that the outer third of each tooth projects over the beveled part of the anvil. Set every other tooth by striking a punch which is fixed above the anvil. Then reverse the saw and set the rest of the teeth. A trip-hammer saw set (Fig. 39) delivers a blow of exactly the same force every time.

4. Set only a small part of the teeth, because otherwise too much resistance to the passage of the wood will be encountered and the cut will be rough and uneven.

5. Miter saws are not set. They are hollow ground and therefore are thinner at the center than at the edge. Ripsaws over 16 in. in diameter are usually swaged like the inside cutter of a dado head. This means spreading the points of the teeth so that they will make a saw kerf wide enough to clear the rest of the saw. A tool called a saw swage (Fig. 40) is used.

Fig. 40.   Saw swage.

145. Filing a Circular Ripsaw.   1. After gumming and setting, the saw is now ready to be filed. If a filing machine, such as is shown in Figure 53, is not available, a clamp for holding the saw while it is filed must be either bought or made.

2. An iron clamp or vise, as shown in Figure 41, is on the market; a wooden clamp, as shown in Figure 42, can easily be made in the shop. The front jaw of this clamp is hinged and slotted for a bolt which can be moved up or down in a similar slot in the rear jaw to which it is fastened. In this way saws of different diameters may be accommodated. The bolt is turned from a piece of 1-in. stock and is threaded on both ends.

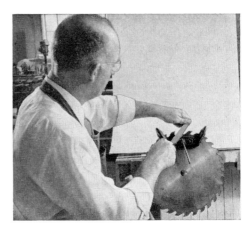

Fig. 41. Cast-iron saw filing clamp.

3. Use a flat mill file with rounded ends, hold the file level and take only light strokes. File the top of the teeth set away from you, then reverse the saw in the clamp and file the rest of the teeth. Some woodworkers prefer to bevel the teeth slightly on top.

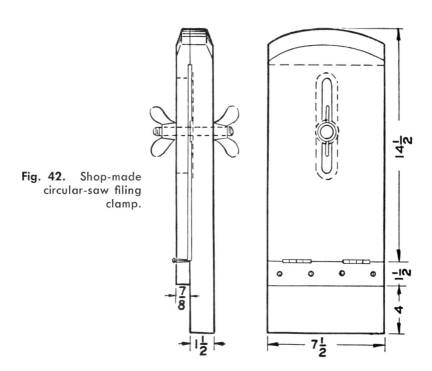

Fig. 42. Shop-made circular-saw filing clamp.

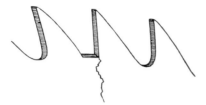

Fig. 43. Crack caused by square gullet on circular ripsaw.

4. If the saw has not been gummed, it is necessary first to file the front edge of each tooth. The rounded edges of the file keep the gullets round. Square gullets often cause the saw blade to crack (Fig. 43).

146. Filing Circular Crosscut Saws. 1. As the crosscut saws have beveled edges like those of a handsaw, it is more convenient to file them when clamped in the iron saw-filing vise (Fig. 41) because that can be tilted to 45 deg.

2. The bevels should not extend all the way down to the gullets, as these should be round (Fig. 44). File the bevels on those teeth that are set away from you, then reverse the saw and file the remaining half of the teeth. Use a flat or triangular file.

Fig. 44. Bevels on circular crosscut saws. Wrong shape of bevel and gullet at X.

147. Filing Circular Miter Saws. 1. File the crosscut teeth of these saws in the same way as the regular crosscut saws. Usually there are no gullets between the crosscut teeth, and the bevel extends all the way down. Follow these bevels as closely as possible, using either a flat or a triangular file.

2. The rip or raker teeth are filed straight across as in a ripsaw, but they should be a trifle lower than the crosscut teeth. Test them by taking a shallow cut in a piece of wood. If the bottom of the saw cut is flat, the raker teeth are too high, and must be filed a little more, but if too sharp lines are scored in each side of the saw cut, it shows that the crosscut teeth are a trifle longer than the raker teeth. When the crosscut teeth are a little longer, a smoother cut will result.

148. Brazing Band Saws. 1. Straighten out any kinks or bends the saw may have received in breaking, and *scarf* the two ends to be soldered; i.e., file their sides to a taper for a distance equal to the length of one or two teeth (Fig. 45). This filing should be done carefully, so that the filed surfaces are perfectly flat and the finished joint is of the same thickness as the rest of the saw.

Fig. 45. Scarfing band saw.

Fig. 46. Brazing clamp.

Fig. 47. Brazing tongs.

A band saw should always have an even number of teeth, so that succeeding teeth will all be set opposite to one another.

2. Clamp the saw in a brazing clamp (Fig. 46) so that it is perfectly aligned. Mix a little borax with water to form a paste, and coat the filed surfaces with this mixture.

This is called a "flux" which keeps the surfaces clean while the heat is applied. A specially prepared flux also may be used.

3. Cut a strip of silver solder the length of the scarf, coat it with the flux, and insert it between the surfaces to be soldered. Silver solder for band-saw brazing is manufactured in rolls of different widths.

4. Heat a pair of brazing tongs (Fig. 47) until they take a bright-red color, and clamp the joint together. The red-hot tongs heat the blade and melt the solder. Keep the tongs clamped on the saw blade until they turn black. If the joint is cooled too quickly, it does not hold. The joint also may be heated by a blowtorch, special brazing lamp, or electric current.

5. When using an electric brazer, Figure 48, the joint should be prepared and clamped as described above. When the current is turned on, heat is automatically applied to both ends of the saw blade. After a few seconds, the joint becomes red and the solder melts. The current is then turned off, and the center clamp is tightened for a few seconds to bring the ends of the joint close together. If a joint cools too quickly, as it is likely to do when the electric heater is used, it becomes very hard and brittle. To prevent it from breaking, reheat it to a dull red color.

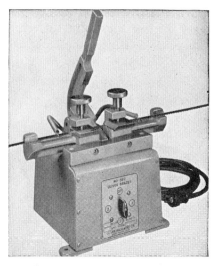

Fig. 48.   Electric band-saw
brazer.

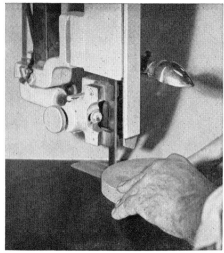

Fig. 49.   Jointing teeth directly
on band saw.

6. Smooth the joint on both sides with a fine, flat file, then finish it with fine emery cloth.

149. Jointing Band-Saw Teeth.   Before band-saw teeth are set or filed, they should be brought to uniform length by jointing. This can be done with a flat mill file, as shown in Figure 1, or it can be done directly on the band saw (Fig. 49).

150. Setting Band Saws.   1. Narrow band saws may be set by hand with an ordinary saw set, or by machine. Band-saw setters are either hand or

Fig. 50.   Hand-operated
band-saw setting machine.

motor driven. They have two hammers, which automatically bend the teeth to alternate sides, and a pawl, which moves the saw past the hammers (Fig. 50). The amount of set and pawl movement or feed is adjustable.

2. To use the setting machine, adjust the amount of set and the feed. Mark the point where the setting begins with chalk. Place the saw on a table or bench so that it can move freely through the machine.

Fig. 51. Band-saw fitting wheels.

Fitting wheels (Fig. 51), which are faced with leather, are very convenient for mounting the saw while it is being set or filed.

151. Filing Band Saws. Filing may be done by hand or by machine. Some machines do both the setting and filing operations. When filed by hand, it is very convenient to use a special vise 20 in. long in connection with the fitting wheels (Fig. 52). If this is not available, an ordinary bench vise may be used and the saw laid in the trough of the bench.

File the band saw straight across in the manner explained for filing hand ripsaws. Use a blunt triangular file with rounded edges, because this gives just the right hook to the front of the teeth on narrow blades. Place the file in each gullet so that it rests on the back of the next tooth, and thus files the front of one and the back of another at the same time. File all the teeth from one side of the saw.

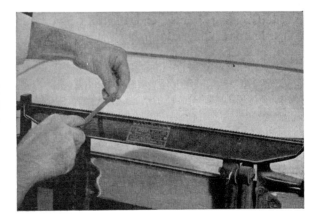

Fig. 52. Special band-saw filing clamp.

 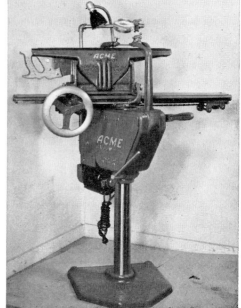

Fig. 53. Automatic saw filer.   **Fig. 54.** Hand saw filing machine.

The machine illustrated in Figure 53 can file practically any kind of circular saws. The one shown in Figure 54 is especially designed to sharpen all kinds of handsaws. The machine shown in Figure 55 illustrates a new technique in saw sharpening. Instead of sharpening the teeth to a fine point with a file or abrasive wheel, it is done by means of an abrasive belt.

152. Grinding Jointer and Planer Knives. 1. On machines equipped with a knife-grinding attachment the knives need not be removed from the cutterhead. Instead, the cutterhead is locked with a pin, which brings one of the knives into grinding position. All the bolts holding the knife are now loosened, after which it is moved up about ⅟₁₆ in. with a special adjusting wrench furnished with the machine (Fig. 56). Use the three-pronged knife-adjusting gauge or the micrometer gauge, shown in Figure 57, to set it as accurately as possible. The bolts are then tightened again and the next knife brought into position.

2. When all the knives in the cutterhead have been moved up the same distance, the grinding motor is bolted to a casting called the "saddle" which is moved back and forth on a steel bar (the bridge) by a continuous screw (Fig. 58).

Fig. 55. Sharpening circular saw teeth with abrasive belt.

3. Adjust the motor so that only a very light cut is taken and move it back and forth over the knife several times. Be careful to move it fast enough so that the knife is not burned. Repeat on the other knives, locking the cutterhead with the pin, so that each one in turn is held firmly in the correct grinding position.

4. When the first knife is again brought into position, the motor is lowered slightly and again moved several times over the knife. Repeat on the other knives and lower the motor each time all the knives have been gone over until all nicks have been ground away and a perfect bevel has been obtained on every knife in the cutterhead.

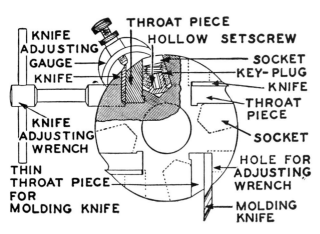

Fig. 56. Section view of knife setter.

Fig. 57. Micrometer knife-setting gauge.

Fig. 58. Planer with knife-grinding attachment in position.

5. Remove the motor from the saddle and bolt a jointing attachment to it. A jointing attachment has a fine whetstone clamped to its lower end which can be adjusted vertically by a screw (Fig. 59).

6. Set it so that it barely touches the knives. Revolve the cutterhead by hand to make sure, then start the machine and move the jointing attachment back and forth over the revolving knives.

7. Stop the machine and examine the knives. If they have not all been touched by the whetstone, move the stone down slightly and repeat the process. Be careful not to joint the knives too much, otherwise a rounded surface or "heel" will be formed behind the cutting edge. Too much heel is likely to cause the knives to pound, heat up, and produce a glazed surface.

8. Knives on older or smaller machines which are not equipped with a knife-grinding attachment, have to be removed from the cutterhead for grinding. Knife-grinding machines have a carriage, which

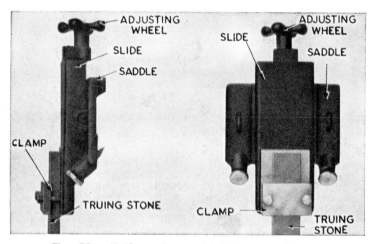

Fig. 59. Knife-setting and jointing attachment.

slides on a fixed bed and moves back and forth in front of a grinding wheel. The movement of the carriage is automatically reversed at each end of the bed so that the machine can be left running with only occasional adjustment (see Fig. 159, p. 135).

9. The knife to be ground is clamped to the carriage and adjusted to the correct grinding bevel, which is from 30 to 40 deg. A pump sends a continuous stream of oil over the knife to cool it.

10. If a special knife grinder is not available, an oilstone grinder (see Fig. 157, p. 134) may be used for grinding thin knives up to 12 in. in length.

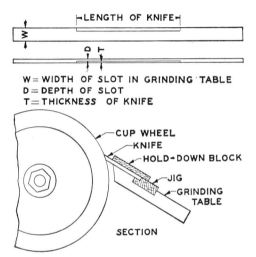

W = WIDTH OF SLOT IN GRINDING TABLE
D = DEPTH OF SLOT
T = THICKNESS OF KNIFE

Fig. 61. Grinding jointer knives on oilstone grinder.

Fig. 60. Knife-grinding jig.

11. A simple jig (Fig. 60), consists of two sticks of close-grained hardwood such as birch or maple. One stick, which slides in the slot in the table, has a recess cut for the knife. The other is simply used to hold the knife against the stone and protect the fingers from the heat generated by the grinding (Fig. 61). This stick may be fastened to the first one with a couple of brads or small screws.

12. When all the knives have been ground, they are weighed on a special knife balance or scale (Fig. 62). If the knives are not exactly of the same weight, they will cause the cutterhead to vibrate and run noisily. This will produce an uneven cut and ultimately damage the bearings. If one or more knives, therefore, are too heavy, they must be reground until their weight equals that of the lightest knife.

Fig. 62. Knife balance.

13. Whetting is done on an ordinary flat oilstone. A jig, as shown in Figure 63, is helpful in whetting the beveled side. The flat side is whetted just like a plane iron.

14. To replace the knives in the cutterhead of a jointer, place a builders'

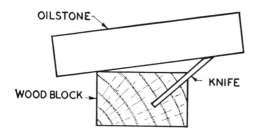

OILSTONE

WOOD BLOCK

KNIFE

Fig. 63. Slotted wooden block for whetting jointer knives.

level or a piece of hardwood with a straightedge on the outfeed table and line up the knives with it (Fig. 64). Screw the bolts in lightly and revolve the cutterhead by hand. If the knife lifts or moves the level, it is too high and must be tapped with a mallet to lower it. When the knife barely touches the level, it is at the correct height and the bolts should be tightened.

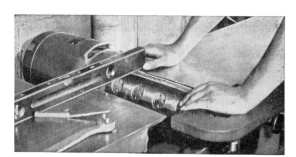

Fig. 64. Adjusting height of knife to outfeed table, using level or straightedge.

Fig. 65. Jointing knives on jointer.

15. Adjust the other knives in the same way, *but take time to do the job well, because smooth and even cutting depends upon it.* Be careful not to cut yourself when tightening the bolts. Try to cover the sharp edge of the knife with a piece of leather or rubber.

16. Move the jointer tables as close together as possible, but be sure that the cutterhead revolves freely. The knives may now be jointed by holding an oilstone on the outfeed table as shown in Figure 65. Wrap a piece of paper around that part of the stone resting on the outfeed table, then bring the infeed table up to the same height and clamp a stop block to it. Turn on the power, hold the stone with both hands, and move it across the tables, pressing lightly on it. This will bring the knives to the exact cutting circle so that each one will do the same amount of work.

17. Similar jigs may be made for trimmer knives, which are sharpened in the same way.

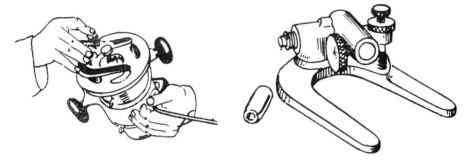

Fig. 66. Grinding attachment for shaper cutters and bits for portable router or shaper.

153. Sharpening Shaper Knives and Router Bits.   1. Flat shaper knives with straight cutting edges are sharpened just like plane irons and chisels.

2. Flat shaper knives with curved cutting edges may be sharpened with various-shaped small emery wheels or with a grinding pencil which can be held in the chuck of a portable router. A grinding pencil is an abrasive stone, shaped like a pencil point. The shape of the curves must first be carefully laid out from templates.

3. Three-lip shaper cutters also can be sharpened with a grinding pencil or small grinding wheels held in a router chuck. An attachment for holding the cutters while grinding them is made for some routers (Fig. 66).

4. Milled shaper cutters (Fig. 93, p. 104) are sharpened simply by grinding a flat bevel on them.

5. Router bits are sharpened on the inside with a special grinding wheel which fits in the chuck of a portable router.

154. Sharpening Hollow Chisels.   1. When hollow chisels become nicked or cracked, they can be reconditioned by grinding away the damaged part.

2. The square end produced as at A, Figure 67, is then milled out as

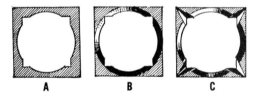

A   B   C

Fig. 67. End views of mortising chisel. A, ground flat; B, reamed; C, corners filed.

Fig. 68. Machine and milling cutter for sharpening hollow chisels.

at B. This may be done on a hand operated milling machine which has a clamp for holding the chisel in a vertical position while a milling cutter is rotated in its end (Fig. 68). Since the milling cutter has a pilot which fits the bore of the chisel, a different cutter must be used for each size chisel.

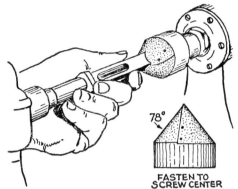

Fig. 69. Sanding cone for sharpening hollow chisels mounted in lathe.

3. A wooden cone may also be turned in a lathe and covered with emery paper. The cone is fastened to a screw chuck mounted on the live spindle and the upper end of the chisel is held on the dead center, which is gradually moved forward as the grinding progresses (Fig. 69).

4. The corners are then filed with a small triangular or auger-bit file as shown at C, Figure 67. Finally, remove the burrs by whetting the chisel on an oilstone.

5. If the chisel is not damaged but merely dull, it may be sharpened on the inside with a grinding pencil and file.

When grinding wheels clog up with particles of steel, oil, and dirt, they can be cleaned with one of three dressing tools: a diamond set in the end of a steel rod, a number of star-shaped wheels placed side by side in a steel holder (emery-wheel dresser), or hard, abrasive stones, plain or circular (Fig. 70). Soaking in kerosene or heating in an oven cleans the wheel of

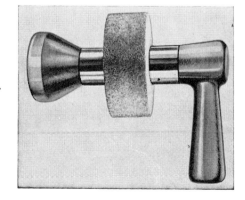

Fig. 70. Emery wheel dresser.

dirt and oil. *When dressing or shaping an emery wheel, be sure to wear goggles.*

Rust Remover. A solution made from the following simple and inexpensive ingredients removes rust from tools and machines very readily: 1 cup lye, ½ cup washing soda, and ½ teaspoon potassium permanganate dissolved in 1 quart of water. Apply the solution liberally to the surface to be cleaned. Small tools may be placed in a large, flat glass tray, such as is used by photographers, and covered with the solution.

REVIEW QUESTIONS, CHAPTER 4

Possible score 55 points

Your score . . . . . .

PART I. COMPLETION QUESTIONS.   Complete the following statements:

1. When a saw has teeth of uneven length, the first sharpening operation is . . . .
2. In order to cut properly without binding, saw teeth need a small amount of . . . .
3. A mechanical saw set sets teeth by means of a small . . . .
4. A hand ripsaw is filed by holding the file at . . . . to the blade.
5. The size of the included angle of crosscut teeth measures . . . .
6. After grinding a plane iron, it is necessary to remove the . . . .
7. Whetting of inside and outside gauges is generally completed with a . . . .
8. The tool used to turn the edge on a scraper is called a . . . .
9. The dull edge of a hand scraper is removed and made straight by careful . . . .
10. A dull auger bit is sharpened by carefully sharpening the . . . . and . . . .
11. A wood-turning tool which resembles an ordinary wood chisel is called . . . .
12. The cutoff tool is also called . . . .
13. Clogged files and rasps are readily cleaned with a . . . .
14. When the gullets of circular saw teeth become too shallow, it is necessary to deepen them by a process called . . . .
15. The set on the teeth of large circular saws is often provided by the process called . . . .

16. When brazing a broken band-saw blade, it is first necessary to .... the two ends.
17. Instead of sharpening tools by means of files and abrasive wheels, it is also possible to sharpen many tools by means of an ....
18. Many jointers and planers come equipped with a specially-built ....
19. After sharpening jointer knives it is important that all knives are checked for ....
20. When grinding wheels clog up with particles of steel, oil and dirt, they can be cleaned with a ....

PART II. TRUE-FALSE QUESTIONS. Indicate, by encircling T or F, whether the following statements are true or false:

21. Handsaws, whether rip or crosscut, are filed with a triangular file.	T	F
22. A handsaw set is so adjusted that it sets the entire tooth.	T	F
23. Handsaw teeth are always set by hand.	T	F
24. A crosscut saw is filed by holding the file at right angles to the saw blade.	T	F
25. Plane irons are sharpened so that the cutting edge is perfectly straight.	T	F
26. Overheating a plane iron is likely to draw the temper from the blade.	T	F
27. After grinding a plane iron edge on a grinder, it is ready for immediate use.	T	F
28. To do successful wood turning it is important that the tools are sharp and properly shaped.	T	F
29. Hand scrapers are used to remove small ridges on a wood surface made by a jointer.	T	F
30. Dull auger bits are best sharpened with an auger bit file.	T	F
31. The nibs of an auger bit are always sharpened from the outside.	T	F
32. The spear-point chisel is like a round-nose chisel except that it is pointed instead of rounded.	T	F
33. For best service, rasps and wood files should be stored properly after use.	T	F
34. It is extremely important that machine tools are kept perfectly sharp.	T	F
35. The teeth of a circular saw are best gummed with a ¾ inch thick abrasive wheel.	T	F
36. Large circular saw teeth can be successfully set with an ordinary handsaw set.	T	F
37. Circular saws are always sharpened by hand.	T	F
38. Square, ragged gullets are more likely to cause cracks in the blade than rounded gullets.	T	F
39. Band-saw blades can be successfully repaired by means of a butt welder.	T	F
40. To joint band-saw teeth, the blade is always removed from the machine.	T	F

PART III.   MULTIPLE-CHOICE QUESTIONS.   Select, by encircling the correct letter, the answer which completes each statement:

41. One of the following processes can be omitted when sharpening a handsaw:
    A. Gumming
    B. Jointing
    C. Setting
    D. Filing
42. The front of each tooth of a crosscut saw makes a certain angle with a line perpendicular to the tooth line. The size of this angle generally is:
    A. 5 deg.
    B. 15 deg.
    C. 30 deg.
    D. 45 deg.
43. The cutting edge of a correctly sharpened plane iron should be:
    A. Concave
    B. Convex
    C. Perfectly straight
    D. Straight with slightly rounded corners.
44. When laying out the rake on a circular saw the extended rake forms a line:
    A. Passing through the saw center.
    B. Tangent to the arbor hole.
    C. Tangent to a circle with a radius equal to half the saw's radius.
    D. Tangent to a circle with a radius equal to two-thirds the saw's radius.
45. When brazing a band-saw blade, one of the following is not needed:
    A. Flux
    B. Silver solder
    C. Brass
    D. Tongs

PART IV.   Matching Questions. Match the terms to the left with the descriptions to the right by placing the correct letter in the parenthesis.

46. ( )	Flux	A. A series of small chisels.
47. ( )	Rust remover	B. The process of removing the wire edge on a plane iron or chisel.
48. ( )	Ripsaw teeth	C. Caused by square, ragged gullets.
49. ( )	Kerosene	D. A mixture of borax and water.
50. ( )	Whetting	E. A mixture of: 1 cup of lye, ½ cup washing soda, ½ teaspoon of potassium permanganate dissolved in 1 quart of water.
51. ( )	Lips of an auger bit	
52. ( )	Alcohol	
53. ( )	Saw swage	F. A tool used to spread the points of circular saw teeth.
54. ( )	Cracked blades	G. Used to weigh jointer knives.
55. ( )	Knife balance	H. Used as a cooling agent on oilstone grinders.
		I. Filed on the upper side only.
		J. Sometimes used to clean dirty files.

CHAPTER 5

Planing and Squaring to Dimensions

Planing and squaring to exact dimensions is the ABC of all good woodwork. It must be thoroughly mastered before any other process can be undertaken successfully. Parts of a project that have not been planed and squared up properly will give continuous trouble as the project progresses.

157. Checking and Adjusting a Plane. Often the beginning woodworker takes it for granted that when he picks up a plane it is automatically in proper working condition. But a number of things can be wrong with this tool. Before starting a planing job, it is always good practice to check the double plane iron first. After removing it from the plane, see whether the cutting edge is sharp. If the edge has small nicks, the plane iron should be taken over to the grinder, and the bevel ground to its proper shape. The cutting edge should be perfectly straight with the corners rounded lightly. A perfectly straight cutting edge leaves little grooves in the wood, whereas a curved or rounded plane iron edge leaves little hollows on the surface. Neither one is satisfactory for a smooth planing job (see Chap. 4, Art. 129, page 143).

After completing the grinding process, one must carefully remove the wire edge on the proper honing stone. Quite often, a plane iron upon checking needs only to be touched up a little by careful honing. It is surprising how this will improve the performance of a plane.

After checking and sharpening the plane iron, reassemble plane iron and chip breakers (Figs. 1 and 2). The chip breaker should be placed within $\frac{1}{16}$–$\frac{1}{32}$ in. of the cutting edge of the plane iron and the two should fit

Fig. 1. Assembling double plane iron.

Fig. 2. Chipbreaker in position.

Fig. 3. Placing double plane in position.

Fig. 4. Placing lever cap in position.

perfectly flat together. Chip breakers that do not fit properly can cause a great deal of trouble, because, when wood particles collect between plane iron and chip breaker, it soon becomes impossible to make any sizable shavings.

To know how to adjust the double plane iron in the plane is also most important. It is here where the beginning woodworker often has a great deal of difficulty. The following procedure should prove helpful in overcoming some of these difficulties:

1. Hold the plane in one hand and insert the double plane iron in the plane, with the chip breaker on top (Fig. 3).

2. With the clamp lever of the lever cap at right angles with the lever cap, place the lever cap on top of the double plane iron (Fig. 4). The lever cap should slip over the lever cap screw.

3. Push down on the clamp lever. If the lever pushes down too easily, set the lever cap screw a little deeper into the frog of the plane. If it is too tight, unscrew it a little. When it gives a light click, it is usually tight enough (Fig. 5).

Fig. 5. Pushing down clamp lever.

Fig. 6. Sighting along sole of plane.

4. Turn the plane upside down and hold it at eye level in a position shown in Figure 6.

5. Hold the plane with one hand, and make the two remaining adjustments with the other hand.

6. If the cutting edge of the plane iron cannot be seen, turn the brass knurled nut until the edge appears as a fine black line through the throat of the plane.

Fig. 7. Adjusting cutting edge.

7. Next, with the lateral adjusting lever, move the plane iron either to one side or the other until the cutting edge is parallel to the bottom of the plane (Fig. 7).

The plane should now be ready for planing. Adjust for either heavy or light cuts, depending on the nature of the work.

158. Procedure for Squaring Small Boards to Dimensions. The squaring up process consists of six steps which should be fully understood and followed in order presented here. Although minor variations can be made in this procedure, generally, woodworkers agree that these six steps are basically sound. The six steps are:

1. Select the best face and plane a true "working face."
2. Plane a "working edge" square with the completed working face.
3. Square one end.
4. Mark off the correct length and square the second end.
5. Lay out the correct width and plane the second edge.
6. Lay out and plane to thickness.

Squaring Up Procedure. 1. Select the better of the two wider sides, and clamp the board end to end between the vise dog and a bench stop (Fig. 8). Never clamp a board side to side, because the pressure will bend it. If it is then planed so that it is flat, it will spring back when the pressure is released and will be curved. If the sides have been planed, it usually can be seen in which direction the face should be planed by observing the edge grain (Fig. 9). Note that opposite surfaces are planed in opposite directions Set the plane to cut a fine shaving, plane off just enough to clean off the surface, and make it perfectly flat. Test this surface with the try square, holding it lengthwise, crosswise, and diagonally at several points. This surface is called the "working face" (Fig. 10).

2. Select the better of the two edges, and plane it until the surface is true and square to the working face (Fig. 11). This edge is called the

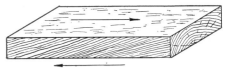

↑ **Fig. 9.** Opposite surfaces are planed in opposite directions.

← **Fig. 8.** Clamping a board for surface planing.

"working edge." Mark the working face and working edge with a pencil (Fig. 12).

Fig. 10. Testing flatness of working face.

Fig. 11. Testing edge for squareness.

3. Set a marking gauge to the desired width. With a rule measure the width from the spur of the gauge to the block. Hold the block of the marking gauge against the working edge, and mark a line on the working face, pushing the gauge, away from you.

If the width of the board is more than 5 or 6 in., the marking gauge

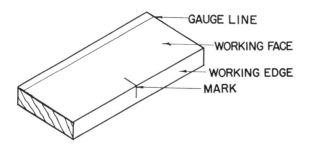

GAUGE LINE

WORKING FACE

WORKING EDGE

MARK

Fig. 12. Squaring board to dimensions. Steps 1 to 3.

cannot be used. If a panel gauge is not available, measure the width with a ruler at two points, one near each end. Then, draw a pencil line, along a straightedge, through these two points. This layout may be completed after step 4.

4. Plane or chisel off a corner outside the gauge line (Figs. 13 and 14), and plane the better end square to both working face and working edge

Fig. 13. Chisel off corner to prevent splitting when planing end grain.

Fig. 14. Removing corners to avoid splitting end grain.

(Figs. 15 and 16). The corner is chiseled off to prevent the wood from splitting when planing end grain. Plane from the working edge toward the unfinished edge. Never chisel off a corner on the working edge. Hold the plane slightly at an angle and make what is called a "shearing cut" (Fig. 17).

5. Measure the length of the piece from the end just planed, and square lines all around, using the try square and a knife or sharp pencil (Fig. 18).

6. Saw off the surplus lumber outside this line, using a bench hook, or clamping the piece in the vise. Chisel off or plane the corner as before, and

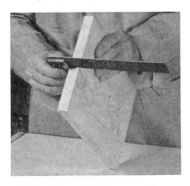

Fig. 15. Testing end for squareness.

Fig. 16. Testing end for squareness.

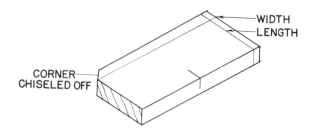

CORNER
CHISELED OFF

WIDTH
LENGTH

Fig. 18.   Squaring board to dimensions.
Steps 4 and 5.

Fig. 17. Making a
"shearing cut."

plane this end to the line marked, so that it is square to both the working
face and the working edge.

7. Plane the edge opposite the working edge to the gauge or pencil line,
and square to the working face.

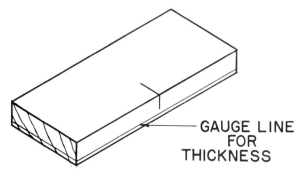

Fig. 19. Squaring
board to dimensions.
Step 6.

GAUGE LINE
FOR
THICKNESS

8. With a marking gauge, gauge the thickness from the working face on
both edges and ends (Figs. 19 and 20).

Fig. 20. Laying out thickness
with marking gauge.

Fig. 21. Planing end of narrow
piece of wood.

9. Plane the last face, opposite the working face, to these gauge lines.

In cases where the board is very narrow or already has the desired width, splitting of the end wood may be prevented if a piece of wood is placed in the vise behind the edge while planing the ends (Fig. 21).

159. Procedure for Jointing Boards for Gluing. 1. Wide surfaces, such as table tops, are built up of two or more boards, whose edges are jointed and glued together. After enough boards have been cut to length to form the width, it is a good plan to arrange them so that the better surfaces of all are up and so that the grain, if possible, runs in the same direction and forms pleasing patterns. The boards to be glued up must be reasonably flat without warp or wind. Warped boards and boards "in wind" can cause considerable trouble. If machines are available, warp and wind is readily removed on the jointer and thickness planer.

2. Mark the direction of the grain and the edges to be joined together. The faces are usually not planed until after the boards have been glued (Fig. 22).

In Article 342, page 487, there is a discussion of a marking system successfully used by the author for many years. Particularly, when a number of wide boards need to be glued up, the system used in Figure 22 could become confusing. This other marking system eliminates much confusion.

3. Place the boards to be joined, two and two, in the vise, so that both faces are out (Fig. 23). Long boards are further clamped together with a hand screw at each end.

4. Plane the two edges at the same time. Even if the edges are not planed absolutely square to the sides, the angles of both are still equal, and when

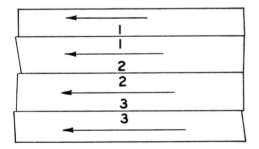

Fig. 22. Arranging boards for jointing.

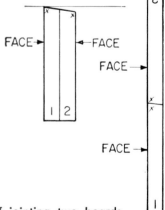

Fig. 23. Method of jointing two boards.

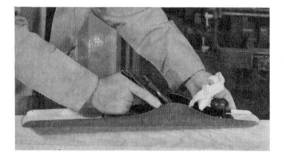

Fig. 24. Planing edges of long boards with jointer plane.

one is placed on top of the other (Fig. 23), the faces will be in line. To make sure that the edges are planed straight, use a fore or jointer plane (Fig. 24).

5. It is of the utmost importance that the edges of both boards make a good joint at both ends, because wood dries faster at the ends, and, therefore, shrinks more rapidly, causing the joints to open. For this reason, it is advisable to plane the edges of the boards in such a way that when one is

Fig. 25. Testing edge-to-edge joints before gluing.

placed on top of the other the joint will be closed at both ends, but there will be a slight opening in the center. Such a joint is called a "spring joint."

6. If a single clamp is put on the boards in the center, they should come together over-all and the two ends should be tight (Fig. 25).

7. The other edges are jointed in the same way, two and two.

Directions for gluing are given in Article 225, p. 293.

160. Procedure for Squaring a Table Top. 1. Select the better face, remove any surplus glue with a chisel, clamp the table top securely to the top of the bench, and plane it *across the grain*. Start planing at one end, continue toward the other end, and repeat (Fig. 26). It may be necessary to plane a small chamfer on the farthest end to prevent splitting.

Planing across the grain is especially recommended when working with cross-grained woods, like birch or mahogany, as it prevents tearing up the

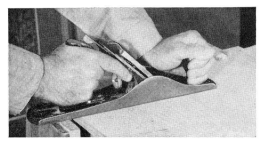

Fig. 26. Squaring table top, planing across grain.

grain. Straight-grained woods, like white pine or cypress, may be planed lengthwise from the beginning of the work. Planing a surface across the grain is a good method of quickly evening it up and reducing it to size.

2. Test the surface frequently lengthwise, crosswise, and diagonally with a framing square (Fig. 27). If, when placing the square diagonally, it touches at both ends, but not in the middle, and if, when placed diagonally in the opposite direction, it touches in the middle, but not at the ends, it is an indication that the board is warped or in "wind." This is remedied by planing the board in the diagonal direction first mentioned, when the square touches at both ends, but not in the middle.

3. When the surface is true over-all, it is planed lengthwise just enough to remove the marks of the cross planing. Use a very sharp plane iron, and set it to cut a fine shaving.

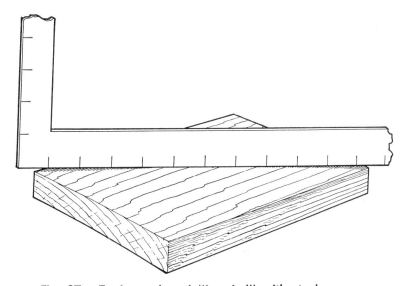

Fig. 27. Testing a board "in wind" with steel square.

Fig. 28. Smoothing with a cabinet scraper.

If the wood is very cross grained, it should be scraped with a cabinet scraper instead of planed (Fig. 28).

4. Plane the better edge true and square to the face, and test it as in Figures 29 and 30.

5. Square a line across the face from the working edge near one of the ends, using a framing square.

6. Saw off any surplus wood, and plane this end square to the working face and the working edge. Do not plane all the way across the end, but plane part way from both edges. Test for squareness with a framing square. Hold large boards while planing as shown in Figure 24. Clamp one side or end in the bench vise and support the other by fastening a hand screw to it and letting it rest on the bench top.

7. Measure the length from the squared end, square a line across the working face from the working edge, saw off the surplus wood, and plane the other end to the line in the same manner as the first one was planed (Fig. 31). Test for squareness with a steel square held against the working edge.

8. Measure the width at both ends, connect these points with a pencil line, and plane the other edge.

9. Gauge the thickness on both edges and ends from the working face.

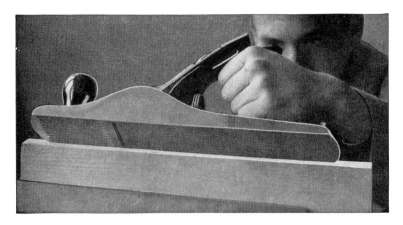

Fig. 29. Testing edge for straightness with plane.

Fig. 30. Testing edge of long board for squareness.

10. Fasten the board face down to the top of the workbench, and plane the last face or underside to the gauge lines, as explained in steps 1, 2, and 3.

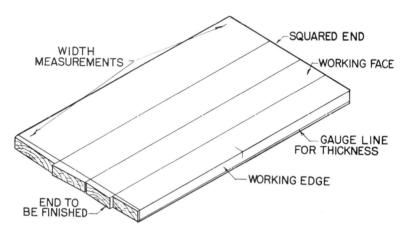

WIDTH MEASUREMENTS

SQUARED END

WORKING FACE

GAUGE LINE FOR THICKNESS

WORKING EDGE

END TO BE FINISHED

Fig. 31. Squaring a table top.

161. Procedure for Making and Squaring a Table Top, Using Machine Tools. The squaring up process with the use of woodworking machinery is much the same as when done by hand. The main difference is that manual power has been replaced by more efficient mechanical power. Also, the order in which the basic six steps are executed may differ slightly from the hand processes. The placement of the machinery in the shop may have something to do with the procedure. An experienced machine woodworker not only works fast, but also tries to save as many steps as possible from one machine to the next.

Figures 32 and 33 illustrate two examples where gluing up of large sections becomes an important part of the construction procedure. Slight warpage

Fig. 32. Chest of drawers.

Fig. 33. Triple dresser.

in either sides, top or bottom could result in serious difficulties when the assembly is made. If the over-all structure is correct and true from the standpoint of warpage, wind, and squareness, the other parts such as drawers, drawer rails, and legs are likely to cause little trouble.

1. Cut the number of boards, which are needed to make up the top on the swing cutoff saw, allowing about ½ in. on the length for squaring.

2. If the boards are not absolutely straight, but are a little in "wind," plane one of the faces of each board on the jointer until it is perfectly flat. Mark the direction of the grain on each board. Then plane the two edges square to this face, except on the outside boards, where only one edge needs to be planed.

3. Run all the boards through the planer to bring them to an even thickness. Remember that the grain runs in opposite directions on opposite surfaces.

4. Place the boards together, taking into consideration the matching of the grain and the direction in which it runs (Art. 159 and Fig. 22). Mark or number the edges to be glued together.

5. Glue and clamp according to directions given in Article 225, p. 293.

6. After the glued top is dry, and any excess glue has been removed, plane it on the planer. Notice the direction of the grain, and take a light cut the first time. When this surface is smooth, reverse the top, and plane the other surface. Continue planing until the top has been reduced to the required thickness.

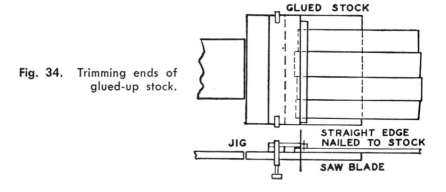

Fig. 34. Trimming ends of glued-up stock.

7. Plane one edge on the jointer, measure the length, and square lines across both ends. If the top is too large to be cut across on the circular saw, it may be cut on the band saw. If several tops are to be sawed, it will be worth while to make a jig of two boards nailed together as shown in Figure 34. The lower and narrower one should be a little thicker than the top to be sawed. Clamp the jig to the band-saw table so that the upper board touches the saw blade, then nail a strip of wood along the line squared across the table top. When this strip is held against the jig, a perfectly straight saw cut will be made.

8. The ends may be squared on the jointer. Begin planing from the squared edge, take a light cut, and push the board slowly across the cutter-head. The grain may tear a little on the edge yet to be finished.

9. If the top has been planed to width, the end-planing should be stopped ½ in. from the last edge and this piece finished by hand. Never end-plane a board less than 12 in. wide. It is also acceptable practice to plane the end grain a little past the midway mark of the width of the board. Reverse the board and complete end planing from the opposite edge. The board should be at least 12 inches wide.

10. If the top is not too wide, it may be ripped to width on the circular saw. In this case, the ripping fence is set to the proper width, and the top run through without further measurement.

11. When the top is wider, the width is measured from the planed edge, and a pencil line is drawn from one end to the other. The waste is sawed off on the band saw, and the edge planed on the jointer.

12. The top may now be sanded smooth on a belt sander, or with a portable sander. No hand planing or scraping is necessary when a sanding machine is available.

162. Procedure for Squaring Legs for Tables and Cabinets. 1. Cut the legs (usually four) to dimensions, allowing sufficient material for squaring.

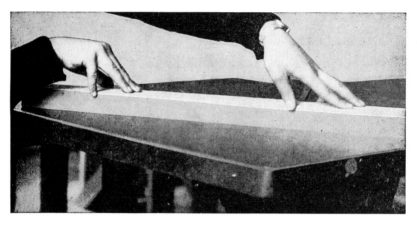

Fig. 35. Testing for "wind."

If the lumber is free from defects, from ¹⁄₁₆ in. to ⅛ in. on each side should be sufficient. For example, a leg that should measure 1½ in. square when finished, should be at least 1⅝ in. in the rough. It is well to allow ½ in. on the length.

2. Select the best two adjoining sides on each leg, and plane them true and square to each other. Test surface planed for "wind" by placing it on a level surface (Fig. 35). Mark the sides squared.

3. When two faces have been squared on each leg, the marking gauge is set to width, and lines are gauged on all legs with the same setting of the marking gauge (Fig. 36).

4. The remaining sides are then planed to the gauge lines square to the first two sides planed. The ends are usually cut to exact length in a miter box.

5. Turned legs having square sections should be planed to finish dimensions in the same way and cut to length before they are put in the lathe. It is important to center them carefully, otherwise the square parts will be out

GAUGE
LINES

Fig. 36. Squaring a table leg.

of line. For turned legs a half inch overlength should be allowed on each end. This will avoid cutting into the live or dead center while turning.

163. Procedure for Squaring Table Legs, Using Machine Tools. 1. Plane one surface of each leg on the jointer. Then hold the planed surface against the fence and plane one adjoining side square to it (Fig. 37). Always check the fence to make sure that it is exactly at right angles with the infeed table.

2. Now set the ripping fence on a circular saw to ½₂ in. more than the finished dimension, and saw the two remaining sides on each leg to width and thickness. In this case they are the same. Hold one of the squared sides against the ripping fence and the other on the saw table. Use a push stick (Fig. 21, p. 69).

3. The two sawed sides are then planed smooth on the jointer.

4. If a planer is available, the unfinished sides can be planed directly to finished dimensions without again using the circular saw or the jointer.

5. In either case, the ends are squared and sawed to length on the circular saw. First square one end on all the legs, using the universal gauge and cutting off as little as possible. Then clamp the stop rod in the universal gauge, adjust the stop and, holding the squared ends against it, saw all the legs to correct length.

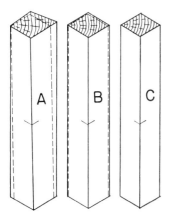

Fig. 37. Steps in squaring table leg. A, two adjoining sides planed square to each other; B, sawed on circular saw to within ¹⁄₁₆ in. of finished dimensions; C, sawed sides planed to finished dimensions.

Fig. 38. Tapering square legs.

TAPER LINES
GAUGE LINES

164. Procedure for Tapering Square Legs for Tables and Cabinets.
1. After the legs have been square, as explained in Article 162, the part to be tapered is measured off and a pencil line squared all around each leg.

2. A marking gauge is then set to the amount of the taper, as for example ¼ in., and four lines are gauged on the end of each leg. The lines of taper are then drawn on two opposite sides with a straightedge from these points to the pencil lines (Fig. 38).

3. If the amount of material to be removed is considerable, it is advisable to saw it off before planing the sides true to the lines.

4. When two opposite sides have been tapered, the taper lines are laid out on the remaining two sides, and the processes are repeated.

165. Procedure for Tapering Square Legs for Tables and Cabinets on the Circular Saw. 1. Suppose the legs are to be 2 in. square and 30 in. long; plane two adjoining edges on the jointer, set the ripping fence on the circular saw to 2 in. full, and rip with the planed edges always against the fence.

2. If the taper is to be ¼ in. on each side and begins 5 in. from the top, make a jig as shown at A, Figure 39. The notches, as will be seen, are ¼ in. each.

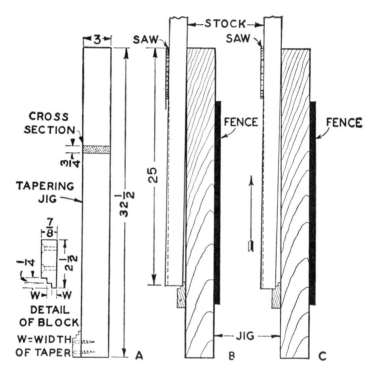

Fig. 39. Tapering table legs on circular saw.

3. Square a line all around one leg 5 in. from the top. Place the other end of the leg in the inner notch as shown at B. Measure the combined width of the leg and jig, in this case 5 in., and set the ripping fence accordingly.

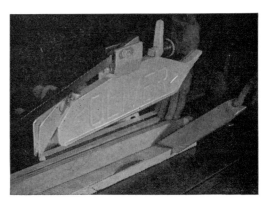

Fig. 40. Hinged tapering jig. Guard raised to show jig.

4. Rip two adjoining sides, then place these successively in the other notch, and rip the remaining two sides. The leg is now tapered equally on all four sides. Use the splitter guard to prevent the stock from being caught by the back teeth of the saw.

5. Smooth the legs with a cabinet scraper, or a belt or portable sander.

The tapering jig shown in Figure 40 consists of two boards hinged together at one end. The length of the taper is measured from this hinged end. For example, if the taper is 16 in. long, this distance is measured off on the jig. If the leg is to be tapered ¼ in., this distance is measured off between the two boards at the 16 in. mark. The advantage of this jig over the first one is that it makes possible a much greater variety of taper sizes.

166. Procedure for Tapering Table Legs on a Jointer. 1. If the length of the taper is 25 in. and the leg is to be tapered ¼ in. on each side, square a line all around one leg at the point where the taper begins. Place the leg on the infeed table so that this line is even with the lip on the outfeed table. Then clamp a stop block to the fence or table at the other end of the leg, and lower the infeed table ¼ in.

2. Place the end of the leg against the stop block, lower the other end

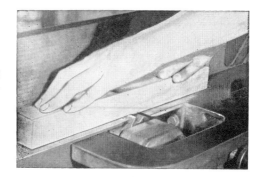

Fig. 41. Tapering leg using hand screw as stop block.

carefully over the revolving cutterhead, and plane the taper on each side of each leg (Fig. 41).

3. It will be noticed that the knives dig in a little at the beginning of the cut, and that the cut starts a little below the line squared around the leg. This unevenness can easily be removed with a few strokes of a hand plane without making the taper go beyond the line marked.

4. If a bench jointer is used, it may be found that the infeed table is shorter than the length of the taper. In such cases the taper is divided in two parts of equal length and a line is squared around the leg at this point (12½ in.) (Fig. 42).

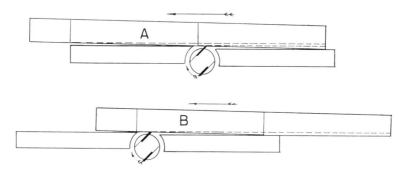

Fig. 42. Tapering long leg on small jointer. A, Cut started at middle of taper. B, Taking finish cut the full length of taper.

5. Lower the table to half the amount of the taper (⅛ in.), and plane the lower half of the taper first. Then, with the same setting, make a second cut the full length of the taper. The leg will now have a ¼-in. taper, 25 in. long.

167. Procedure for Planing Short Tapers.* 1. The best results in planing short tapers are obtained if you pull the stock over the knives. This is also the safest way. Set the infeed table to the depth of the taper. Stand behind the outfeed table, place the starting line over its lip, and lower the end until it touches the infeed table.

2. While in this position, slip a small block under the elevated end of the leg. Mark the place where it touches the leg, and nail it in place with fine brads (Fig. 43). Clamp a stopblock to the infeed table, and plane the tapers by pulling the stock toward you.

---

* For a more complete discussion on tapering and other machine operations, see: Hjorth, H., and Holtrop, William F., *Operation of Modern Woodworking Machines,* Chap. 1, pp. 1–39.

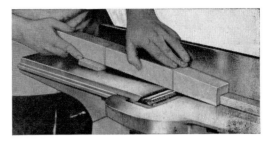

Fig. 43. Planing short taper on jointer.

REVIEW QUESTIONS, CHAPTER 5

Possible score 45 points

Your score . . . . . .

PART I. COMPLETION QUESTIONS. Complete the following statements:

1. Planing and . . . . to dimensions is the ABC of all good woodwork.
2. A dull plane iron is first sharpened on a . . . .
3. The terms stoning, honing, and . . . . are often used interchangeably.
4. The plane part that prevents a plane iron from digging into the wood is the . . . .
5. The tool that holds the plane iron firmly in position is the . . . .
6. A plane iron is set for depth of cut by turning the brass, knurled . . . .
7. The plane iron is moved from one side to the other by means of the . . . .
8. The first step in the squaring up process is the selection of a true . . . .
9. The thickness is laid out by means of a . . . .
10. A most useful testing tool in the squaring up process is the . . . .
11. When planing end grain, the plane is held slightly at an angle, making a . . . .
12. Boards to be glued up must be reasonably flat without . . . . or . . . .
13. Two boards to be glued edge to edge are planed slightly hollow. This type of joint is called a . . . .
14. When a board cannot be successfully planed smooth with a plane, it is best made smooth with a . . . .
15. When table legs are wider at the top than at the bottom, they are . . . .
16. Tapered legs are readily cut on the circular saw with a . . . .
17. Tapers can be cut on the jointer by lowering the . . . .
18. The surfacer is primarily used to plane stock to the proper . . . .
19. The shortest length that can be safely planed on the jointer is . . . .
20. The shortest length that can be safely planed on the planer is determined by the distance between . . . . and . . . .

PART II. TRUE-FALSE QUESTIONS. Indicate, by encircling T or F, whether the following statements are true or false:

21. Before starting to plane, one should learn how to adjust a plane properly.   T   F
22. A perfectly straight plane iron performs best.   T   F
23. A careful woodworker makes it a practice to sharpen plane irons and chisels by frequent honing.   T   F
24. When assembling a plane iron, the chip breaker is best placed within ¼ inch of the cutting edge.   T   F
25. A chip breaker should fit properly against the flat side of the plane iron.   T   F
26. When planing, the thickness of cut is regulated with the lateral adjusting lever.   T   F
27. When squaring up a board, the first step consists of selecting and planing the best working face.   T   F
28. When gluing up several boards, the various boards should be identified by a proper marking system.   T   F
29. Table legs are best squared up by running them through the planer.   T   F
30. By taking certain precautions, end grain can be successfully planed on the jointer.   T   F

PART III. MULTIPLE-CHOICE QUESTIONS. Select, by encircling the correct letter, the answer which completes each statement:

31. One of the following machines is not used when cutting tapers:
    A. Surfacer
    B. Jointer
    C. Circular saw
    D. Band saw
32. A properly sharpened plane iron edge should be:
    A. Convex
    B. Concave
    C. Perfectly straight
    D. Straight with lightly rounded corners
33. The third step in the squaring up process of a board is:
    A. Plane the second edge
    B. Square one end
    C. Plane to thickness
    D. Plane a working edge
34. When assembling a plane, the last step is:
    A. Assemble plane iron and chip breaker
    B. Make the lateral adjustment
    C. Adjust for depth of cut
    D. Push down the clamp lever
35. When gluing two boards edge to edge, the edges should be:
    A. Slightly hollow
    B. Perfectly straight
    C. Slightly rounded

PART IV. MATCHING QUESTIONS. Match the terms to the left with the descriptions to the right by placing the correct letter in the parentheses:

36. (   ) Chip breaker
37. (   ) Squaring up process
38. (   ) Shearing cut
39. (   ) Marking system
40. (   ) Fore plane
41. (   ) Cabinet scraper
42. (   ) Taper
43. (   ) Stop block
44. (   ) Planing and squaring
45. (   ) Clamp lever

A. A cut made straight across the end grain of a board.
B. A long plane particularly useful in edge planing long boards.
C. That part of plane that holds the plane iron in place.
D. Placed within $\frac{1}{16}$–$\frac{1}{32}$ in. of the cutting edge of a plane iron.
E. A cut which becomes progressively narrow toward one end.
F. Two important operations in good woodworking.
G. Consists of six basic steps.
H. A scraper held in a steel frame.
I. A method of marking parts of a project to avoid confusion.
J. A necessary device when making short tapers on the jointer.
K. A cut made across end grain at a slight angle.

CHAPTER 6

Joints Used in Woodworking and Cabinetmaking

Whenever two pieces of wood are fastened together, some type of joint must be used. Woodworking joints range from the very simple to the more complex and their selection depends on the type of job that needs to be done. The corners for a simple box to store toys are often put together with what is known as a butt joint. Such corners are usually held together with glue, nails, or screws. From the standpoint of joints, the project shown in Figure 1 is very simple. The legs were fastened against the sides with round-head screws, the sides were fastened to the top quite likely with glue, finishing nails, or flat-head screws. Though simple from the standpoint of joints, this coffee table has nevertheless a sturdy and strong appearance.

But when making an attractive night stand as shown in Figure 2, one cannot use simple joints as described above and a knowledge of the more elaborate wood joints and how to make them becomes necessary. A person thinking about making such a project, better ask himself in advance: how do I go about making the two 19 in. wide tops out of stock that is only 8 in. wide? How do I fasten the top and center rails to the legs? And how does one go about making neatly fitting and easy sliding drawers? These few questions readily show that much planning and know-how is necessary.

Fig. 1. Coffee table.

Fig. 2. Night stand.

194

This chapter, under seven separated headings, discusses the numerous ways in which wood is joined together, not only from the standpoint of appearance but particularly from the standpoint of strength.

Part I.   GROOVED JOINTS

Grooved joints are a group of joints which have the following characteristics in common: They all have a groove or recess cut into one member, either with the grain or across the grain, into which the edge or end, in whole or in part, of another member is fitted. This type of joint is used extensively in all cabinet construction, as for example, in door, panel, and drawer construction, in shelving, picture frames, built-in furniture, etc. The carpenter uses grooved joints in flooring, wainscoting, tank construction, concrete forms, store fixtures, etc.

170. Procedure for Making a Rabbet Joint.   A rabbet is a groove cut on the edge or end of a piece of wood (Fig. 3). To make this joint by hand use the rabbet and fillister plane shown in Figure 52, p. 33.

1. Adjust the plane iron to cut the proper thickness of shaving as in ordinary planing. Be sure that the blade projects evenly through the bottom of the plane. See that the edge of the blade is exactly in line with the side of the plane.

2. The spur, which is fastened to the side of the plane with a little screw, is now set to a cutting position. It is important to have it sharp.

3. Set the two gauges on the plane to the desired width and depth.

4. Clamp the board to be rabbeted to the bench. Hold the plane level, and press the width gauge against the edge of the board. Take every stroke evenly and carefully. The spur scores the wood so that the rabbet will be cut to an even width. Continue until the depth gauge bears against the upper surface of the board.

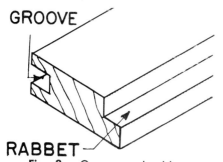

Fig. 3.   Groove and rabbet.

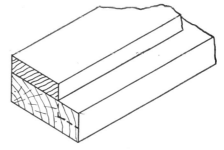

Fig. 4.   Strip of wood clamped to board as a guide for the rabbet to be planed.

Fig. 5. Scoring line with knife.

Fig. 6. Scoring with a chisel.

5. If the gauges cannot be used on a thin or narrow board, a strip of wood can be nailed or clamped to the board as a width gauge. The depth should be marked along the edge with a marking gauge (Fig. 4).

6. On narrow boards it is easier to saw and chisel a rabbet than to plane one. Mark the width and depth of the rabbet with a marking gauge and then saw across the grain with a backsaw.

7. A straight saw cut can be made when a small triangular groove is first cut on the waste side of the line marked for the width. First score the line as deeply as possible with a knife or a chisel. Hold the try square right on the line when scoring (Figs. 5 and 6). The groove can now be cut with a chisel as shown in Figures 7 and 8.

↑ Fig. 8. Cutting triangular groove with chisel bevel down.

← Fig. 7. Cutting triangular groove with chisel.

Fig. 9.   Block hand-screwed to
piece guiding backsaw.

Fig. 10.   Cutting end wood with
chisel, bevel down.

8. Another way to make a straight saw cut is to clamp a piece of wood right on the line (Fig. 9).

9. The rabbet is cut to depth with a chisel as shown in Figures 10 and 11. The final smoothing and cutting to uniform depth should be done with the bevel of the chisel up or with a router plane.

Fig. 11.   Finishing rabbet with
chisel, beveled side up.

171. Procedure for Making a Groove.   1. A groove is a recess or slot cut along the grain (Fig. 3). It differs from a rabbet in having three surfaces — two sides and one bottom; the rabbet has only two — one side and one bottom. Grooves are cut on the sides and front of drawers for the bottom (Fig. 12). They are also made in the frame around a panel and in the edges of flooring and other tongue and grooved building materials.

2. Grooves are planed with a matching plane (Fig. 53, p. 33) or with a plow plane (Fig. 13). A matching plane makes a groove on the edge of one board and a tongue to match or fit it on another.

3. *Groove and rabbet joints,* as shown in Figure 14, are used a good deal in furniture construction, for example where the sides and legs of a cabinet are joined. The groove is first made in the legs, after which the rabbet is planed to fit it.

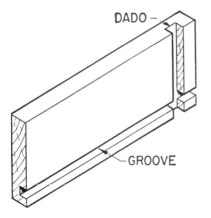

Fig. 13.   Plow plane.

Fig. 12.   Drawer
side groove
and dado.

This procedure is followed because the plow plane cuts a groove to a specific width. The rabbet can be cut to any desired size.

This joint is sometimes called a barefaced tongue joint.

172. Procedure for Making a Dado Joint.   1. A dado is a groove made across the grain from one edge to the other. Dado joints are used in shelves, bookcases, cabinets, stepladders, boxes, etc.

2. A practice joint (Fig. 15) may be made from a piece of wood squared to about 4 in. wide by 8 in. or more long.

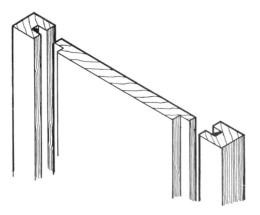

Fig. 14.   Barefaced tongue joint.

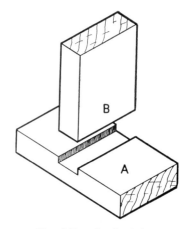

Fig. 15.   Dado joint.

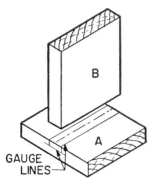

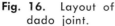

Fig. 16.   Layout of
dado joint.

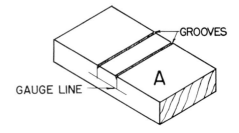

Fig. 17.   Dado ready for sawing.

3. Square a line across the center and saw the board in two with a backsaw.

4. Square a line across the center of one of the pieces at A, Figure 16, and lay out half the thickness of the other piece, B, on each side of this center line. Square lines across piece A at these points. Test the layout by placing B on top of A. Mark the depth with a marking gauge. Dado joints are usually ¼ in. deep.

Remember that a *dado is always cut across the grain* and never with the grain.

5. Saw on the waste side of the lines, using one of the methods described in Article 170 to obtain straight cuts (Fig. 17). Cut away the waste stock between the saw cuts with a chisel narrower than the dado, and finish the bottom of the cut with a router plane (Fig. 18). Chisel and plane from both edges toward the middle.

6. Fit the planed end of piece B, Figure 15, into the dado. If it is too loose, nothing can be done about it except to make a new joint. If it is too tight, a few shavings may be planed off piece B until it fits snugly into the dado.

Fig. 18.   Finishing gain with router plane.

173. Procedure for Making a Gain or Stopped Dado Joint. 1. A gain joint (Fig. 19) is a dado joint that does not go all the way across a surface. It is therefore also called a stopped dado joint. It is used for the same jobs as the dado joint, but is neater in appearance.

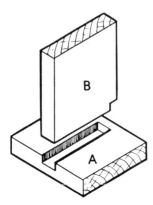

Fig. 19. Finished gain joint.

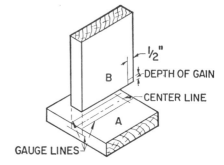

Fig. 20. Layout of gain joint.

2. Square the piece, cut it in half, and lay out the joint as explained in Article 172. Lay off the distance where the dado stops on both members, which is about ½ in. from the front edge (Fig. 20).

3. Gauge the depth on the rear edge of piece A, and also on the front edge of piece B with the marking gauge.

4. Chisel out the gain, using a ¾-in. chisel, and holding the beveled side toward the inside. Strike light blows with a mallet, being careful to follow the lines (Fig. 21).

5. Cut a small groove all around, and then go over it again striking heavier blows (Fig. 22).

6. Finish the gain with a chisel and router plane (Fig. 18).

7. Saw out the notch in the front edge of B, and fit the pieces together.

This joint is used on such pieces of furniture as bookshelves, where the plain dado joint would be unsightly.

174. Procedure for Making a Dado-and-Rabbet Joint. 1. This joint (Fig. 23) is similar to the groove-and-rabbet joint, except that it is made across the grain. It is used principally in boxes and boxlike construction as chests, cabinets, and drawers.

2. The two pieces forming the joint are first squared to dimensions. The thickness of the rabbet member, A, is then gauged on the dado member B, with a marking gauge (Fig. 24).

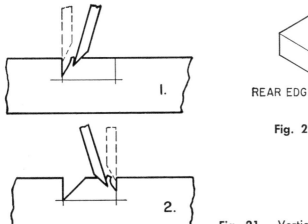

1.

2.

Fig. 21.   Vertical chiseling.

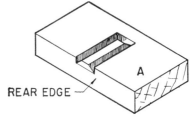

REAR EDGE

A

Fig. 22. Chiseling gain.

3. The depth of the rabbet, *d,* which is usually ½ to ⅔ the thickness of the stock, is then gauged on both members.

4. The width of the rabbet is equal to the depth of the dado or about one half the thickness of the stock. Gauging this dimension, *w,* on both members completes the layout of the joint.

5. The dado is first made according to directions given in Article 172, after which the rabbet is sawed and chiseled as described in Article 170. Try the fit of the rabbet in the dado before reaching the depth line to make sure that the joint will fit tightly. Do not drive it together as that will cause the short piece at the end of B to split off and spoil the joint.

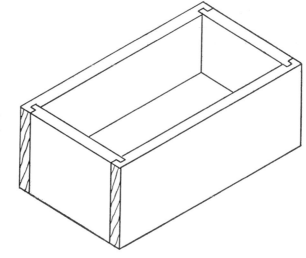

Fig. 23.   Dado-and-rabbet joint.

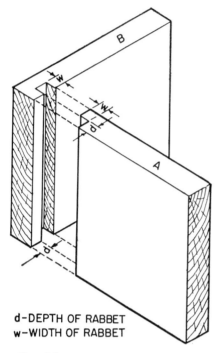

d-DEPTH OF RABBET
w-WIDTH OF RABBET

Fig. 24.   Dado-and-rabbet joint.

175. Procedure for Cutting a Rabbet With Machine Tools. A *rabbet* may be cut on the circular saw as follows:

1. Lay out the width and depth of the rabbet on the end of one of the pieces to be rabbeted (Fig. 25). Be sure to mark the end of the first piece which comes in contact with the saw. It is necessary to mark only one piece.

2. If the width is cut first, measure it from the ripping fence to the tooth set to the left or away from the ripping fence. Check the measurement by holding the stock against the saw and the ripping fence before starting the machine. If you would set the fence according to the scale marked on the table, the width of the rabbet would be increased by the width of the saw cut (A, Fig. 25).

3. Set the saw above the table to the correct depth for the rabbet.

4. Remove both the splitter and saw guards, because they will be in the way.

5. Place one side of each board on the saw table, start the machine, and run all the pieces through. Hold them against the fence with the left hand, but use a push stick in the right hand next to the fence (Fig. 26A).

6. For the second cut, raise the saw above the table to the width of the rabbet, and set the fence as explained in step 2. Hold the side of the

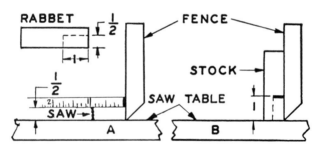

Fig. 25.   A, measuring the width of a rabbet from the outside of the saw blade to the fence; B, cutting the depth of a rabbet.

board that was on the table during the first cut against the ripping fence, and check the measurement (B, Fig. 25). When the pieces now are run through, a rectangular strip of wood will be cut away. The friction between this strip of wood and the saw often carries the wood backward with the speed of an arrow (Fig. 26B).

To avoid having these strips thrown backward, the second cut of a rabbet often is made as shown in Figure 26C. This practice avoids any possible binding of the strips. It is necessary that all pieces be of exactly the same thickness. If not, there is likely to be a slight difference in the size of the rabbets.

7. By using a dado head, rabbets may be made with a single cut. This saves time if many pieces have to be cut.

8. Rabbets may be planed on the jointer (Figs. 48 and 49, pp. 81 and 82).

9. Rabbets may also be cut on a shaper or a router. Straight work is held against the fence when rabbeting along the grain (Fig. 27). When

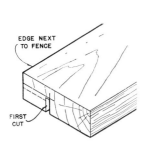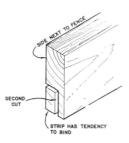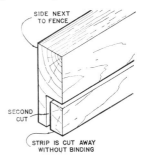

| **Fig. 26A.** First cut of rabbet. | **Fig. 26B.** Second cut of rabbet. | **Fig. 26C.** Making a rabbet. |

rabbeting endwood the stock is clamped to a slide in the table (Fig. 28). Curved work is guided along a shaper collar (Fig. 29). A follower (Fig. 105, p. 109) is used over the bit on a portable router. Curved work can only be rabbeted on a shaper or router.

10. *Grooves and Dadoes* on straight work are usually cut on the circular saw with a dado head (see Fig. 15, p. 65). The two outside cutters or saws alone will cut a full ¼ in. The inside cutters vary in thickness from ¹⁄₁₆ to ¼ in.

11. To set up the dado head, first screw the sleeve to the saw arbor. Remember it is a left thread. One outside cutter is then put on, and as many inside cutters as needed. The inside cutters should be distributed so that the cutting points are about evenly spaced. The second outside cutter is now put on the sleeve, as well as one or two spacing collars, which should extend at least ¹⁄₁₆ in. beyond the thickest part of the sleeve. Finally the

regular saw collar and nut are put on and the whole assembly is tightened with a wrench.

12. Be sure the dado head revolves freely before turning on the power. Set it to correct height over the table, and make a trial cut to check both

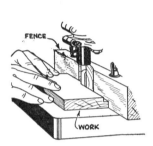

Fig. 27. Rabbeting on a router.

Fig. 28. Cutting rabbets on a sliding jig.

Fig. 29. Cutting with two-wing cutters.

depth and width of cut. If the cut is too wide or too narrow, the dado head must be reset. Sometimes a piece of cardboard, added to the inside cutters, will give just the right width needed. Grooving saws are used for narrower grooves. They may be obtained in differing thicknesses.

13. Grooves are cut as in ordinary ripping. Dadoes are cut with the same setup of the dado head, but the edge of the stock is held against the cutoff gauge or the universal gauge. The ripping fence is used as a stop against which the end of the board slides (Fig. 30). There can be no danger of a kickback, because the cut goes only part way through the wood.

14. Stopped grooves are often made on the legs of cabinets, as in Figure 31. To do this, set the ripping fence and dado head to correct width and height. The width is figured from the outside surface of the legs. Measure

Fig. 30. Cutting a dado, using ripping fence as stop. Saw guard cannot be used.

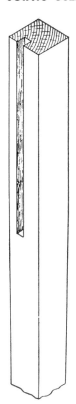

Fig. 32.   Cutting groove in leg
for panel.

Fig. 31.   Stopped
groove.

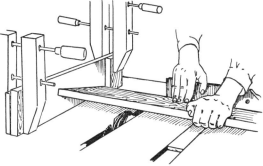

Fig. 33.   Cutting stopped dado or gain.

the length of the groove to be cut from the front of the dado head toward the rear of the table, and clamp a stop block to the table at this point. Beginning the cut at the end, two of the legs can now be grooved with this setting. The other two must be cut from the point where the grooves stop toward the end of the leg. The length of the groove is therefore measured from the back teeth of the dado head toward the front, where a stop block is clamped to the ripping fence (Fig. 32). Start the machine, hold the end of the leg against the stop block and its side against the ripping fence, and lower it slowly over the revolving dado head. Then push it forward until the cut has been completed. As no guard can be used, great care must be taken to avoid an accident.

15. Stopped dadoes are cut in the same manner (Fig. 33), holding the edge of the board against the universal gauge and using the ripping fence as a stop for the end of the board.

16. Grooves can also be cut on the shaper and router, much in the same

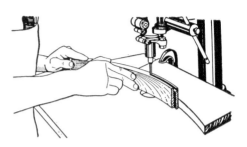

Fig. 34. Cutting grooves along fence.

Fig. 35. Grooving curved stock.

way as rabbets are cut. Straight work is guided along a fence (Fig. 34), curved work along a jig (Fig. 35).

17. Dadoes are cut on a shaper by clamping the stock in a vertical position to a sliding jig (Fig. 36). They may be cut on a router by making a jig that will slide across the table (Fig. 37).

18. The ends of stopped grooves and dadoes cut on a circular saw or shaper must be squared by hand with a chisel.*

---

* For a more detailed discussion on cutting rabbets and dado joints, see: Hjorth, H., and Holtrop, William F., *Operation of Modern Woodworking Machines,* Chap. 1, pp. 1–39.

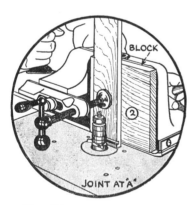

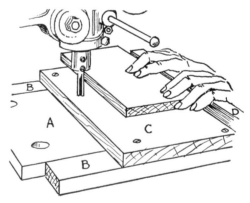

Fig. 36. Cutting dadoes. Board clamped to tenoning jig.

Fig. 37. Jig for cutting dadoes on a router.

Part II.   DOWEL JOINTS

Dowels are used extensively in all modern furniture construction. They are used in reinforcing boards glued edge to edge, in segment work, and as a substitute for the mortise-and-tenon joint. A dowel joint can be made more rapidly than a mortise-and-tenon joint, and does not require as much skill. When well made, it is much superior to a poorly made mortise-and-tenon joint. The patternmaker uses dowels in split patterns.

Dowels are round sticks of wood made of birch or maple. They are either smooth or grooved. The standard sizes measure from ¾₆ to 1 in. in diameter, and 36, 42, or 48 in. in length. They also may be obtained in usual working lengths, pointed, grooved, and ready for use. The purpose of the grooved surface is to allow glue and air to escape when the dowel is driven into the hole bored for it. It is also a good idea to countersink dowel holes slightly so that the wood will not be forced up around dowels when they are driven home.

178. Procedure for Making a Doweled Butt Joint.   1. Square the pieces to dimensions.

2. Gauge a line through the center of the ends and edges to be joined from the face of each piece.

3. Determine the position of the dowels, and set the marking gauge equal to the distance between the outside edge and the center of the dowel nearest to it. With this setting, gauge lines crossing the center lines on all the pieces (Fig. 38).

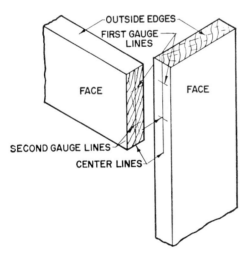

Fig. 38.   Gauging for dowels.

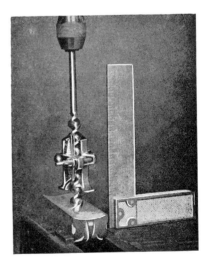

Fig. 39.   Boring for dowel.

4. Now set the marking gauge equal to the distance between the outside edge and the center of the next dowel, and gauge lines as before. The important point to remember is always *to gauge from the same sides and edges.*

5. Bore holes with an auger or dowel bit of the same size as the dowels, where all gauge lines on all the pieces intersect. The dowels should be of a diameter to give sufficient strength to the construction, without weakening the members to be joined. The diameter should be from one third to one half the thickness of the stock. Clamp an auger-bit gauge to the bit so that all the holes are bored to the same depth.

6. The ordinary auger-bit gauge is too long to fit on a dowel bit. For these bits a gauge can easily be made by running the bit through a small block of wood, which is then cut to the right length (see Fig. 84, p. 42). When this block of wood is slipped over the bit until it butts against the chuck of the brace, the bit should project the distance to which it is desired to bore the hole (Fig. 90, p. 230).

7. Watch the boring carefully so that all holes will be perpendicular when finished. It is recommended to stop boring after every few turns, and sight the work to determine if the bit is perpendicular both to the side and end of the board (Fig. 39). Any error may then be corrected before the holes are bored to their full depth.

8. Cut the dowels about ⅛ in. less in length than the combined depth of the holes. Point them a little with a knife or coarse sandpaper so that they may enter the holes more easily. Cut a small groove along the side of the smooth dowels to permit glue and air in the bottom of the holes to escape. Avoid making the dowels too short, as the wood around the part of the hole, not filled, will shrink and make a depression in the surface (Fig. 40).

9. Put glue in the holes of one member with a small round brush, or a small stick with a little cotton waste wrapped around one end. Dip one end

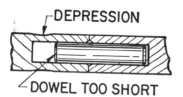

Fig. 40. Depression caused by a short dowel.

Fig. 41. Doweled frame ready for gluing.

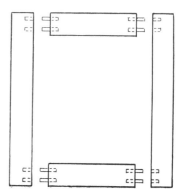

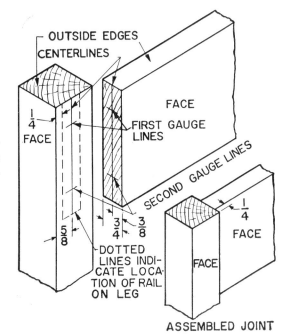

Fig. 42. Dowel joint between table leg and rail.

OUTSIDE EDGES
CENTERLINES
FACE
FIRST GAUGE LINES
SECOND GAUGE LINES
$\frac{1}{4}$
FACE
$\frac{5}{8}$
$\frac{3}{4}$
$\frac{3}{8}$
DOTTED LINES INDI-CATE LOCA-TION OF RAIL ON LEG
$\frac{1}{4}$
FACE
FACE

ASSEMBLED JOINT

of the dowels in the glue, and drive them home with light blows of a ham-mer or mallet. Wipe off surplus glue with a piece of waste.

10. Put glue in the holes and on the edges of the members which make contact and also on the dowels which protrude from the members into which they are glued (Fig. 41). Join the pieces together and clamp (see directions for clamping, Arts. 225, p. 293, and 227, p. 296).

11. When the members of a joint are not to be flush as, for example, the legs and rails of a table or stool, the center lines are gauged with different settings of the marking gauge (Fig. 42).

12. If the rails are ¾ in. thick, the marking gauge is set to ⅜ in. for gauging the center lines on them. If they are to join the legs ¼ in. from their outer surfaces, this distance must be added to the setting of the gauge. The center lines on the legs are therefore gauged ⅝ in. from their faces.

179. Procedure for Making a Draw-Bolt Joint. Although this joint is not strictly a dowel joint, it may be described under this heading, because dowels are generally used for locating the parts (Fig. 43).

1. Draw-bolt joints are used in timber construction, in stands for motors or machines, in workbenches, and in other construction subject to strain and vibration. Its advantage over other joints is that it can be tightened when it works loose.

2. The horizontal member or rail is joined to the vertical member with one or two dowels as explained in the previous article. The dowels are glued into the rail only.

3. The hole for the bolt is bored through both pieces while they are clamped together. It should be of the same size as the bolt and a little longer.

4. Another hole is then bored or chiseled in the rail for the nut of the

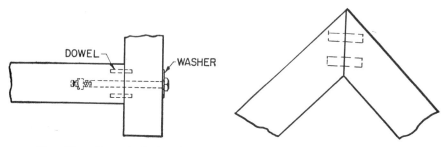

Fig. 43.   Draw-bolt joint.   **Fig. 44.**   Doweled miter joint.

bolt. If the rail is thin, the hole goes right through it, but if the rail is thick the hole should be only deep enough so that the nut will fit into it. It should be made so that the nut cannot move out of place and so that the end of the bolt will go through it and get a good grip. A washer should be placed under the head of the bolt to prevent it from digging into the wood.

Note that holes for dowels are always bored at right angles to the surfaces to be joined, even if these surfaces are not at right angles to the sides. Typical examples are rims for round tables, side rails for chairs, miter joints (Fig. 44), and segment work (Fig. 45).

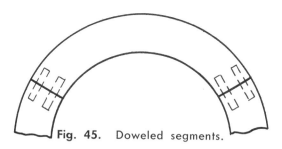

Fig. 45.   Doweled segments.

180. Procedure for Doweling Boards Edge to Edge.   1. When boards for a table top are to be glued together, they are first placed side by side on a bench and arranged so that the grain forms pleasing patterns and runs in the same direction. They are then numbered or marked as in Figure 22, p.

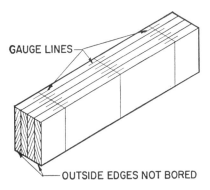

GAUGE LINES

OUTSIDE EDGES NOT BORED

Fig. 46. Doweling boards
edge to edge.

Fig. 47. Self-centering doweling
jig.

179, and jointed two and two as in Figure 23, p. 179. Do this job as carefully as if no dowels were to be used, *because dowels will not hold poorly jointed edges together.*

2. When all the joints fit (Fig. 25, p. 180), the boards are all gauged lengthwise in the center from the face of the boards. Clamp all the boards together side by side as in Figure 46, and square lines all around them. The holes for the dowels are to be bored where these lines intersect the gauge lines. If a little hole is made with the brad awl at these points of intersection, it will help to center the auger bit quickly and accurately. Remember that no dowel holes are to be bored in the two outside edges of the top.

3. Bore the holes, glue the dowels and clamp as explained in steps 7 to 10, Article 178.

A doweling jig enables anyone to bore straight and perpendicular holes. It can be clamped over the edge or end of a piece of wood and has cylindrical metal guides for ¼, ⁵⁄₁₆, ⅜, ⁷⁄₁₆, and ½-in. bits.

The doweling jig shown in Figure 47 is a so-called "self-centering" dowel jig because the guide holes center themselves automatically in the center of a board. This jig cannot be used in work where the dowel holes are placed off center.

181. Procedure for Joining Legs to a Turned Column With Dowels.

1. Sand the legs on a spindle sander or sanding cylinder mounted in the lathe. Support each leg on the tool rest, and move it from side to side until the desired curvature has been obtained, so that it fits snugly against the column (see Fig. 61, p. 370).

It is also important that the upper part of the leg, which fits against the column, is square with the lower part which is to stand on the floor. Test

Fig. 48. Testing for squareness with a steel square.

for squareness with a steel square (Fig. 48) before and after sanding in the lathe. If one of the legs should not be square, the column of the table would be out of plumb.

2. Gauge center lines on the ends of the legs as described in Article 178, step 2. It is important that these lines be gauged exactly in the center, because the legs are to fit against a cylindrical column. If the holes to be bored for the dowels are a little off center, the joints will be open on one side.

3. Lay out vertical lines on the column at the points where the legs are to join it. This is done as follows: Wrap a strip of paper around the column and cut it so that the ends just meet. Remove it and fold it into three or four equal parts, depending upon the number of legs to be doweled into the column. Wrap the paper strip around the column again, and mark these divisions on it with a pencil (Fig. 9, p. 384). Place the column in the lathe, move the tool rest of the lathe close up against it, and mark the lines along its upper edge from these points (see also directions for reeding, Art. 278).

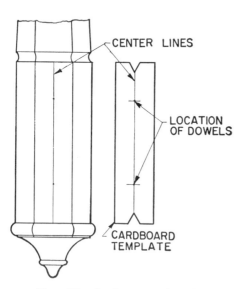

CENTER LINES

LOCATION OF DOWELS

CARDBOARD TEMPLATE

Fig. 49. Laying out dowels on turned column.

4. Make a cardboard template of the same length as the joint, mark a center line on it, and punch two holes where the dowels should be (Fig. 49).

5. Place the template on the column and legs so that the center lines coincide, and mark the position of the dowels.

When the underside of the column is flat as in this case, the horizontal gauge lines may also be

Fig. 50.   Leg to be joined to turned column with dowels.

Fig. 51.   Gluing last of three legs to turned column.

gauged on both column and legs by holding the block of the marking gauge against their lower edges (Art. 178, step 4).

6. Bore holes for the dowels as explained in Article 178 (Fig. 38, p. 207, and 50), and glue the legs to the column as described in Article 231.

182. Procedure for Boring Dowel Holes With Machine Tools.   1. Holes for dowels can be bored on a boring machine, a mortiser with boring attach-

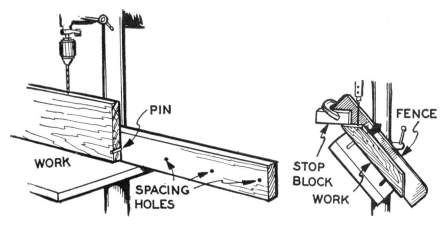

Fig. 52.   Boring dowel holes in the edges of boards to be glued together.

Fig. 53.   Boring dowel holes in mitered frame.

ment, a drill press, or a router. However, only shallow holes can be bored on the router, because router bits are very short.

2. When boring holes in the edges of the boards for a table top, an auxiliary fence should be made and screwed to the regular fence. This is then adjusted and clamped to the table, so that the holes will be bored in the center of each edge. Lay out the holes on one board, and bore a spacing hole for each dowel in the auxiliary fence, which should extend beyond the table (Fig. 52).

3. A pin is put in the first spacing hole, the end of one of the boards butted against it, and the first dowel hole bored. The pin is then put in the second spacing hole, the board moved against it, and another dowel hole bored. In this way all the holes will be spaced exactly alike on all the boards without any further laying out.

4. Holes in 45-deg. miter joints may be bored with the table tilted to 45 deg. (Fig. 53). Similarly, holes may be bored in surfaces at other angles by tilting the table the required number of degrees and supporting the work on jigs and stop blocks.

5. Holes may be bored in a turned column, by making a cradle for it and clamping it to the fence as shown in Figure 118, p. 243.

The horizontal double spindle boring machine illustrated in Figure 76, p. 97, is a popular machine in the small cabinet and school shop.

Part III. LAP OR HALVING JOINTS

In lap or halving joints, half the thickness of each member is cut away, so that when jointed together their upper and lower surfaces will be flush. These joints are used in carpentry, patternmaking, and cabinetmaking. The carpenter uses lap joints in framing the timbers forming the sill and plate of a house and where timbers cross each other. The patternmaker uses them in making the arms for pulleys, etc. The cabinetmaker uses them in connecting crossrails to the sides of a cabinet, in chair seats, in picture frames, in joining stretchers which cross diagonally, in molded work, and faced-up grounds for doors. These joints also have many other applications.

185. Procedure for Making an End-Lap Joint. 1. For a practice joint, square one piece of stock to the following dimensions: ¾ in. thick, 2 in. wide, and 12 in. long. Cut it in half and mark the face of each member plainly.

2. Lay out the width (2 in.) from one end of each piece, and square lines all around.

3. Place one piece on top of the other in the position they are to occupy with the face of both pieces up (Fig. 54).

4. Then set a marking gauge to half the thickness of the pieces (⅜ in.)

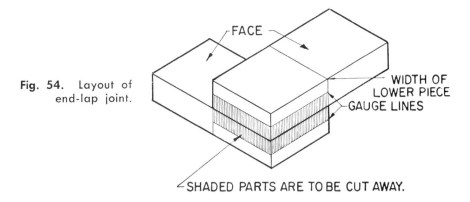

Fig. 54. Layout of end-lap joint.

FACE

WIDTH OF LOWER PIECE

GAUGE LINES

SHADED PARTS ARE TO BE CUT AWAY.

and gauge a line around the end of each piece *from the face of both pieces.*

5. The parts to be cut away are then marked. It is the lower part of the top piece and the upper part of the bottom piece.

6. If the lines were not gauged exactly in the center, the two pieces when cut would still be flush, because if too little were cut from one piece, proportionately more would be cut from the other. The most important thing in laying out lap joints, therefore, is to *gauge from the face of both members.*

7. The shoulder cuts across the grain are now made on both pieces. As it is very important to make them straight, perpendicular, and to the line, it is best to cut triangular grooves in which to start the backsaw, or to clamp a piece of wood as a guide right on the line (see Figs. 5, 8, and 9, pp. 196 and 197).

8. The cheek or side cuts may be made either with a backsaw or a ripsaw. Each piece is clamped diagonally in a bench vise and sawed on the waste side of the gauge line. In this position both the end and one side can be seen at the same time (Fig. 55).

9. Follow the gauge line and continue sawing until the shoulder cut has been reached. Then reverse the piece, clamp it vertically in the vise, and finish the saw cut. As the top and one side have been sawed, it is only necessary to follow the gauge line on

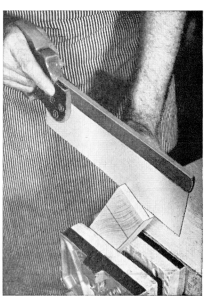

Fig. 55. Sawing cheek cut of end-lap joint.

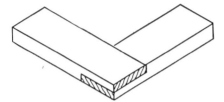

Fig. 56. Finished end-lap joint.

the second side. The first saw cut helps to guide the saw.

10. When the pieces are fitted together, their upper and lower surfaces should be flush, and the side of one should fit accurately against the shoulder of the other (Fig. 56). Any adjustment can be made with a chisel.

186. Procedure for Making an End-Lap Joint With Rabbet. This joint is used when framing a mirror, a wooden panel, or a pane of glass.

1. If possible, square a piece of wood long enough for the whole frame, plane the rabbet, and saw into lengths.

2. The joint is laid out as an ordinary end-lap joint, except that the width of the rabbet is subtracted on one piece (B) when laying out the shoulder cuts (Fig. 57).

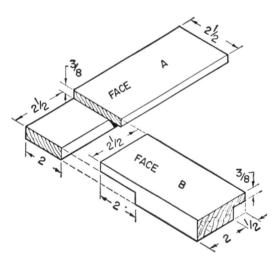

Fig. 57. Layout of end-lap joint with rabbet.

3. The pieces are gauged *from the face* so that the gauge lines are even with the rabbet.

4. The shoulder cuts are made as explained in the previous article. When the side cuts are made, the piece from which the upper part is cut away (A) will be reduced in width by the width of the rabbet, while the other piece (B) still has its full width.

187. Procedure for Making a Cross-Lap Joint. In cabinetmaking this joint is used more than any other lap joint. Some typical examples are: crossrails, both plain and shaped, for taborets, tables, stools, and cabinets, as well as crosses for hall trees, flowerpot stands, trellises, etc. The pattern-maker uses cross-lap joints when making spokes for wheels and pulleys, and the carpenter also uses them in various timber constructions.

1. The members of a cross-lap joint generally are of the same thickness and width, and cross each other in the middle at right angles. Cross-lap joints, however, may be made at different angles and the parts may also be of different dimensions. To make one of the common cross-lap joints, square a piece of stock, long enough for both parts, to dimensions.

2. If the joint is to be in the center, cut the pieces to exact length, place them side by side, and square a line across them in the center (Fig. 58). Test the accuracy of this measurement by reversing one of the pieces. If the center lines still meet when the ends are flush, the measurement is correct.

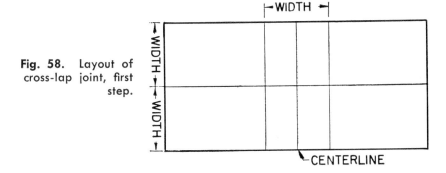

Fig. 58. Layout of cross-lap joint, first step.

3. Lay out half the width of the pieces on each side of the center line, and square lines across both pieces at these points. Test the measurements as before and check on the width of the cut by placing one piece on top of the other in the position these pieces are to occupy. Square these shoulder lines all around each piece.

4. Mark the faces and *gauge the depth lines from the face* of each piece between the shoulder lines.

5. After marking the parts to be cut away, make the shoulder cuts as explained in Article 185, and Figures 5, 7, 8, and 9, pp. 196, 197. It is better to make these so that they are a trifle too small, and then plane a few shavings off the edges until they fit perfectly.

6. To aid in chiseling away the waste stock, a few extra saw cuts should be made between the shoulder cuts (Fig. 59). These will serve as a depth

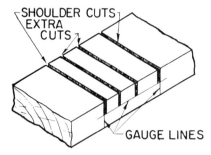

Fig. 59. Shoulder and center cuts for middle- or cross-lap joints.

gauge and prevent splitting off chips below the depth line. Hold the bevel of the chisel down and begin cutting well above the gauge line (Fig. 60). Chisel from both edges toward the middle. Finish the cut with the bevel of the chisel up (Fig. 61) or with a router plane (Fig. 62).

Fig. 60. Chiseling middle- or cross-lap joint, bevel down. Roughing cut.

7. Cross-lap joints are also made on the edges of the stock as shown in Figure 63. The procedure is the same.

8. *Middle-lap joints* (Fig. 64) are used especially in house framing and timber construction. One member is made as an end-lap joint and the other as a cross-lap joint. They are usually made at right angles to each other,

Fig. 61. Chiseling middle- or cross-lap joint, bevel up. Finishing cut.

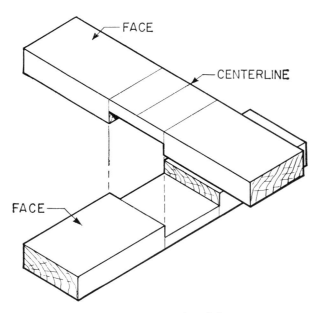

Fig. 62. Cross-lap joint.

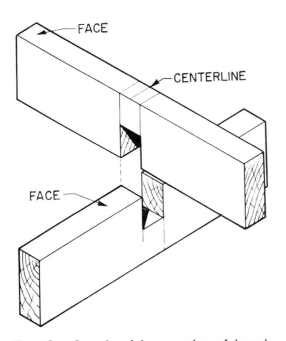

Fig. 63. Cross-lap joint on edge of board.

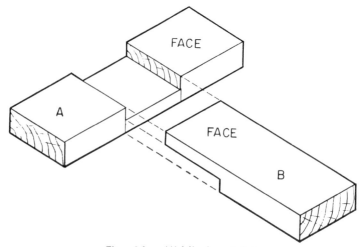

Fig. 64. Middle-lap joint.

either in the center of one piece or at some other point between the ends. They are laid out and cut exactly as end-lap and cross-lap joints.

188. Procedure for Making a Mitered Cross-Lap Joint. If in Figure 65 the piece of stock shown there was one of the mullions* in a glass panel door (French door), the procedure for making the cross-lap joint for the horizontal and vertical mullions would be a great deal more complicated than explained in Article 187.

The end view of a mullion for such a door would appear as shown in Figure 65. It shows two glass rabbets at the bottom and a simple decoration on the top.

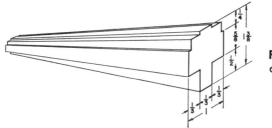

Fig. 65. Cross section of a mullion.

Assuming that the stiles, rails, and mullions have first been properly identified and laid out (see Arts. 342 and 343, p. 487 ff.) and all mortises and tenons have been cut, proceed as follows:

---

* NOTE: Mullions are sometimes called muntins or munnions.

1. Cut the glass rabbets on the unmarked side of stiles, rails, and mullions. In 1⅜ in. stock they can be made ½ in. deep. The width of the rabbet is equal to ⅓ the width of the mullion. Do this operation with a rabbet plane. If machines are available, use either the circular saw, jointer, or shaper.

2. Cut the decorative molding on the marked side of all the parts. Do this with the proper molding plane or complete this operation with the shaper or router.

3. Hold one of the mullions in the vise and with a fine-tooth dovetail saw make two cuts halfway down the two center lines of the layout (Fig. 66).

4. Carefully remove this cut portion with a sharp ¼ in. chisel. Do not cut beyond the halfway mark (Fig. 67).

Fig. 66. Sawing out center of cross-lap joint.

Fig. 67. Removing cut portion.

5. Repeat step 4 for the other mullion but now make the two cuts from the opposite side (Fig. 68).

6. Remove this cut portion with a ¼-in. chisel (Fig. 69).

7. Next give the mullion a quarter turn and fasten it in the vise. With a sharp 1-in. chisel make a 45-degree cut, starting at the outer layout line (Fig. 70).

Fig. 68. Sawing second mullion.

Fig. 69. Removing cut portion.

Fig. 70. Making a 45-degree cut.

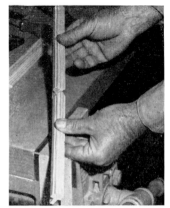

Fig. 71. One half of cross-lap joint.

8. Repeat this operation for the three other areas. When the four 45-degree cuts have been made, the completed half of the mitered cross-lap joint appears as shown in Figure 71.

9. Hold the other mullion in the vise in a like manner and remove the V-shaped portion between the outer layout lines. Do not cut beyond the molding. The completed half of the cross-lap joint appears as shown in Figure 72.

10. Cross the two mullions and press the joint together (Fig. 73). If it is too tight, make the necessary adjustments. The completed joint should appear as shown in Figure 74. In door and window construction it is accepted practice to have the vertical mullions continuous on the outside and make the saw cuts on the inside. By following this procedure, there is less chance that water will collect in the joints.

Fig. 72. Second half of joint completed.

Fig. 73. Assembling two mullions.

Fig. 74. Completed cross-lap joint.

189. Procedure for Making a Dovetail-Lap Joint. 1. This joint (Fig. 75) is a modified middle-lap joint. As it cannot be pulled apart, is it used especially where there is a pull or tension strain. It is used a good deal in such pieces of furniture as cabinets and chests of drawers, which have an upper rail connecting and holding the two sides together (Fig. 76).

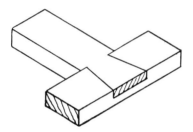

Fig. 75. Dovetail-lap joint.

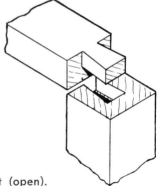

Fig. 76. Dovetail-lap joint (open).

2. The joint is laid out as an ordinary middle-lap joint after which the angle of the dovetail is marked on the upper piece B, Figure 77.

3. The angle is obtained as follows: Square a line across a board, and step off six equal spaces on it. From the end of the sixth space, step off one to the right and parallel to the edge of the board (Fig. 78). A line drawn from this point to the starting point of the first line gives the correct angle for dovetails. Set a sliding T bevel to this angle and lay it out on the end of piece B.

4. Make the shoulder cut as explained in Article 185, but continue it around both edges to the line of the dovetail.

5. Then make the cheek cut as in a regular end-lap joint. Finally saw along the lines marked for the dovetail.

6. The upper piece B now has the shape shown in Figure 79. Place it on top of piece A, and mark its outline with a knife or sharp pencil. Saw and chisel the recess as in an ordinary cross-lap joint (Art. 187). Then fit the pieces together.

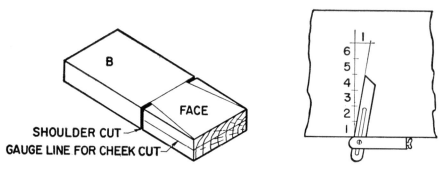

Fig. 77. Shoulder cut on dovetail-lap joint.

Fig. 78. Laying out angle of dovetails.

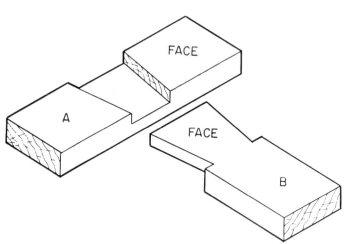

Fig. 79. Dovetail-lap joint.

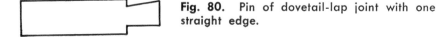

Fig. 80. Pin of dovetail-lap joint with one straight edge.

7. When a dovetail-lap joint is made on the end of a leg as in a cabinet (Fig. 76), the dovetail is made shorter than the width of the leg. The joint is laid out as before, but the recess in the leg must be cut with a chisel.

8. Dovetail-lap joints may also be made with only one slanting side as in Figure 80.

190. Procedure for Making Lap Joints on the Circular Saw.   1. End-lap joints may be cut on the circular saw in the same way as tenons are cut (Art. 201).

2. Cross-lap joints can also be cut on the circular saw, but in this case a dado head is used.

3. Set the dado head to the correct height above the table and hold each part of the joint with one edge against the universal gauge. Adjust the ripping fence so that when the end of the piece bears against it, the dado head will cut the part of the recess nearest to it.

4. Reverse the piece, hold the other end against the ripping fence, and the opposite end of the recess will be cut. If there is any wood left in the center of the joint, this can be cut away by moving the ripping fence to the right.

5. Instead of using the ripping fence as a stop, a piece of wood may be clamped to the universal gauge as shown in Figure 81.

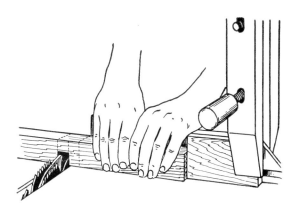

Fig. 81. Cutting cross-lap joint with dado head. Stop block clamped to miter gauge.

Part IV.   MORTISE-AND-TENON JOINTS

The mortise-and-tenon joint is without exception the most important and most used joint in cabinet construction. It is made with several variations. Some of the most important of these are: blind, pinned, haunched, barefaced, through, wedged, slip, and keyed joints (Fig. 82).

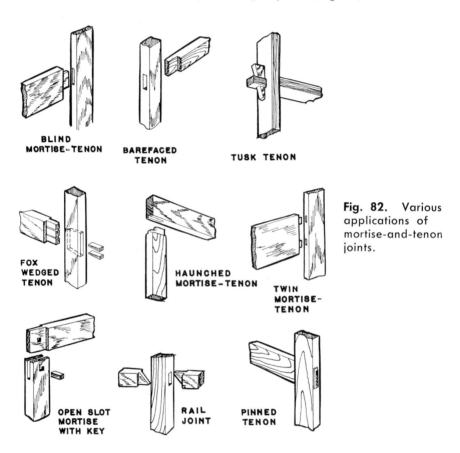

BLIND MORTISE-TENON

BAREFACED TENON

TUSK TENON

FOX WEDGED TENON

HAUNCHED MORTISE-TENON

TWIN MORTISE-TENON

Fig. 82. Various applications of mortise-and-tenon joints.

OPEN SLOT MORTISE WITH KEY

RAIL JOINT

PINNED TENON

A carpenter uses a mortise-and-tenon joint both in timber construction and in interior woodwork. Cabinetmakers use this joint in all of their better construction. The three pieces of furniture shown in Figure 83 all have some mortise-and-tenon joints. So do the pieces of the bedroom furniture illustrated in Figure 84. For over-all strength and holding power this joint is difficult to surpass.

Fig. 83. Use of well-
fitting mortise-and-
tenon joints.

Fig. 84. Double
bed and matching
night stands.

193. Procedure for Making a Blind Mortise-and-Tenon Joint. This type
of mortise-and-tenon joint is used in most cabinetwork, because it is neater
in appearance than other joints. It requires three principal operations to
make any mortise-and-tenon joint. These operations are: laying out, making
the mortise, and making the tenon.

Laying out. 1. Square the pieces to dimensions, and mark their faces
plainly.

2. Determine the length of the tenon, i.e., the distance it is to enter the
other member, and square a line all around its end at that point which is
the shoulder.

3. Mark the total width of the tenon member on the mortise member at
the point where they are to be joined.

4. Determine the thickness of the tenon; it is usually from one third to
one half the thickness of the stock. Set the points of a mortising gauge to

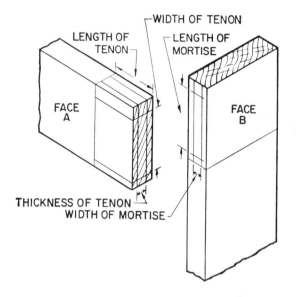

Fig. 85. Layout of mortise-and-tenon joint.

this distance, and adjust the block of the gauge, so that the double lines will be marked in about the center of the piece.

5. Gauge *from the face* on the end and edges as far as the lines which mark the shoulder (Fig. 85).

6. If the faces of the members are to be flush, gauge the mortise with the same setting of the gauge from the face of the piece. If the mortise member is thicker than the tenon member, as for example in a table leg,

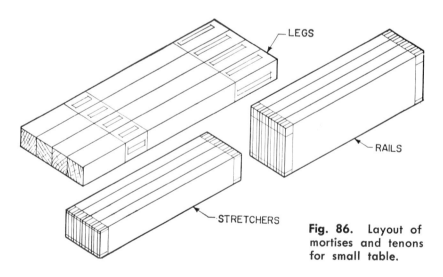

Fig. 86. Layout of mortises and tenons for small table.

and the rail or tenon member is to be set in, for example ¼ in. from the face of the leg, the block of the mortise gauge must be moved accordingly, *but not the setting of the two points.*

7. A tenon is rarely made the full width of the member, but an additional cheek cut is laid out, making it narrower. If the mortise is near the end of a piece, at least ½ in. should be taken from the width of the tenon so that the end wood of the mortise will not tear out when it is chiseled. Lay out this cheek cut on both tenons and mortises.

8. In a mortise-and-tenon construction there usually are several joints with the same dimensions. *These must all be laid out at the same time with the same setting of the gauge* in order to produce accurate work (Fig. 86). In addition, mortises in legs should always be gauged from the outside or face surfaces. When four legs are required, as in tables, stools, or cabinets, it will make it more convenient if they are placed in the position they are to occupy and are marked left front, right front, left back, and right back. Furthermore, all outside faces may be marked "out" (Fig. 87).*

---

* For a marking system that may be less confusing *see* Article 342, p. 487.

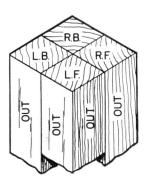

Fig. 87. Marking table legs before laying out mortise.

Fig. 88. Chiseling mortise. Paper strip glued to chisel for depth gauge.

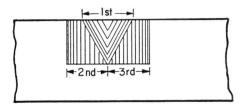

Fig. 89. Diagrammatic sketch of steps in chiseling a mortise.

If a mortising gauge is not available, an ordinary marking gauge may be used. Set it first to mark the gauge lines nearest the faces of the pieces, then set it to mark the farther gauge line, and mark all the pieces again from the face of each.

Making the Mortise. The mortise can be made in two ways, either by chiseling the hole with a mortising chisel, or by boring a number of adjoining holes and then cutting away the waste between them.

9. In the first method, a mortising chisel of the same width as the mortise to be chiseled is used. Clamp the piece on top of the bench and begin by cutting out wedge-shaped pieces in the center of the mortise until the required depth is reached. This depth may be determind by gluing a strip of paper around the chisel (Fig. 88). Now make a series of perpendicular cuts toward both ends of the mortise, holding the bevel of the chisel toward the center of the mortise. Break the shavings loose by moving the handle of the chisel toward the center of the mortise. Pare the ends of the mortise (Fig. 89).

10. In the second method, a series of adjoining holes are bored with an auger or dowel bit of the same diameter as the width of the mortise (Fig. 90). Clamp an auger-bit gauge to the bit, or make one of a block of wood (Art. 178, step 6, p. 208) so that the hole bored will be slightly deeper

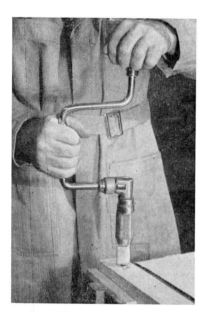

Fig. 90. Boring holes to start mortise.

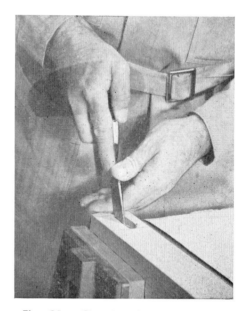

Fig. 91. Cleaning bored mortise.

Fig. 92.   Sawing cheek cuts.

Fig. 93.   Tenon cheek cuts.

than the length of the tenon. Be careful to bore the holes perpendicularly (Figs. 39 and 90).

11. Clamp the pieces firmly in the vise or on top of the bench, and chisel out the pieces of wood left between the holes bored. Chisel perpendicularly until the gauge lines have been reached (Fig. 91).

Making the Tenon. 12. If the cheek cuts are made first, the thin pieces of wood that are sawed off will not split away before the cut has been completed. Clamp the piece diagonally in the vise as shown in Figure 92, so that the gauge lines on the end and one side can be seen at the same time. Use either a backsaw or a ripsaw, depending upon the size of the tenon, and saw until the line marking the shoulder cut is almost reached.

13. Then reverse the piece in the vise, clamp it in a vertical position, and finish the saw cut. It is necessary to watch only the gauge line in front of you, because the diagonal saw cut already made serves as a guide for the saw. Finish the other cheek cut in the same manner, but do not saw below the lines marking the shoulder cut.

14. If one or two more cheek cuts reduce the width of the tenon, these should also be sawed as shown in Figure 93.

15. The shoulder cuts are made in the same way as those on lap joints. Score the lines all around with a sharp knife (see Fig. 5, p. 196) or a chisel (see Fig. 6, p. 196). Then make a shallow triangular groove in which to

Fig. 94. Sawing shoulder cut.

start the backsaw, as in Figures 7 and 8, p. 196. When sawing the shoulder cuts, hold the piece of wood on a bench hook (Fig. 94) or clamp it in a vise. Trim off any unevenness with a sharp chisel, and bevel the edges of the tenon (Figs. 95 and 96).

16. Fit the pieces together, and make any necessary adjustments.

Only hand pressure should be necessary to bring the members of the joint together. Excessive force may cause the mortised member to split.

When the tenoned member of a blind mortise-and-tenon joint has only two cheek cuts, it is called a "stub mortise-and-tenon joint."

17. If the shoulder cuts are not perfect, the tenoned member will not fit snugly against the edge of the mortised member. A poor shoulder cut may be repaired by scoring a new line all around it (step 15). Cut as deeply with the chisel as possible (Fig. 6, p. 196), and then make perpendicular chisel cuts on this line from both sides as in Figure 96. Finish by clamping the piece in a vise with the tenon up, and cut from the edges with a ½-in. chisel (Fig. 97).

18. As this trimming naturally shortens the tenoned member, corresponding members must be shortened the same amount, even if their shoulder

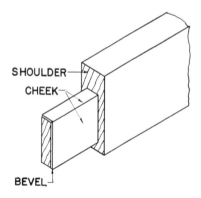

SHOULDER

CHEEK

BEVEL

Fig. 95. Finished tenon.

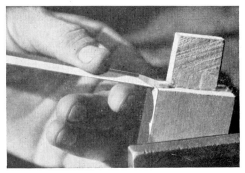

Fig. 96. Straightening uneven shoulder cuts with chisel.

Fig. 97. Removing remaining parts on shoulder with chisel.

cuts are perfect. *Tenoned members of equal length must measure exactly the same between shoulders.*

19. A blind mortise-and-tenon joint is sometimes strengthened by driving a pin through it. On reproductions of Elizabethan or Jacobean tables, benches, or stools, such pins are a feature of the design and are usually made square or triangular. When the appearance is unimportant, ordinary dowels are used. Such joints are called "pinned mortise-and-tenon joints" (Fig. 98). It goes without saying that all tools used in making a mortise-and-tenon joint should be sharp and in perfect condition.

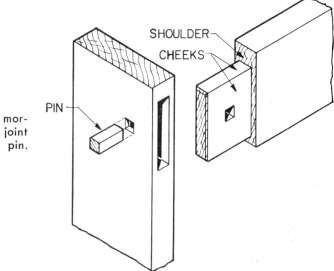

Fig. 98. Blind mortise-and-tenon joint with pin.

194. Procedure for Making a Glass Door With Blind Mortise-and-Tenon Joints. In the construction of windows and glass doors (French doors), one must take into account that on the outside a series of rabbets are cut which hold the windowpanes. The inside is generally finished with some kind of decorative molding. When fitting such a window or door together, the procedure is quite different from the procedures discussed so far. Assuming that the parts of the door have been marked and laid out properly (see Arts. 342 and 343) proceed as follows:

1. Cut all mortises and tenons, using either hand tools or machines. One stile, one rail and two mullions appear as shown in Figure 99.

Fig. 99. Mortises cut in stile; tenons cut on rail and two mullions.

2. Cut the glass rabbets on the unmarked side of stiles, rails, and mullions. In 1⅜-in. stock they can be made ¾ in. deep. They are usually ¼ in. wide or one third the width of a mullion. When using hand tools do this with a rabbet plane. When using machines, do it on the circular saw, jointer, or shaper.

3. Next cut the decorative molding on the marked side of all the parts. Do this with the proper molding plane or complete this operation with the shaper or router.

4. Hold one stile in the vise and make a fine saw cut on the inside mark of the mortise. This cut is made exactly to the depth where the molding stops (Fig. 100).

5. With a sharp 1-in. chisel remove this section of the molding until it appears as shown in Figure 101.

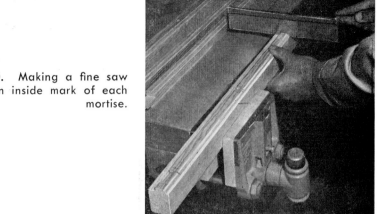

Fig. 100. Making a fine saw cut on inside mark of each mortise.

Fig. 101. Removing molding, and haunching rail mortises.

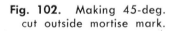

Fig. 102. Making 45-deg. cut outside mortise mark.

6. From the outside mark of the mortise make a 45-degree cut as shown in Figure 102.

7. To prepare the mortise for the mullions repeat step 4, with this difference that two saw cuts are made at the inside marks.

8. With a sharp ¼-in. chisel remove the wood between these saw cuts to the depth of the molding.

Fig. 103. Completing mullion mortises.

9. From the outside marks make two 45-degree cuts as shown in Figure 103. Also complete this mullion mortise in the rail.

10. In completing the tenons on the rail and mullions indicate the size of the haunches by holding the tenon over the mortise as shown in Figure 104.

11. Place the rail vertically in the vise and cut the haunches lengthwise (Fig. 105).

Fig. 104. Laying out positions of haunches.

Fig. 105. Cutting tenons lengthwise.

Fig. 106. Completing haunches.

Fig. 107. Starting cut at inside mark on rail.

12. Place the rail horizontally in the vise and complete cutting the haunches as shown in Figure 106.

13. From the inside mark on the rail make a 45-degree cut, using a sharp 1-in. chisel as shown in Figure 107.

14. Repeat the operation for the mullions.

15. Test all tenons for correct fit. Make any necessary adjustments. Check for squareness with the stile (Fig. 108).

16. After completing the mitered cross-lap joint the completed corner unit appears as shown in Figure 109. See procedure for making a mitered cross-lap joint, page 220.

Fig. 109.   Completed corner unit.

Fig. 108.   Testing joints
for squareness.

195. Procedure for Making a Haunched Mortise-and-Tenon Joint. 1. This joint is used in panel construction. First make the grooves in all the pieces. These must be of the same width as the tenons are to be, which is usually one third the thickness of the members.

2. Lay out the mortises and tenons, as described in Article 193, but do not extend the upper cheek cut all the way to the shoulder of the tenon. A piece of the tenon just large enough to fill up the groove is left at this point (Fig. 110).

The object of this joint is to give lateral stiffness.

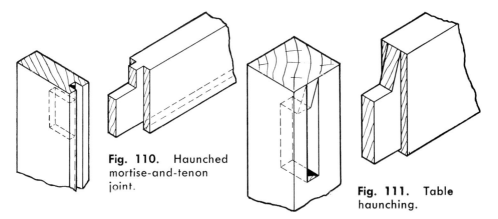

Fig. 110. Haunched mortise-and-tenon joint.

Fig. 111. Table haunching.

3. A modified haunched joint is the table- or taper-haunched joint (Fig. 111). This is used on tables to give stiffness to the rails, or in places where the appearance of the regular haunched joint would be objectionable.

4. A double tenon is made on the lower rail of a door if the rail is more than 8 in. wide. The joint is haunched both on the ends and between the tenons (Fig. 112).

196. Procedure for Making a Barefaced Mortise-and-Tenon Joint. When the rails and legs of tables and stools are made flush, very little wood is left between the mortise and the face of the leg if a regular tenon is used. To strengthen the joint in such cases, the tenon is made on the inside part of the rail and therefore has only one shoulder (Fig. 113). Note that bare-

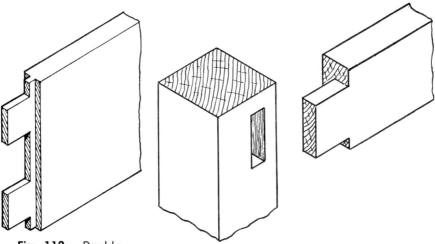

Fig. 112. Double haunched tenon.

Fig. 113. Barefaced mortise-and-tenon joint.

faced mortise-and-tenon joints can be used only when the mortise member is thicker than the tenon member.

197. Procedure for Making a Through Mortise-and-Tenon Joint. 1. This joint is laid out and made in the same manner as a blind mortise-and-tenon joint (Art. 193) except that the tenon extends through the mortise member and therefore is made a little longer than the mortise is deep. The mortise is chiseled from both edges.

2. The tenon is either planed off flush with the mortise member, or is rounded off and left to project a little.

3. A "wedged mortise-and-tenon joint" is a through mortise-and-tenon joint in which wedges are driven into the end of the tenon so that it cannot pull out. The end of the mortise is chiseled a little wider. When the wedges are driven home, the tenon will spread and fill the hole completely (Fig. 114).

198. Procedure for Making a Slip Joint. A slip joint is simply a through mortise-and-tenon joint made on the ends of two pieces (Fig. 115). In this case, the mortise, which is open on three sides, is sawed on the inside of the lines instead of bored. The waste pieces are cut out with a chisel. This joint is very strong and is used on various types of frames (Fig. 22, p. 422).

199. Procedure for Making a Keyed Mortise-and-Tenon Joint. This joint differs from the other mortise-and-tenon joints in that it can be taken apart. It can also be tightened by driving in the key. It is therefore used much in the same way as a draw-bolt joint (Fig. 43, p. 210), on benches and other heavy wood construction.

1. The keyed joint is a through mortise-and-tenon joint with a tenon at least twice as long as the mortise.

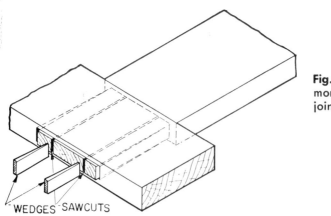

Fig. 114. Wedged mortise-and-tenon joint.

WEDGES SAWCUTS

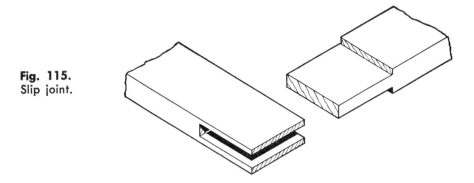

Fig. 115.
Slip joint.

2. Make the through mortise-and-tenon joint as explained in Article 197, and when that fits, lay out a through mortise on the projecting end of the tenon.

3. This mortise should be rectangular in shape. The end nearest the end of the stock must be slanted a little toward the underside, but the opposite or inner end should be perpendicular and cut back at least ⅛ in. beyond the face of the large mortise member (Fig. 116). When the mortise has been cut, the upper edge of the rectangular hole in the tenon therefore should be a little longer than the lower edge.

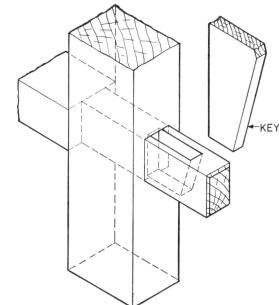

KEY

Fig. 116.   Keyed mortise-and-tenon joint.

4. A key is now made to fit this mortise. The rear edge of the key is square to the two ends, but its front edge is tapered to fit the mortise.

5. When this key has been driven home, its rear edge bears against the face of the mortise member, drawing the joint tight. If the mortise, made through the tenon, had not been cut back ⅛ in., the joint could never be tightened, because the wedge could not be driven in any farther.

200. Procedure for Making a Mortise on a Mortising Machine. 1. Insert a mortising chisel and bit of the proper size in the machine, and see that the rear edge of the chisel is parallel to the vertical rear fence of the table. The bit should be adjusted so that it clears the cutting edges of the chisel, because friction will overheat both bit and chisel (Art. 111, p. 91).

2. Clamp the piece to be mortised on the table. Press down the foot pedal, and bring the bit down near the top of the wood without starting the machine. Adjust the table so that the bit is centered between the two gauge lines, indicating the width of the mortise. If table legs are to be mortised, one outside surface is placed on the table and the other against the fence. If the fence has a lip, this should be adjusted so that the leg just slides under it and will not be pulled up on the upward movement of the ram.

3. Adjust the machine to cut the desired depth, see that the lengthwise movement of the table is set so that the entire length of the mortise can be cut without changing the position of the piece held in the clamp.

When several pieces are to be mortised alike, various stops on the table can be set so that the pieces are mortised automatically with the same spacing and length of mortise. In this way only one piece has to be laid out.

4. Start the machine, and bring the chisel down by stepping on the foot pedal. Make successive cuts next to the first cut until the entire length of the mortise has been chiseled. The first cut should be made to only half the depth, because the chisel is likely to bind in the wood, so that the spring on the machine cannot return the ram to its first position. This would cause overheating. Make the last cut the full width of the chisel; otherwise the chisel may slide sideways and be bent.

5. Pieces that will not lie flat on the table as, for instance, legs with turned parts, must be held on a flat base as in the jig shown in Figure 117.

Fig. 117. Leg with turned parts held in a jig while being mortised.

Fig. 118. Cutting mortises in circular stock.

6. When mortises are to be cut in turned stock, it is of the utmost importance to clamp the stock in the machine in such a way that the mortise, if continued, would pass right through the center of the turned piece. This may be accomplished as shown in Figure 118. A rectanguar block of the same width as the diameter of the turned piece is cut on the band saw, so that it forms a rest or cradle for the cylindrical piece to be mortised. A line is marked in the center of the block as shown.

Lay out the mortises on the turned column as explained in Article 181. From these points draw lines across the end of the column. Each line passes through its center and continues to the opposite side.

Place the column in the cradle, so that the lines coincide, as shown in Figure 118. Clamp securely and adjust the table so that the chisel is centered over the line marked on the side.

This method may also be used when legs are to be doweled to a turned column (Fig. 50, p. 213).

201. Procedure for Cutting Tenons on the Circular Saw. 1. When a number of tenons have to be cut to the same dimensions, the pieces must all be planed or sawed to the same thickness and the ends squared and cut to exact length.

2. Lay out only one piece and make the shoulder cuts first. Set the crosscut saw to correct height above the table, and, using the ripping fence as a stop, measure the length of the tenon from the fence to any saw tooth set to the left (Fig. 119).

Some woodworkers prefer making the cheek cuts first and make the shoulder cuts second in order of completion. Especially when no tenoning jig can be used on the ripping fence or the ripping fence is not very high, this procedure has merit. If one would cut tenons on the circular saw without the support of a tenoning jig and shoulder cuts are made first, it is difficult to hold the stock in an upright position against the ripping fence when the cheek cuts are made (Fig. 119).

Fig. 119. Making shoulder cuts on circular saw.

3. Hold the edge of the piece against the universal gauge and cut both sides and edges (Fig. 120). On table rails and similar pieces the edges of the tenons are cut deeper on top (Fig. 93). In such cases the sides and one edge are cut first on all the pieces. The saw is then raised higher over the table and all the upper edges are cut (Fig. 120).

4. The cheek cuts are made with a ripsaw. If an attachment like that

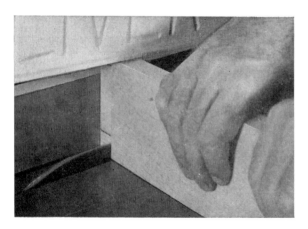

Fig. 120. Sawing shoulder cut on edge of rail.

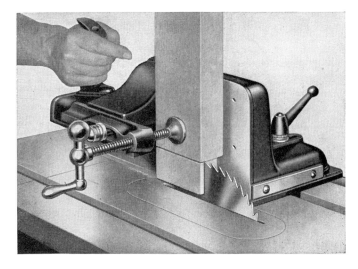

Fig. 121.
Tenoning
attachment.

shown in Figure 121 is not available, a jig illustrated in Figure 122 and 123 should be made. With such a jig, cheek cuts can be made quite safely.

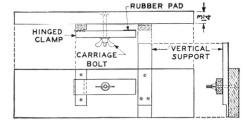

Fig. 122. Tenoning jig.

5. Clamp the pieces in the jig, and adjust the ripping fence so that the saw cut will come on the outside of the gauge lines farthest away from the ripping fence. When the jig now is held against the ripping fence and pushed

Fig. 123. Making
cheek cuts using home-
made jig.

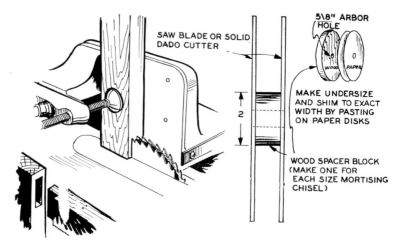

Fig. 124. Making cheek cuts with two saws and spacing block.

past the saw, the waste wood from the cheek cut will fall on the table.

6. Reverse the piece in the jig, and make the other cheek cut. The waste pieces on the edges may be cut off by hand or on a band saw.

7. If the stock is not of exactly the same thickness, it is necessary to make both cheek cuts from the same side. In this case, make the outside cheek cut first on all the pieces and then reset the ripping fence to make the second cheek cut.

8. It is possible to make both cheek cuts simultaneously if two saws of the same diameter and with a spacing block between them are put on the saw arbor (Fig. 124).

9. The mortise member of a slip joint may be cut in the same manner. The saw cuts are made on the inside of the lines, and any waste wood remaining between them may be removed by one or two extra saw cuts in the middle.

10. The mortise on a slip joint may be made in a single cut by using a dado head.

11. Tenons may also be cut with a dado head. In this case the edge of

Fig. 125. Cutting tenons with dado head. Saw guard cannot be used.

the piece is held against the universal gauge and the end against the ripping fence. The ripping fence is adjusted so that the dado head will cut just outside the shoulder line.

12. Set the dado head accurately to height and make the first cut. This will take in both the shoulder cut and part of the cheek cut (Fig. 125). Move the piece to the left and make one or two more cuts, but *do not change the setting of the ripping fence.* Make the other cheek cut in the same way.

13. When cutting tenons by this method, the stock must be planed to exactly the same thickness and the dado head set very carefully to height above the table, otherwise tenons will be either too thin or too thick.

Part V. MITER JOINTS

Miter joints are used in picture frames, in furniture construction, and in moldings around panels, doors, mirrors, windows, interior and exterior trim. When miter joints are used in the construction of glass doors as shown in Figure 126, it would be necessary to strengthen the joints with dowels, splines, or some other reinforcing device; otherwise the weight of the glass is likely to break the glue joints. Wherever feasible, projects made of plywood are often constructed with miter joints. In this way the unattractive edges do not show (Fig. 127).

A miter joint is a neat but weak joint, because its surfaces only butt against

Fig. 126.   Use of glass doors.

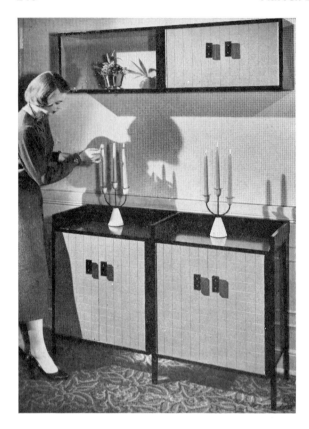

Fig. 127. Use of mitered corners in cabinets.

each other and in most cases contain about 50 per cent endwood. As glue does not hold well in endwood, miter joints are usually reinforced in various ways. The making of a miter joint may be divided into the following three principal operations: cutting, gluing, and reinforcing the joint.

204. Procedure for Cutting a Miter Joint. 1. Most moldings fit around a square or rectangular surface and are therefore cut at 45 deg. (Fig. 128). The angles for other polygons are found by dividing the number of sides into 180 deg. and subtract the quotient from 90 deg. Examples: pentagon,

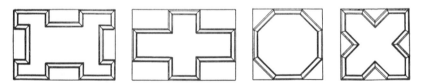

Fig. 128. Panels decorated with moldings.

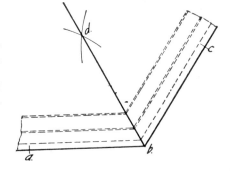

Fig. 129. Bisecting an angle. Lay off ab equal to bc. Draw arcs with equal radius from centers a and c, intersecting at d. Angle abd is the miter.

$$90 - \frac{180}{5} = 54 \text{ deg.; hexagon, } 90 - \frac{180}{6} = 60 \text{ deg.; octagon, } 90 - \frac{180}{8} =$$

67½ deg.

2. In any case the miter cut of any angle may be found by bisecting the angle as shown in Figure 129.

3. Having determined the angle of the cut, the length of the piece to be mitered is the next to be found. If it is a molding for a picture frame, take the length of the picture or glass and add to that twice the width of the molding less the rabbet (Fig. 130). Directions for making moldings are given in Article 286.

4. A miter box of wood or metal is used when cutting miters by hand. The iron miter box has the advantage over the wooden one in that it can be set to cut the most common angles and its saw runs in metal guides which hold it perpendicular. It is well to clamp the stock to be mitered to the back of the miter box while making the saw cuts (Fig. 131).

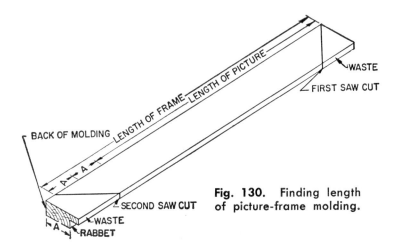

Fig. 130. Finding length of picture-frame molding.

5. If the joints should not fit exactly, they may be touched up by planing, sawing, or sanding. Planing a miter joint is difficult and should be attempted only by the more experienced workers. Sawing a miter joint to fit is done as follows: Bring the two members of the joint as close together as possible, and clamp them to a board at right angles to each other. Then saw right through the joint, using a backsaw or a crosscut saw. The saw

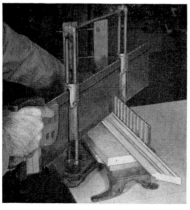

Fig. 131. Making a miter cut.

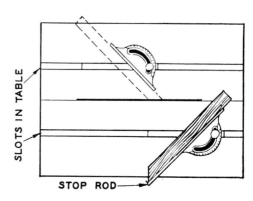

Fig. 132. Cutting miters with two miter gauges.

cuts away the high spots on both pieces so that, when they are unclamped and brought together again, they will fit perfectly. Sanding can only be done when a disk sander is available.

6. Miters may be cut on the circular saw by removing the ripping fence

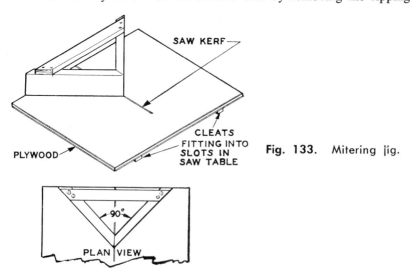

Fig. 133. Mitering jig.

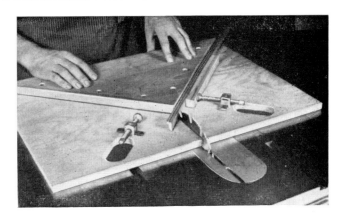

Fig. 134.
Mitering jig
with clamps.

and using the two universal gauges in the slots milled in the table. If a 45-deg. miter is to be made, set both gauges to 45 deg., as shown in Figure 132. Make the first cut with the gauge to the right, set a stop rod to length in the gauge to the left, and cut the second miter.

7. If the mitered pieces are to be short as in Figure 128, this method cannot be used. Instead, a jig, as shown in Figure 133, should be made. It is made of ⅜ or ½-in. plywood. Two cleats, which fit in the slots in the saw table, are glued and screwed to its underside. A piece of 1½-in. stock is mitered to form an angle of 90 deg., braced and screwed to the upper side.

8. The pieces to be mitered are held first against one side and then against the other as the jig is pushed over the saw. Do not saw into the jig any farther than necessary. A mitered stop block may be nailed or clamped along one side as shown in Figure 134. Both long and short, wide and narrow pieces can be accurately mitered in this jig, but only at an angle of 45 deg. Miters may also be cut on the radial saw.

205. Procedure for Gluing Mitered Frames. 1. A good way to glue

Fig. 135.
Clamping
mitered frame
while gluing.

mitered frames, especially the larger ones, is by using four bar clamps as shown in Figure 135.

2. Since the mitered ends contain about 50 per cent end grain, the glue is likely to be absorbed and sink into the open pores in the endwood very quickly, thus leaving little glue on the miters and causing what is called a "starved" joint.

3. To avoid this it is recommended to first "size" the mitered ends. Sizing means to apply a rather thin coat of glue, which will run into pores and fill them up. When the sizing coat has set, the regular glue is applied to the pieces which are laid on the bench or other flat surface. Place a piece of paper under each joint to prevent it from sticking to the bench and protect its surface from glue spots.

4. Place the first two clamps on their sides, so that the clamp dogs are close to the mitered corners. The other two clamps are placed with their notched backs up. Tightening one or two clamps and loosening others will gradually bring all four miter joints in line. If the miter joints are not flush on top, place a dowel on the piece that is high and drive it down even with the others.

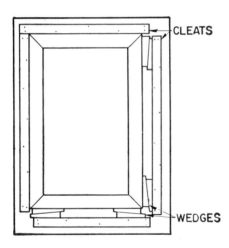

Fig. 136. Gluing a picture frame by wedging.

5. Smaller frames may be clamped in a jig like the one shown in Figure 136. Four cleats are nailed or screwed to each other to a board. Two sides of the frame are placed against two of these cleats. The other two sides of the frame are forced tightly against the first two by driving double wedges between them and the other cleats.

6. Mitered frames may also be clamped with a hand screw on each corner as in Figure 137. In this case triangular blocks are first glued to the

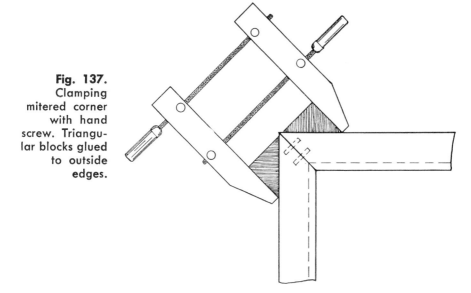

Fig. 137. Clamping mitered corner with hand screw. Triangular blocks glued to outside edges.

outside edges of the frame, two to each corner. If pieces of paper are placed between the blocks and the frame, the blocks will be easy to chisel off after the frame has been glued, because the paper will split. This method of gluing is particularly useful when long miters are made on the edges and ends of boards, as for example on mitered columns, boxes, chests, etc. (Fig. 138).

Longer pieces with a notch cut into them for the hand screws may also be clamped to the sides, thereby avoiding gluing (Fig. 139).

There are also special clamps on the market for the express purpose of

Fig. 138. Gluing a spline miter joint.

Fig. 139.
Method of clamping mitered box.

clamping up projects with miter cuts. Some of these so-called picture frame clamps secure one corner at a time. This makes it a rather time-consuming procedure. The more advanced picture frame clamps fasten all four corners at once. They are used particularly in shops where picture frames are made daily.

To the author most of these methods seem involved and time consuming except for the commercial method. A much more simple and equally effective way is discussed in the following article.

206. Procedure for Gluing a Picture Frame Using String and Blocks. The materials needed for this method are: a piece of sturdy string, long enough to go around the picture frame to be assembled; eight little wooden blocks approximately 1 by 1 by 1 in. in size, and a good, slow-setting glue. The string should be strong enough to withstand the severe pressure that will be exerted upon it.

1. Cover the bench top with a piece of paper to avoid gluing the frame to the bench.

2. Make a trial assembly by tying the string loosely around the frame (Fig. 140).

3. Place two blocks between the string and each frame member.

4. Now move these blocks, in pairs, toward each corner (Fig. 141).

5. Apply enough pressure so that the miter joints fit. Check the frame for squareness (Fig. 142). If the miters do not fit, make any necessary correction.

6. If in the trial assembly the frame lines up satisfactorily, remove string and blocks.

7. Apply glue to all the miter joints (Fig. 143).

8. Repeat steps 2, 3, 4, and 5. Push the blocks far enough into each corner so that the string does not cut into the corners of the frame.

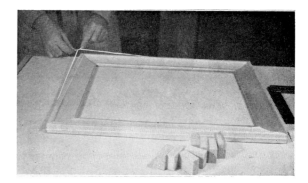

Fig. 140. Making a trial assembly.

Fig. 141. Equalizing pressure in corners.

Fig. 142. Checking frame for squareness.

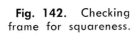

Fig. 143. Applying glue to joints.

9. Make a final check for squareness and let the frame dry in this position for two or more hours.

10. If necessary, reinforce each corner with small finishing nails.

By using two or more strings, one can use this simple but effective method on such projects as small wall cabinets (Fig. 127).

207. Reinforcing Mitered Joints. Because of the inherent weakness of miter joints, they should always be reinforced. The most common methods of reinforcement are: nails, slip feathers, splines, and dowels.

Picture frames are always nailed together by glaziers and others who make picture frames to order. The joints are not glued, but the nails used, called picture points, have greater holding power than ordinary brads and finishing nails.

1. Slip feathers are thin pieces of wood or veneer, which are glued into the corners of the frame. Remove the clamps after gluing, and handle the frame carefully so that the joints do not open up. Then clamp the frame in a bench vise so that one corner projects over it, and make a saw cut as shown in Figure 144.

2. Glue and insert a piece of veneer into the saw cut (Fig. 145). The veneer should fit tightly and its grain run at right angles to the miter joint. Clamp each corner with a hand screw.

3. When dry, chisel off the projecting ends of the veneer and smooth the edge of the frame with plane and sandpaper. This joint is called a *slip-feather miter joint* (Fig. 146).

4. These saw cuts may also be made on the circular saw by holding the frame in a homemade jig as shown in Figures 147 and 148.

5. On wide moldings, such as casings of door frames, the reinforcing

Fig. 144. Making saw cuts for splines.

Fig. 145. Gluing splines.

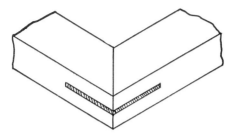

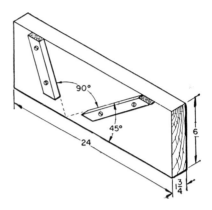

Fig. 146. Slip-feather miter joint.

Fig. 147. Jig for cutting mitered frame for slip feather.

piece of veneer may be entirely concealed within the joint. A cut is made in the center of each mitered surface with a very small circular saw like those made for shaper spindles. The veneer is cut to fit the circular hole (Fig. 149) and is glued at the same time as the miter joint.

6. Splines are thin pieces of wood used to reinforce beveled edges and ends. The bevels may be planed by hand or on a jointer, or they may be sawed on a circular saw by tilting the ripping fence, the saw, or the saw table (Fig. 150). In the latter case the ripping fence is moved to the left of the saw, so that the stock being beveled will rest against it, thus preventing a kickback.

7. The ripping fence is then moved up to the saw, and a shallow cut is made in the edge at right angles to the bevel (Fig. 151).

8. The spline is made so that the grain runs at right angles to the joint. It may be cut from a board ⅛ in. thick, and it may be only 1 in.

Fig. 148. Spline cuts made on circular saw.

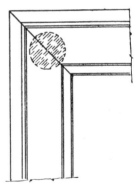

Fig. 149. Door casing with concealed slip feather.

Fig. 150. Cutting bevel. Saw guard removed while taking photo.

long, but it must be as wide as the joint is long (Fig. 152). The reason for this is that wood will withstand a pull or tension along the grain from end to end, but not across the grain from edge to edge. This joint is called a *spline miter joint*. It is glued as shown in Figure 138.

A spline may be planed to thickness by inserting it into a groove or dado made in a board (Fig. 153).

9. When dowels are used to reinforce a miter joint, the holes are laid out as on an ordinary dowel joint (Art. 178). Gauge a center line lengthways

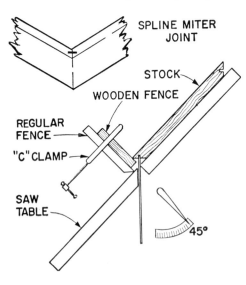

SPLINE MITER JOINT

STOCK

WOODEN FENCE

REGULAR FENCE

"C" CLAMP

SAW TABLE

45°

Fig. 151. Cutting groove for spline.

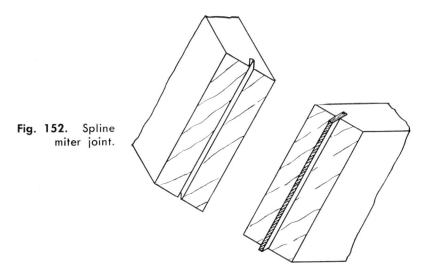

Fig. 152. Spline
miter joint.

and two lines crossing that. Bore the holes at the points of intersection and at right angles to the mitered surfaces, using the depth gauge. Cut the dowels to length, point them on both ends, and glue them into one member of each joint. Glue and clamp as explained above and shown in Figure 137.

10. If it does not matter that the ends of the dowels show on the outside edge of the frame, it is much easier first to glue the frame as in Figure 135. Then remove the clamps, fasten one corner at a time to the top of the workbench with a hand screw, and bore one or two holes from one edge to the other and at right angles to the joint (Fig. 154). Trim the ends of the dowels flush with the edge of the frame.

11. Picture frames are often made with a molding or rectangular strip of wood nailed around the outside edges. Such a strip effectually conceals the dowels (Fig. 154).

208. Procedure for Cope Moldings.   1. Mitered joints often open up in

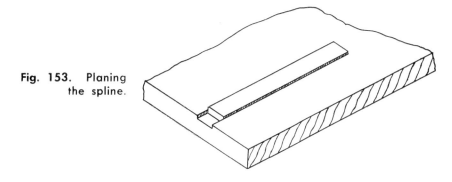

Fig. 153. Planing
the spline.

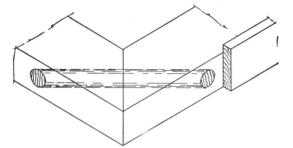

Fig. 154. Through dowel miter joint. Strip of wood around edge conceals dowel ends.

the inside part of the joint (Fig. 155) because the wood shrinks across the grain, but not along the grain (Art. 376).

2. To overcome this defect, moldings are sometimes coped, that is, a section is cut out of the end of one member so that it fits exactly over the

Fig. 155. Open miter joints due to shrinkage.

curves and flat surfaces of the other member (Fig. 156). This is done as follows:

3. If the moldings to be fitted form an angle of 90 deg. with each other, square the end of one of the members, and miter the other in the usual way at an angle of 45 deg. (A, Fig. 156). The mitered part of this member is now cut away with a coping saw. The saw is held so that its blade is at right angles, or slightly less than a right angle, with the back of the molding. The line of the miter cut on the face of the molding must be followed

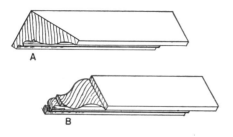

Fig. 156. A, Molding material at 45 deg.; B, The same molding coped.

closely in sawing the coping (B, Fig. 156). If the cut is made carefully, the coped member will now fit accurately over the squared member, and the joint will look exactly like a mitered joint. The same method is followed in coping moldings at other angles.*

Part VI.   DOVETAIL JOINTS

This type of joint is the strongest and neatest of all joints used in cabinet-making. As it takes both time and skill to make dovetail joints, they are used only in the better class of work. Dovetail joints are used mostly in drawer construction, and in box construction (Fig. 157).

Fig. 157.   Dovetail joint.

211. Procedure for Making a Through, Multiple, Dovetail Joint.

1. Square the pieces to dimensions.

2. Square a line around the end of each member equal to a trifle more than the thickness of the other member.

3. Determine the number of dovetails to be cut, and divide the end of one piece into that number of equal spaces (Fig. 158).

The strongest joint is one having the tails and pins equal, but for the sake of appearance, the tails are usually made larger than the pins.

4. Square lines across the end of the board at the points of division. From these lines and from the sides of the piece, lay out a distance that is equal to one half the greatest width of the pin (Fig. 158).

5. Lay out the angle of the dovetails as follows: Square a line across a board, and step off six spaces with a divider (see Fig. 78, p. 224). At the

---

* For a more detailed discussion on "Miters" and how to cut them, see: Hjorth, H., and Holtrop, W. F., *Operation of Modern Woodworking Machines,* Chap. 1, pp. 1–39.

sixth point, erect a perpendicular parallel to the edge of the board. Lay out one space on the perpendicular, and draw a line from this point to the edge of the board where the first line begins.

6. Set the sliding T bevel to this angle, holding the stock against the edge of the board and adjusting the blade to coincide with the line.

7. Mark the pins from the points laid out on the end of the board, as shown in Figure 158.

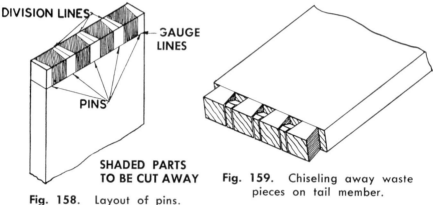

Fig. 158. Layout of pins.

Fig. 159. Chiseling away waste pieces on tail member.

8. Square these lines down on both sides of the board.

9. Mark plainly the parts to be cut away (Fig. 158).

10. Saw on the waste side of the lines with a dovetail saw or a fine backsaw.

Fig. 160. Marking tails.

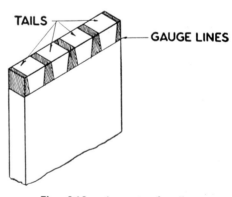

Fig. 161. Layout of tails.

11. Chisel away the waste pieces, cutting halfway through the board from one side, and then reverse the board and finish chiseling from the other side (Fig. 159). Be careful to make these cuts perpendicular, and do not go beyond the line.

12. Having finished the pins, lay the other board on the bench with the working face up. Place the board with the pins on the end of this board, so that the widest part of the pins is on the gauge line.

13. Mark the shape of the pins with a scratch awl, knife, or fine pencil point on the side of the other piece (Fig. 160).

14. Square these lines across the end of the board with a try square and pencil, and also mark the angles with the T bevel on the other side of the board (Fig. 161).

15. Mark the waste pieces, and saw and chisel as before (Fig. 159).

16. Fit the pieces together, but do not force them so as to break or fracture any of the tails or pins (Fig. 162).

Some woodworkers prefer to lay out the tails first, especially if duplicate pieces are to be made.

SHADED PARTS TO BE CUT AWAY

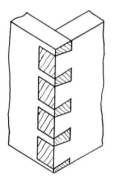

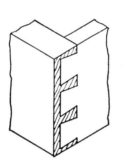

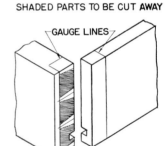

| Fig. 162. Through dovetail joint. | Fig. 163. Half-lap dovetail joint. | Fig. 164. Layout of half-lap dovetail joint. |

212. Procedure for Making a Half-Lap, Multiple, Dovetail Joint. This joint (Fig. 163) differs from the through dovetail joint in that the tails do not extend all the way through the joint and, therefore, do not show on one side. It is used in drawer construction.

1. Gauge a line on the end of one member, A, Figure 164, indicating the distance the tails are to extend.

2. With the same setting of the marking gauge, mark lines around the end of the other member, B, holding the block of the gauge against its end. These lines indicate the length of the tails.

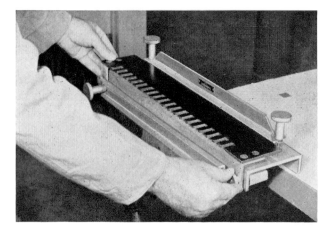

Fig. 165. Dovetail jig fastened in workbench vise.

3. Lay off the thickness of the member having the tails, B, on the other member, A. B is usually thinner than A.

4. Lay out, cut, and fit the pins and tails as explained in Article 162.

When constructing a drawer, the groove for the bottom should be plowed before the pins are laid out so that it will fall within one tail (Art. 215).

In industry, dovetails are made with special dovetail machines. The work is done fast and accurately. In the smaller shop and school laboratory dovetail joints can be successfully made with a portable router. The following accessories are needed: (1) a dovetail cutter which fits the chuck of the router; (2) a dovetail jig which holds the pieces of wood to the dovetailed; (3) a follower disk, which matches in size the cutter and the dovetail jig. Figure 165 shows the dovetail jig fastened on the work bench. Figure 166 shows how the jig is loaded.

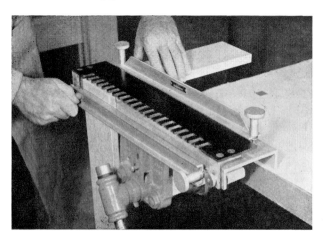

Fig. 166. Loading jig with drawer front and side.

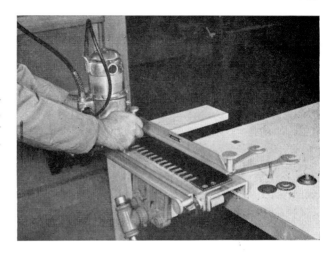

Fig. 167. Router placed in position to cut dovetail.

If the two pieces of stock represent the front and the side of a drawer, the drawer front must be clamped in a horizontal position and the side must be clamped in a vertical position with its upper end flush with the top of the front.

Figure 167 shows how the router cuts the dovetail, which in its completed form, looks like the joint shown in Figure 168. In order for one to make successful dovetail joints with the router a careful setup is necessary with accessories that match each other correctly. It is advisable to make a few practice joints to make sure that the setup is correct.

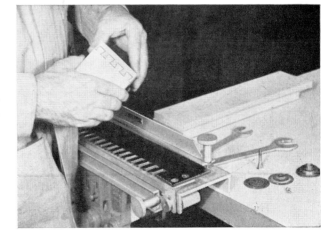

Fig. 168. Completed dovetail.

Part VII.   MISCELLANEOUS CONSTRUCTION

The various joints discussed so far are more or less basic to all types of wood construction. There remains to be discussed a group of joints which is difficult to classify in as much as some of them are made in combination with two or more other joints. Also some of the typical construction jobs, such as drawer construction, are better discussed and treated as a whole instead of breaking them down into smaller units of work.

Drawers are such a common item in pieces of furniture, cabinets and built-ins that one should know how to go about making them; they can be constructed with close-fitting dovetail joints (Fig. 157).

215. Procedure for Making a Drawer

1. The first step in all drawer construction is to fit the front piece carefully to the opening which the drawer will occupy. It should fit rather tightly in this opening in order to allow for smoothing after the drawer has been put together.

2. The two sides and the back are then squared to dimensions, after which a groove is plowed in the front and side pieces for the bottom. The groove is usually made ⅜ in. from the lower inside edge of the sides and the front.

3. One of the simplest kinds of drawers has a rabbet cut on each end of the front piece. The sides are glued and nailed into these rabbets. The nails are set below the surface so that the sides can be planed after the drawer has been assembled (Fig. 170A). An improvement on this joint, called the rabbet and tongue, is shown in Figure 170B. It is both neater and stronger.

4. The bottom is pushed into the grooves cut for it in the sides and the front. It should extend to the ends of the sides to allow for shrinkage. *It should never be glued into the grooves,* because it must be allowed to expand or contract under different climatic conditions. It should preferably

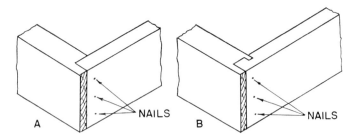

Fig. 170.   Plain rabbet and rabbet-and-tongue joints in drawer construction.

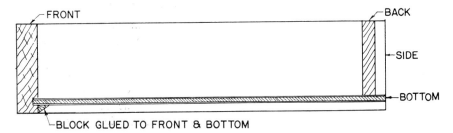

Fig. 171. Typical drawer section.

be made of ³⁄₁₆ or ¼-in. plywood, because this does not shrink or swell as much as solid wood.

5. The back is joined to the sides with dado or dado-and-rabbet joints. Its lower edge rests on top of the bottom which is fastened to it with a few small, flathead screws.

It is also acceptable practice to fasten the bottom to the back with a few small nails. The nails should not completely be driven home. If, because of shrinkage, the bottom must be removed, or pushed forward, all one has to do is remove the screws or pull the small nails.

6. The bottom may also be held in place with triangular blocks glued to its underside and to the lower inside surface of the front. In this way it can never pull away from the front (Fig. 171).

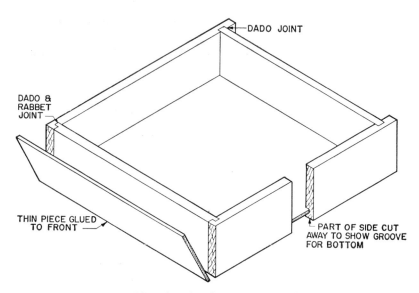

Fig. 172. Simple drawer construction.

7. If the bottom is made of solid wood, the grain should always run from side to side and never from front to back, and that is regardless of the shape of the drawer. The reason for this is that when the wood shrinks and the grain runs from front to back, the bottom becomes narrower and therefore no longer fills the grooves cut for it in the sides. If made with the grain from side to side it will pull out of the front groove upon shrinkage. The screws in the back then can be loosened, and the bottom can again be pushed forward and fastened as before. If it is made the wrong way and pulls away from the sides, cracks will appear. The only remedy for this is to glue another piece to the bottom to make it wider.

8. When gluing the front, sides, and back together, be sure that the drawer is square and that its lower edges are level. It is a good plan to place it on a level surface while the glue is drying. See also Article 229.

9. Another type of drawer is shown in Figure 172. In this drawer the front is joined to the sides with dado-and-rabbet joints. The back, bottom, and sides are joined together as previously explained. A separate piece is glued to the front.

10. After gluing and planing the drawer, the endwood on the front may be concealed by gluing a ¼- or ⅜-in. board to it. It may be planed flush or it may be rounded and extended about ⅜ in. over the sides and upper edge.

11. On the better home and office furniture the front and sides of drawers are usually joined with half-lap, multiple, dovetail joints (Fig. 157 and 173). On the very best work, the back and sides are also joined with through, multiple, dovetail joints. Such a drawer cannot possibly come apart. The sides of dovetail drawers are usually made of hardwood and their upper edges are rounded.

12. The pins on the drawer front often are cut back about 1/16 in. in order

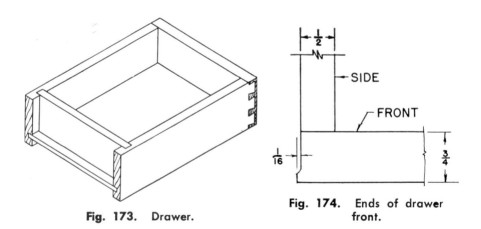

Fig. 173.   Drawer.

Fig. 174.   Ends of drawer front.

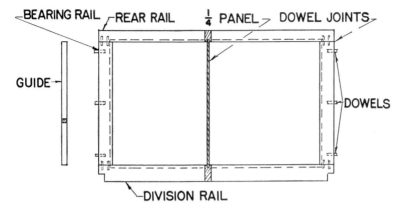

Fig. 175. Drawer-rail frame.

to give clearance to the sides and still have them fitting closely in the drawer opening (Fig. 174).

216. Procedure for Making Drawer Rails and Guides. The weight of a drawer is carried or supported on a framework called the "rails." Its movement is controlled by narrow cleats called "guides," which are fastened to the rails.

1. The rails usually consist of the front rail or division rail, the rear rail, and two side rails or bearing rails, mortised or doweled together. A ¼-in. plywood panel is generally framed in between these rails, at least in the bottom frame where it helps to keep out dust (Figs. 175 and 176). When

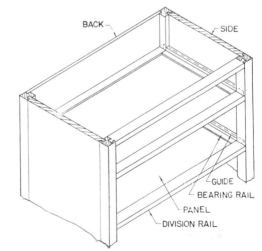

Fig. 176. Framing of drawer rails into cabinet.

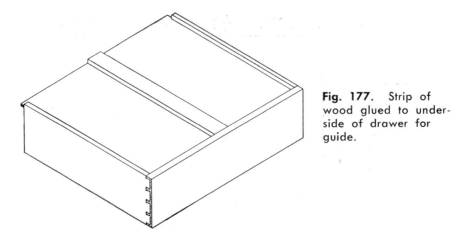

Fig. 177. Strip of wood glued to underside of drawer for guide.

the drawer to be supported is very wide, an extra central rail, mortised into the front and rear rails, is added to the framework. The frames may be joined to the sides of the cabinet with dowels or dado joints.

2. Drawer guides may be made of two narrow cleats of wood glued and nailed to the bearing rails, one on each side of the drawer. This method of guiding can only be used when there is sufficient room for the guides between the front and rear legs as in Figure 176.

3. Another method which will serve in all cases, is to make a single guide in the center. A thin piece of wood, about 1 to 1½ in. wide, is glued and screwed to the underside of the drawer. It runs from front to back and is planed flush with the lower edge of the drawer front (Fig. 177).

4. A corresponding grooved board is notched over the front and rear rails and fastened to them with screws (Fig. 178).

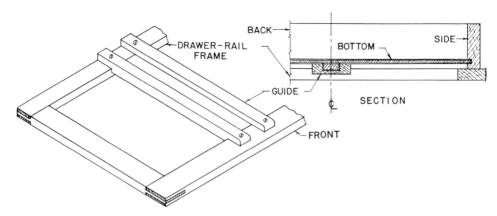

Fig. 178. Isometric and sectional view of central drawer guide.

5. The guides should be fitted so that the drawer runs easily and smoothly. A well-fitted drawer can be pushed in by pressing lightly on either side of it with only one hand.

6. Small blocks should be glued either to the rear or front rails for the purpose of stopping the inward movement of the drawer at the right point.

Metal drawer guides are often used on desks, filing cabinets and other types of office furniture.

217. Procedure for Making a Panel Structure.   The object in panel construction is to provide a means by which a large surface of wood can shrink or swell within a comparatively narrow frame, which also will prevent it from warping or twisting. Panel construction is used a great deal in furniture work and in doors, wainscoting, and other interior trim.

The best type of frame is joined with the haunched mortise-and-tenon joint (Fig. 110, p. 239), but the slip joint (Fig. 115, p. 241), the end-lap joint (Fig. 57, p. 216), and the miter joint (Fig. 146, p. 257) also are used.

1. Square the pieces forming the frame to dimensions (Art. 158). Plow a groove on the inside edges of the frame (Art. 171), and make the joints in the four corners (Art. 195).

2. The panel, which is made either of plywood or of several boards glued together, then is dressed to dimensions. Plywood panels are always flat (Fig. 179), but those made of solid wood are often raised, which means that a bevel is planed all around their edges (Fig. 180). This is usually done on a

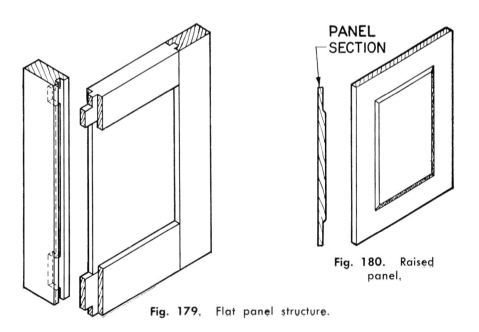

PANEL
SECTION

Fig. 180.   Raised panel.

Fig. 179.   Flat panel structure.

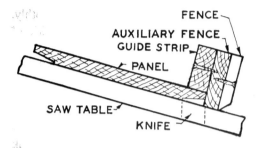

FENCE

AUXILIARY FENCE

GUIDE STRIP

PANEL

SAW TABLE

KNIFE

Fig. 181. Panel raising with molding head.

shaper, but it may also be done on a small circular saw equipped with a molding head (Fig. 181). If necessary, the bevels may also be sawed on a circular saw and smoothed by hand.

3. Clamp the panel and frame together without glue, and then test for fit and squareness.

The panel should fit well in the grooves, not too loose and not too tight. It should be just a little shorter and narrower than the inside length and width of the frame plus twice the depth of the groove.

4. Take apart and glue the joints at the four corners of the frame, but do not put any glue on the panel nor in the grooves.

5. Frames for panels may also be molded on the edges around the panel. This work, which is called "door sticking," is done on the shaper.

6. Two cutters are put on the spindle at the same time, one shaping the edge and the other cutting the groove for the panels.

7. The reverse of these cutters are then put on the spindle and the ends of the horizontal members or rails shaped. One cutter makes a tenon to fit in the groove and the other copes a molding that will fit perfectly over the shaped edges of the stiles or vertical members (Fig. 182).

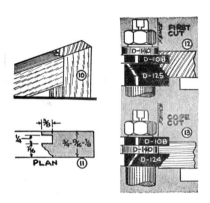

Fig. 182. Door stuck on one side.

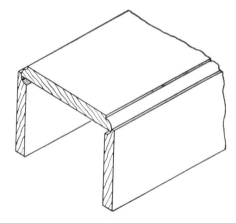

Fig. 183. Rule joint.

8. The tenon is made only long enough to fill the groove. This is sufficient for light work, but if greater strength is needed the joints may be reinforced with dowels.

9. If a shaper is not available, a small molding may be made, mitered in the corners and glued or nailed to the inside edges of the frame.

Although panel construction is used in different types of the work, it is not as popular now as some years ago. Particularly in kitchen cabinet work, "dust catching" panel doors are being replaced by all flat doors.

218. Procedure for Making a Rule Joint.   This joint is used on table tops, whose size is extended by means of drop leaves hinged to it. A table of this kind usually has one fixed part and two leaves. The rule joint, because of its neater appearance, is used instead of the butt joint on the better class of tables (Fig. 183).

1. Square the pieces to dimensions, being particularly careful to see that the two edges are square and true.

2. Set the marking gauge to half the thickness of the knuckle of the hinge; then gauge lines on the end grain of the boards on both ends, holding the block of the gauge against the underside of the boards (Fig. 184A and B).

3. The hinges are like butt hinges, but one leaf is longer than the other. The screw holes are countersunk on the rear side of the hinges, so that the knuckle can be set into the wood and come flush with the underside of the top. This type of hinge is called "back flaps." If they are not obtainable, serviceable ones can be made from ordinary hinge hasps (Fig. 16, p. 314).

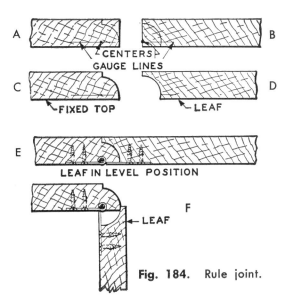

Fig. 184. Rule joint.

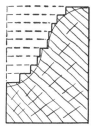

Fig. 185. Sawing molding by making a series of parallel cuts.

4. Set a pair of dividers to about ⅛ in. less than the distance from the gauge line to the top of the board. Beginning at the end of the fixed board, lay off this radius on the gauge line, and mark the center; then scribe a quarter circle as shown in Figure 184A.

5. With the same radius, but using the point of intersection of the gauge line and the end of the board as centers, scribe a quarter circle on the leaf board (Fig. 184B).

6. On the first board, plane a rabbet ⅛ in. deep and equal in width to the radius of the quarter circles (Fig. 184C).

7. Plane the concave and convex curves with molding planes, or work them out with chisel, gouge, and sandpaper. This shaping work is helped greatly if a circular saw is available, because a number of parallel cuts may be made on it right up to the gauge lines (Fig. 185). In this way the rule joint is cut roughly to shape. The small triangular pieces left by the saw cuts serve as depth gauges while the curves are gradually worked to shape with a gouge and chisel. Smooth with scrapers, which have been filed to the right shape, and with sandpaper backed with molded blocks.

One can also cut the concave curve in Figure 184D by using a slanting fence on the circular saw or with the use of a coping head (Fig. 186).

8. The concave curves on the leaves must be cut slightly below the gauge lines so that the two members of the joint will not rub against each other. Continue working on the joint until the two pieces fit together.

9. Place the pieces face down on a bench, and gauge a line for the hinges on the board with the convex edges. The gauge line is made directly over the centers and parallel to the edge. The knuckles of the hinges are placed on this line and the outline of the hinges is marked.

10. Chisel the gains so that the hinges will be flush with the wood, and cut grooves for the knuckles.

Fig. 186. Making ogee cut.

Fig. 187. Rule joint
hasp.

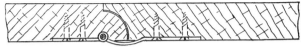

If the top has two leaves, as is usually the case, it follows that the two rule joints are laid out and worked at the same time.

11. To avoid having the gains show when the leaves are folded, it is recommended to bend the hinge hasp so that it will clear the edge of the fixed top (Fig. 187).

12. A rule joint can be made much easier on the shaper if cutters of the right shape and size are available. Lay out the joint as explained in the foregoing and cut the quarter-round shape on both edges of the fixed centerboard.

13. The cutter for the leaves should be of the reverse shape and have a radius about $\frac{1}{32}$ in. larger, so that the leaves, when hinged, can be opened without squeaking and rubbing off the finish on the convex edges.

219. Procedure for Making Supports for Table Leaves. For centuries cabinetmakers have devised methods of extending or increasing the area of table tops when occasion demanded. One of the oldest and most common

Fig. 188. Early
English gate-leg
table.

extension tables is the gate-leg table. The leaves are supported on a swinging leg joined to a movable rail called a "fly-rail" (Fig. 188). Other types of extension tables have hinged, sliding, and pivoted supports for their leaves.

1. *The finger joint* is a movable, interlocking joint made of wood. It has two parts, the movable bracket and the fixed piece, which is fastened to the table rail (Fig. 189).

2. Square the two pieces to dimensions, and divide the width of the boards into five equal parts. Lay off these divisions on one end of each board, and square lines across the ends from these points.

3. Set a marking gauge equal to the thickness of the boards, and with this setting, gauge a line on the face of both boards, holding the block of the marking gauge against the ends of the boards just marked.

4. From these gauge lines, lay off lines at an angle of 60 deg. across the upper edges of the board. From the points where the 60-deg. lines meet the rear edges, gauge or square lines across the rear faces of the boards.

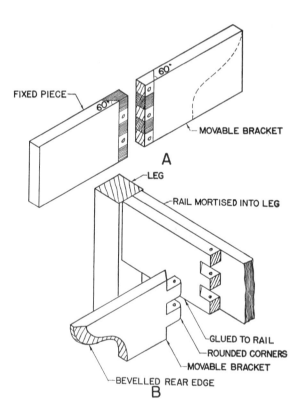

Fig. 189. Finger joint.
A, Layout of joint.
B, Joint ready for assembly.

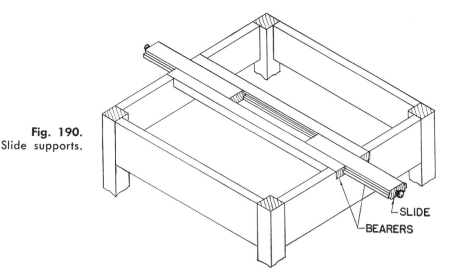

Fig. 190.
Slide supports.

SLIDE
BEARERS

5. The division lines squared across the ends are now carried around on both faces of the boards until they intersect the gauge lines.

6. The boards should then be placed end to end, the parts to be cut away should be marked, and saw cuts made on the waste side of the lines. Use a backsaw or a dovetail saw for this work, and chisel out the waste pieces.

7. Fit the joint together, and mark the center where the hole is to be bored for the pin. Place the pieces at right angles, and bore the hole. A 5- or 6-in. nail or a ¼-in. dowel may be used as a pin.

It is advisable to bore the hole on a boring machine or in a drill press, if one is available, in order to insure perpendicularity.

8. When the joint is pinned together, it will be seen that the "fingers" on the movable piece will project a little when it is half open. These ends should now be rounded off as shown in the drawing.

9. The end of the movable part of the bracket is usually shaped and beveled on its rear side, so that it may be easily grasped with the hand.

10. The other part of the bracket is glued or screwed firmly to the fixed rail of the table.

A piece of a continuous hinge is sometimes substituted for a finger joint, but is not as strong nor as neat looking.

1. *A slide support* for a hinged table leaf consists of three narrow boards, each about 1½ in. wide and 1 in. thick. The length depends upon the size of the leaf.

2. A tongue is cut on each edge of the central board, or "slide," and a

corresponding groove is cut in one edge of each of the other two boards, or "bearers." The tongues should fit in the groove, so that the slide will move easily between the bearers (Fig. 190).

3. The bearers are fastened to the rails as well as to the underside of the top.

4. A notch is cut in the table rails for the slide and bearers.

5. A stop usually is placed both on the slide and on the leaves. These stops limit the movement of the slide.

6. The front edge of the slide is either shaped or provided with a knob by which it can be pulled out under the leaf of the table.

1. *A pivoted rail* is one of the simplest and most common forms of support for drop leaves.

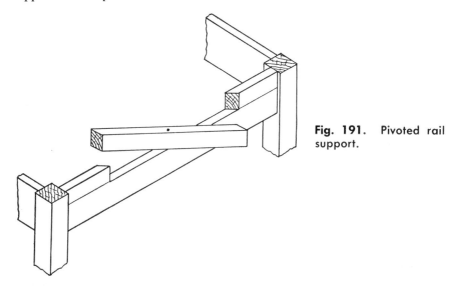

Fig. 191. Pivoted rail support.

2. A section of the upper part of the rail, about 1½ to 2 in. wide, is cut away and another piece is fitted into this opening, to form a swinging rail. In order to make a neater joint, the ends of the swinging rail are beveled to fit against corresponding bevels in the table rail (Fig. 191).

3. The easiest way to make this type of support is to cut a strip of wood a little longer than the side rails and equal in width to the swinging rail. Lay out the length and 45-deg. angles of the swinging rail in the center of this piece, and then saw on these lines. The two shorter end pieces are now glued to the edge of another board after which it is planed to the same width as the other rails, cut to length, and joined to the legs which haunched mortise-and-tenon joints.

4. The swinging rail can then be fitted to the opening and pivoted in

the center. Use a ¼- or a ⁵⁄₁₆-in. dowel for a pivot, and let its end extend a little up in the underside of the fixed part of the table top.

220. Combination Miter Joints.   In addition to the joints described previously, there are many others used in cabinet and furniture construction. The three shown in Figure 192 are useful particularly in the construction of modernistic furniture where wide boards often have to be joined so that no end grain shows.

The housed miter joint can be made of stock either even or uneven in thickness. When the pieces are even, the saw blade is tilted at 55 deg. Uneven stock is mitered with the saw tilted at 45 deg.

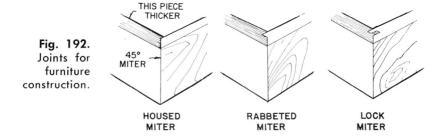

Fig. 192.
Joints for
furniture
construction.

THIS PIECE
THICKER

45°
MITER

HOUSED
MITER

RABBETED
MITER

LOCK
MITER

Procedure for Cutting a Housed Miter Joint; Stock of Even Thickness

1. With the use of a sliding T bevel set at 55 deg. make a careful pencil layout at the end of two pieces to be joined together.

2. Tilt the saw blade so that it makes an angle of 55 deg. with the table. The pointer on the scale should be at 35 deg.

3. Place the miter gauge in the table slot to the right of the saw. Check the gauge for squareness.

4. Hold the edge of the stock against the miter gauge.

Fig. 193.   Cutting
at 55-degree
angle.

Fig. 194. Preparing the second piece for a housed miter joint.

5. After adjusting the blade for height turn on the motor. The saw blade should extend from ⅛ to ¼ in. above the stock.

6. Make the 55-deg. cut (Fig. 193). This completes the first part of the joint.

7. To make the second part of the joint, first remove the miter gauge and replace it by the ripping fence.

8. Without changing the angular position of the saw blade, lower it to a position where it will cut through the thickness of the stock.

9. With the second piece of stock held in an upright position, hold it firmly against the ripping fence.

10. Next move the ripping fence over to a point where the saw will cut just to the left of the angular layout line.

Make any fine adjustments with the micrometer knob. Lock the fence in place.

11. Turn on the motor and make the angular cut (Fig. 194). For wide pieces of stock use a feather board for additional support. Use a mortising jig if one is available.

12. To complete this part of the joint, return the saw to a vertical position. Lower the saw to a point from ⅛ to ¼ in. above the table. See pencil layout for exact amount.

13. Place the miter gauge to the left of the saw and move the ripping fence so that the distance from the outside of the blade to the fence equals the thickness of the stock.

14. With the edge of the stock held firmly against the miter gauge and the end touching the ripping fence, make the final cut (Fig. 195). Test first for correct depth of cut on a piece of scrap wood.

Fig. 195. Final cut for a housed miter joint.

The procedure for making this joint when stock is of uneven thickness is as described previously, with the exception that the saw blade is tilted at 45 deg. Although this joint is more time consuming in its construction than the typical miter joint, it has significant advantages. One of these is the ease with which a project can be assembled. Also this type of joint allows for more glue surfaces, which in turn add strength to a project.

Rabbeted Miter Joints

This joint, as the name indicates, is part miter and part rabbet (Fig. 196). It has excellent holding qualities. The rabbeted miter joint can be used advantageously for cabinet bases and sides. Being more complicated than the housed miter joint, it is more difficult to make.

Fig. 196. Rabbeted miter joint.

Lock Miter Joints

The lock miter joint shown in Figure 192 again is an improvement over the housed miter joint and the rabbeted miter joint. This joint is best made with the dado head, cutting to a width and depth of ¼ in. Blade changing is necessary and a careful pencil layout is imperative.

REVIEW QUESTIONS, CHAPTER 6
Part I, II, III, and IV

Possible score 55 points

Your score . . . . . .

PART I. COMPLETION QUESTIONS. Complete the following statements:

1. Whenever two or more pieces of wood are fastened together, it becomes necessary to use some type of . . . .
2. A groove cut on the edge or end of a piece of wood is called a . . . .
3. A recess or slot cut along or across the grain is called a . . . .
4. A groove made across the grain from one edge to the other is called a . . . .
5. The best tool to use for cleaning out dado joints is the . . . .
6. A dado head is made up of two blades and a number of . . . .
7. On some circular saws, in order to use a dado head, it is necessary to extend the arbor by means of a . . . .
8. When boards are glued together edge to edge, they are often reinforced with . . . .
9. To drill holes of a certain depth, use an . . . .
10. In heavy construction, different members are often fastened together by means of . . . .
11. One of the most useful doweling jigs is the so-called . . . . doweling jig.
12. Dowel holes are readily bored on the drill press and a horizontal . . . .
13. When the ends of two pieces of wood are joined together at a right angle, by cutting away half the thickness of each member, the pieces form an . . . .
14. When two pieces of wood are joined in the middle at right angles, they form a . . . .
15. A glass panel door (French door) is made up of two stiles, two rails and a number of . . . .
16. Without exception, the most important and most useful joint in cabinet construction is the . . . . and . . . . joint.
17. For an accurate layout of mortises it is best to use a . . . .
18. To make a tenon two cuts are made, cheek cuts and . . . . cuts.

19. The lower rails of doors often are quite wide; they are generally made with a .... tenon.

20. When cutting tenons on the circular saw, it is safest to use a ....

PART II. TRUE-FALSE QUESTIONS.   Indicate, by encircling T or F, whether the following statements are true or false:

21. When making mortise-and-tenon joints, the tenons are always cut first.   T   F
22. Tenons always have two cheeks and two shoulders.   T   F
23. Tenons cannot be made with the dado head.   T   F
24. Probably the simplest of woodworking joints is the butt joint.   T   F
25. Grooves and dados are identical except that the first is always cut lengthwise with the grain.   T   F
26. Mortises are best cut with sharp, properly fitting chisels.   T   F
27. Dado joints are generally cut to a depth of ½ inch.   T   F
28. The inside cutters of a dado head range in thickness from ⅟₁₆ to ¼ inch.   T   F
29. The purpose of the spiral groove in dowels is to allow glue and air to escape from the hole.   T   F
30. The self-centering dowel jig automatically adjusts itself in the center of the thickness of a board.   T   F
31. The horizontal double spindle boring machine is extremely useful when making good fitting dowel joints.   T   F
32. A mullion is one of the cross members in a French door.   T   F
33. In window and door construction the horizontal mullions are always continuous from the outside.   T   F
34. For over-all strength and holding power a mortise-and-tenon joint is surpassed by a dowel joint.   T   F
35. When laying out mortises and tenons, the gauge lines are always made from the face or working side of each member.   T   F
36. It is good practice to make mortises first and tenons next.   T   F
37. A ripsaw is the proper saw to make the shoulder cuts on tenons.   T   F
38. A haunched mortise-and-tenon joint is especially appropriate when making panel doors.   T   F
39. When mortising turned legs, it is proper to make some type of jig or cradle for good support.   T   F
40. Cheek cuts can be made simultaneously by means of two saw blades and a spacing block.   T   F

PART III.   MULTIPLE-CHOICE QUESTIONS.   Select, by encircling the correct letter, the answer which completes each statement:

41. Of the following joints which one is the easiest to construct?
    A. Dowel joint
    B. Miter joint
    C. Lap joint
    D. Butt joint

42. In typical drawer construction one of the following joints is not used:
    - A. Rabbet joint
    - B. Miter joint
    - C. Dado joint
    - D. Grooved joint

43. Another name for lap joint is:
    - A. Halving joint
    - B. Dado joint
    - C. Rabbet joint
    - D. Miter joint

44. One of the following is not a part of a glass or French door:
    - A. Mullion
    - B. Stile
    - C. Slide
    - D. Rail

45. A tenon consists of all but one of the following parts:
    - A. Cheeks
    - B. Shoulders
    - C. Rabbet
    - D. Haunch

PART IV. MATCHING QUESTIONS. Match the terms to the left with the descriptions to the right by placing the correct letter in the parentheses:

46. ( ) Groove
47. ( ) Matching plane
48. ( ) Gain joint
49. ( ) Dado head
50. ( ) Lap joints
51. ( ) Mitered cross-lap joint
52. ( ) Dovetail lap joint
53. ( ) Mortise-and-tenon joint
54. ( ) Cheeks
55. ( ) Shoulders

A. A dado joint that does not go all the way across a surface.

B. Used by carpenters in joining the plates and sills of a house.

C. Often used when joining the top rails and legs of a desk.

D. Crosswise cuts which form the length of a tenon.

E. Generally considered the best of all wood joints.

F. A tool which makes a groove and a tongue to match.

G. Lengthwise cuts that form the thickness of a tenon.

H. A combination of two blades and a number of inside cutters.

I. A recess or slot cut along the grain of a piece of wood.

J. Used when crossing the mullions of a French door.

K. Another name for dado joint.

L. Used to reinforce mortise-and-tenon joints.

M. Used to support turned legs.

REVIEW QUESTIONS, CHAPTER 6

Parts V, VI, and VII

Possible score 45 points

Your score . . . . . .

PART I. COMPLETION QUESTIONS.   Complete the following statements:

1. Miters are readily cut with the use of a . . . .
2. Miters are cut on the circular saw by using the . . . .
3. Picture frames can be glued up by means of cleats and . . . .
4. They can also be glued up by means of hand screws and . . . .
5. Probably the simplest way to glue picture frames together is by means of a . . . . and . . . .
6. Thin pieces of wood or veneer glued into the corners of frames are called . . . .
7. The process of cutting out the end of a piece of molding so that it fits exactly over the curves and flat surfaces of another piece is called . . . .
8. Dovetail joints are used extensively in . . . .
9. A portable machine often used to make dovetails is the . . . .
10. Drawers are made either flush or with a . . . .
11. In simple drawer construction the corners are made by means of a . . . .
12. The bottom of a drawer slides in . . . . cut in the front and the two sides.
13. Instead of wood, drawer guides are often made of . . . .
14. The joint used on drop leaf table tops is called a . . . .
15. The lock miter joint is a type of . . . .

PART II. TRUE-FALSE QUESTIONS.   Indicate, by encircling T or F, whether the following statements are true or false:

16. Most miter joints are cut at 45 degrees to fit around square or rectangular surfaces.   T   F
17. The angles of a polygon are found by dividing the number of sides into 360 deg. and subtracting the quotient from 90 deg.   T   F
18. To avoid a so-called "starved" glue joint, it is recommended to "size" the mitered ends of a miter joint.   T   F
19. Clamping a picture frame by means of the string method is unsatisfactory since the string always breaks.   T   F
20. Framing shops use picture clamps which fasten all corners at once.   T   F
21. Splines are thin pieces of wood used to reinforce beveled edges and ends.   T   F
22. Dovetail joints are always made by hand.   T   F
23. A dovetail joint consists of pins, and tails.   T   F
24. The portable router is a convenient tool to make dovetail joints with. T   F
25. Drawers are always made with a lip.   T   F
26. In drawer assembly the last operation consists of fastening the drawer bottom in place with glue and nails.   T   F

27. Drawers run either on side or center guides or both.   T   F
28. In modern kitchens, conventional panel doors have been largely
    replaced by flush doors.   T   F
29. To hang the leaves on a drop-leaf table, an ordinary set of hinges
    is required.   T   F
30. A pivoted rail is a complicated and rather uncommon form of
    support for drop leaves.   T   F

PART III. MULTIPLE-CHOICE QUESTIONS. Select, by encircling the correct
letter, the answer which completes each statement:

31. The angle for pieces shaped into an octagon measures:
    A. 67½ deg.   C. 75 deg.
    B. 60 deg.   D. 54 deg.

32. One of the following is not a part of a dovetail joint:
    A. Tail   C. Pin
    B. Feather

33. In front drawer construction, one of the following joints is not used:
    A. Rabbet   C. Dado
    B. Dovetail   D. Rabbet and tongue

34. One of the following distinguishes drop-leaf hinges from ordinary hinges:
    A. Knuckle   C. Leaves
    B. Back flaps   D. Pin

35. Of the following table leaf supports, which one is the simplest?
    A. Finger joint   C. Pivoted rail
    B. Slide support   D. Fly rail

PART IV. MATCHING QUESTIONS. Match the terms to the left with the
descriptions to the right by placing the correct letter in the parentheses:

36. ( ) Polygon   A. Used to reinforce picture frames.
37. ( ) Sizing   B. One of the two parts of a dovetail
38. ( ) Splines   joint.
39. ( ) Coping   C. A many sided figure.
40. ( ) Pins   D. A joint used in drawer construction.
41. ( ) Follower disk   E. Those parts of a framework that sup-
42. ( ) Rabbet and tongue joint   port the drawers.
43. ( ) Rails   F. Used in drop-leaf table construction.
44. ( ) Raised panel   G. The practice of giving wood a pre-
45. ( ) Rule joint   liminary coat of glue.
                                     H. A panel with a bevel planed around
                                        the edges.
                                      I. A method of fitting one piece of a
                                        molding neatly over another.
                                      J. One of the necessary attachments
                                        needed when making dovetails with
                                        the portable router.
                                     K. A panel with rounded corners.
                                     L. Used on gate-leg tables.

CHAPTER 7

Gluing and Clamping

Gluing and clamping is one of the most important phases of the wood-worker's art, because the strength and appearance of the finished product is in direct proportion to the skill and accuracy with which this job has been done. Methods of clamping vary a good deal according to the work in hand, and often special blocks or fittings have to be devised.

223. Properties and Uses of Glue. Woodworking glues may be divided conveniently into two main groups, namely glues made of materials of natural origin and the synthetic resin glues. The latter are of more recent development and are the products of modern chemistry. The major natural glues are the following:* (1) animal glue; (2) vegetable (starch) glue; (3) casein glue; (4) soybean (vegetable protein) glue; (5) liquid glue; and (6) blood albumin glue.

Animal glue is made from the hide parings, bones, sinews, and other waste parts of cattle, horses, pigs, sheep, etc. This offal is soaked in lime water for several weeks and then washed and boiled several times. A foam, which is skimmed off, forms at each boiling. The finished product is a gelatinous mass which is dried and sold in sheets, flakes, or coarse powder. Good grades of animal glue are brittle and transparent.

Animal glue must be soaked in cold water overnight before it is ready to be heated. Sheet glue, which is very hard and brittle, must be broken into small pieces with a hammer. The sheets should be put into a bag or cloth during the breaking-up process, otherwise the glue will be scattered all over the floor. The pieces are then put into a double-boiler gluepot, covered with water, and allowed to soak overnight. If it is a good grade of glue, the small hard pieces, when examined the following day, should have absorbed most of the water in which they were soaking. They should also have swelled to several times their original size, and be soft and jellylike.

The proportions of glue and water vary according to the grade of glue and the kind of wood to be glued. A certain standard grade of glue is mixed in the proportions of 1 part of glue to 2 parts of water for hardwoods, but only 1½ parts of water for softwoods.

Obtain these proportions from the manufacturer, weigh the glue and water,

---

* Source: U. S. Department of Agriculture, Forest Products Laboratory, Technical Note, No. 257, Feb., 1953.

and let it soak in the glue pot overnight. Be sure to clean both gluepot and brushes thoroughly, because old scraps of glue will pollute a new batch. The old-style gluepot was just a cast-iron double boiler with water in the outer vessel. Very often, when it was not watched, the water would boil away and then the glue would boil over and spoil.

It was found that when glue was heated to more than 145 deg., its binding powers were greatly diminished. This led to the invention of the modern gluepot, which has no water jacket, but is heated electrically and automatically to only 145 deg. It is recommended to use a type that has a lid, because that helps to prevent evaporation.

Repeated heatings weaken the glue and it also becomes thicker through evaporation. As the glue should be quite thin and run freely from the brush, more water has to be added and this further weakens the glue.

Vegetable (*starch*) *glue* is made by grinding the wood of the cassava bush* into a fine, flourlike powder. This powder is mixed with water to which a quantity of caustic soda is added (usually 3 per cent by weight). The mixture is then heated. Vegetable glue is used cold, but is so viscous and stringy that it can only be applied by mechanical glue spreaders. It is not suitable for shopwork, but is used in the plywood industry and for laying linoleum.

Casein glue is made from the curds of skimmed milk to which an alkali is added. The finished product is a fine, yellow powder.

This powder is mixed with an equal amount of cold water by volume. The glue powder is poured into the water while stirring briskly for about a minute. The mixture then is allowed to stand for about 15 minutes, after which it is again stirred for a minute.

The glue is now ready to use. It is much thicker than animal glue, but squeezes easily out of a joint when it is pressed together. Casein glue does not set for 15 to 20 minutes and therefore gives the operator plenty of time to glue and clamp his work.

Casein glue is water resistant and can be used in temperatures below 70 deg. It is used for all ordinary gluing jobs, in veneering, and in gluing up beams, partitions, and other structural forms used in modern carpentry.

As the glue is mixed fresh every day, it is always of uniform strength. It has the disadvantage of staining all wood. There is a casein glue, however, that is stainless, but it is less water-resistant.

Soybean (*vegetable protein*) *glues* are quite similar to casein glues and are made from dried protein of soybeans. They are cheaper and generally produce lower-strength joints than casein glues. At present they are mainly used for veneer gluing, particularly of the softwood species. They are little

---

* The cassava bush grows in Brazil, Africa, the Malay States and in other tropical countries. It is from the root of this plant that tapioca is obtained.

used in hand woodwork or small scale operations. Their moisture resistance is similar to that of casein glues.

Liquid glues are natural glues offered in ready-to-use form. Originally made from animal waste, they are more recently made from animal-glue bases by special treatments. These glues can differ considerably in quality from sample to sample, but the better ones produce joints comparable to those of hot animal glue. They are popular in the small shop and in hobby work.

Blood-albumen glue is made of beef blood to which an alkali is added. It is made into flakes which readily dissolve in water after a preliminary soaking of about an hour. It is used to glue plywood panels which must be heated while being clamped. As this glue is waterproof, it is also used in the manufacture of canoes and airplanes. It is not suitable for shopwork. Formerly used a great deal in veneering, this type of glue has been replaced by the synthetic-resin glues.

*Synthetic Resin Glues.** These glues were introduced to the woodworking industry about 1935. Their development and general acceptance on a large scale began during World War II and continues to increase. They are the product of our modern chemical laboratories, deriving their origin from such raw materials as coal, air, petroleum, natural gas, and water.

The synthetic resin glues are classified either as thermosetting or thermoplastic. The first type undergoes irreversible chemical curing reactions to produce insoluble, infusible glue films in the joint. The other synthetic glues, and in particular polyvinyl-resin emulsion glues, are thermoplastic, which means that they do not undergo any chemical curing during the gluing process but remain in a reversible state and soften on subsequent heating. The chemical curing process for the thermosetting glues is often accelerated by adding catalysts to certain glues within this group. For easier spreading, some glues may be modified with fillers, such as walnut-shell flour; or extenders may be added, such as wheat or other cereal flours as a means of keeping their cost down.

Some of these glues are sold either in ready-to-use package form or in powder form to be mixed with water. Many others must be prepared by mixing their basic ingredients at the time of use. The manufacturer's instructions for their use should be closely followed:

The following synthetic resin glues are discussed here in greater detail. *Urea-resin glues* are thermosetting glues and are available in powder and liquid form with or without additional catalysts, fillers, or extenders. They are formulated to cure at room temperature (70° F.) or at hot-press temperatures of 240° to 260° F.

---

* Source: Department of Agriculture, Forest Products Laboratory, Technical Note, No. 258, Feb., 1953.

The glue lines produced are colorless to light tan and have little dulling effect on tools.

Unextended urea-resin glues are highly resistant to water and moisture, but become sensitive at temperatures of 150° F. or higher, especially at high-humidity conditions. They are for these reasons not recommended for exterior use. The addition of fortifiers may partly eliminate the foregoing shortcomings.

Phenol-resin glues are normally dark-reddish liquids and require hot pressing at 280° F. or higher. A few of these glues are supplied in powder form to be mixed with water or some other solvent. Because they generally require high curing temperatures, phenol-resin glues are mainly used for plywood production. When formulated for intermediate temperature setting, they are used for laminating heavy timbers, a technique which is developing rapidly in the lumber manufacturing industry. Ordinarily they are not suitable for small scale shop operations or hobby work.

Resorcinol-resin glues are dark reddish and are generally supplied as liquids to which a liquid or powdered catalyst is added. They have much the same characteristics as the phenol-resin glues with this distinct advantage that they cure well at temperatures around 70° F. They are, however, the most expensive of the current woodworking glues. In combination with phenol resin glues they are made appreciably cheaper without losing their original good qualities.

These glues are also used in laminating processes where a high degree of durability to exteriors or other severe service is required. At least one brand of resorcinol-resin glue is available in small retail packages and is of particular interest to the amateur boatbuilder.

Melamine-resin glues are available as colorless hot-press glues at a cost which compares favorably with the other synthetic resin glues. They are limited in use to a few special applications. More often they are used to fortify and thus improve the durability of urea-resin glues.

Polyvinyl-resin emulsion glues are the newest type of wood glue and are available in a ready-to-use liquid form that sets at room temperature to a colorless glue line. Unlike the other resin glues described, they do not cure by a chemical reaction but set by losing water to the wood. They remain somewhat elastic and thermoplastic in the glue line. They are known to cause trouble under lacquer finishes, particularly when boards are glued up with poorly fitting glue joints. Also when glue joints have not been given sufficient time to dry, subsequent lacquer coats are likely to soften the glue joints. In many types of construction and assembly work they are becoming increasingly popular, especially now that they are placed on the market in convenient plastic squeeze bottles.

224. General Directions for Gluing. *Animal Glue.* When using animal glue the work must be done very quickly, because the glue sets and chills so fast. The whole gluing job must therefore be well thought out and planned in advance. The temperature of the room should be at least 70° F. or higher. It is also good practice to place the parts of the project to be assembled in this room a day in advance. This is another precaution to avoid chilling.

Any significant gluing job should be done with a freshly prepared "batch" of glue. Glue that has been reheated several times may have lost much of its strength, especially if it has been heated once or twice to the boiling point. If this is the case fill the glue container with warm water and let it soak overnight. Clean the container thoroughly and fill it with enough flake glue to do the job. Cover the dry flakes with enough water so that they are all submerged and let them soak for about two hours. Next, heat this solution in a double boiler. Animal flake glue should never be heated over a direct open flame. If the glue appears too thick, add some clean hot water. It should have the consistency of thick cream. It is better to have the glue a little too thin than to have it too thick.

With these advance preparations made, proceed as follows:

1. Have all pieces to be glued ready so far as tool operations are concerned. Mark them plainly to show how they are to be joined.

2. Prepare blocks needed to protect the finished surfaces from being marred by clamps or hand screws. Have a few extra ones on hand.

3. Adjust all necessary clamps and hand screws to the right opening or width between jaws.

4. Place them in a convenient position together with the framing square,

Fig. 1. Hold the work over the gluepot when applying hot glue.

try square, mallet, rule, chisels, or other tools necessary for the gluing job.

5. Clamp the pieces together without glue, in order to make sure that every part fits as it should and to find out the best way to apply the clamps.

6. Close all doors and windows so that no cold draft chills the glue while it is being applied. Chilled glue does not penetrate into the pores of the wood, nor can it be squeezed out of a joint. It, therefore, makes a poor bond, and such a joint comes apart when the glue later hardens and dries.

7. Apply the glue quickly to both members of each joint, but be careful not to smear it or get glue spots on finished surfaces. As far as possible hold each part over the gluepot while applying the glue so that the excess can drip back into the pot (Fig. 1).

8. Clamp the pieces together as quickly as possible and then check the job for squareness or flatness as the case may be.

9. Scrape off the surplus glue with a dull chisel after it has set but before it has dried hard.

It is usually advisable, and very often necessary to have one or more helpers when gluing.

Procedure When Using Casein and Resin Glue. 1. When using casein or resin glue the method of procedure is about the same, except that speed is not so important as these glues set slower (in about 15 minutes).

2. With regard to temperature, the same precautions should be taken with resin glue, but casein glue can be used just as well in a cold room and on cold wood. Clean off casein and resin glue with a piece of clean cotton waste moistened with hot water.

Apply polyvinyl resin glue directly from the squeeze bottle and spread it evenly with your fingers or a brush. This popular glue can be purchased in handy plastic containers, which are readily refilled from a quart or gallon jar.

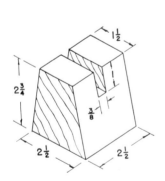

Fig. 2. Bar clamp block.

Fig. 3. Clamping boards edge to edge.

225. Procedure for Gluing Two or More Boards Edge to Edge. 1. Joint the edges as explained in Article 159, and number or mark the boards in the order they are to be placed.

2. Prepare four blocks, as shown in Figure 2, for the two clamps to be placed underneath the boards at each extremity.

3. Place the boards on top of these clamps, and put a third clamp on top of the boards in the center (Fig. 3). Tighten up the center clamp only, and see if the joints are tight all along and especially at the ends. The joints should be so tight at the ends that it is impossible to move the boards up or down by pressing on them with the hands.

4. Loosen the center clamp, and adjust the other two to the right opening.

5. Apply glue simultaneously to the two edges by holding the boards in an inclined position (Figs. 4 and 5).

Fig. 4. Applying glue simultaneously to edges of two or more boards.

Fig. 5. Applying polyvinyl-resin emulsion glue directly from handy "squeeze" bottle. Spread evenly with fingers or a brush.

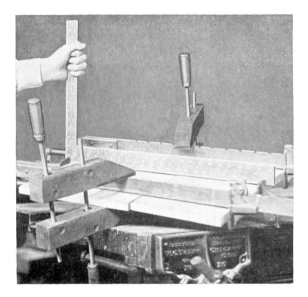

Fig. 6. Testing glued boards for flatness.

6. Tighten the center clamp on top of the boards first, and then the two underneath at either end.

7. Bring the surfaces of the boards to the same level by striking them with a mallet. This should be done after the clamps have been tightened.

8. Test for flatness with a framing square (Fig. 6). If the boards bulge in the center, this condition usually can be corrected by clamping them to the iron clamp below with one or two hand screws.

Fig. 7. Clamped glued-up table top.

Fig. 8. To prevent buckling place hand screws on the end of the boards.

9. Sight along the boards to see that they have not been sprung out of shape in the gluing process.

10. When large table tops consisting of several boards are to be glued, it is necessary to use three or more clamps below and two or more above. Two or more heavy pieces of wood, as 2 by 4 in., with one straight edge are also clamped across the top with hand screws so as to make it level (Fig. 7).

If the glued boards are about as wide as a large hand screw, place a hand screw on the ends of the board as shown in Figure 8.

11. As boards glued together to form tops must be planed after gluing, no particular care need be taken in this case to protect the surfaces or outside edges.

12. When the gluing process has been completed, the boards with the clamps attached may be lifted out of the gluing blocks (Fig. 3) and placed against a wall to dry.

226. Procedure for Gluing Bookshelves. 1. Finish and sandpaper the inside faces of the sides and both faces of the shelves, and try them together before applying the glue. Number all the joints.

2. Prepare short heavy blocks about 2 by 2 in. and as long as the sides are wide. Two blocks and two clamps are needed for every shelf. Each block should have one planed side. Blocks, as shown in Figure 9 will not bend when clamped and therefore keep sides flat.

3. Place one of the sides flat on the bench with the inside face up. Apply glue to the dadoes with a small brush and to both ends of the shelves.

4. Insert the shelves in their corresponding dadoes, apply glue to the dadoes in the other side, and place that side on top of the shelf ends so that each enters in the dado cut for it.

5. Drive the joints together by striking on the upper side with a mallet, protecting this side from being marred by placing a piece of wood over each joint while it is being driven together.

6. Place the bookcase in an upright position, and apply the clamps. The heavy blocks extending across the sides will prevent them from bulging in the middle, which they are very likely to do when clamps are forcing the front and rear edges together, especially when the joints are tight.

Fig. 9. Squaring bookcase.

7. Try for squareness by placing a try square on both ends of each shelf. If the shelves are not quite square with the sides, this defect can easily be remedied by changing the clamps from their horizontal position to a slightly oblique one (Fig. 9).

8. Clean off the surplus glue, both on the upper and lower parts of the shelves as explained in Article 215.

227. Procedure for Gluing a Frame or Panel.   1. Place two clamps in the blocks as explained in Article 225.

2. Number the mortise-and-tenon joints, and try them first without glue.

3. Apply glue both to the mortises and tenons. For the mortises a small, flat brush is needed. A small stick wrapped with a piece of waste or rag at one end may also serve the purpose. Protect finished sides by placing small blocks between them and the clamps.

4. If a panel is to be inserted between the four members of the frame, no glue should be applied either to the panel or the groove into which it fits. A panel should be free to expand or contract in accordance with the moisture it absorbs or gives off to the surrounding air.

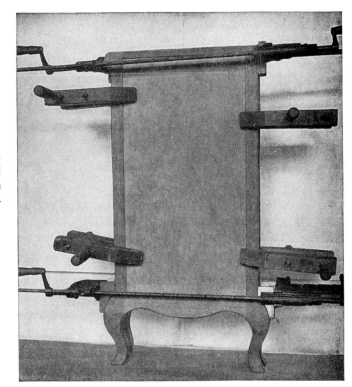

Fig. 10. Cabinet panel clamped with hand screws.

5. Test the frame for squareness by placing a try square in the inside corners. Correct any angles being out of square by shifting the clamps or, in extreme cases, by applying a clamp diagonally. Also test for flatness and "wind" by placing a steel square across the rails and glued points. Correct any unevenness by clamping heavy pieces across the frame.

6. In cabinets, or stools, having two opposite sides alike, each side is glued up as explained before, after which they are clamped together with hand screws, inside faces together (Fig. 10). This tends to correct any twisting of legs or rails, and will insure perfectly square joints when the cabinet or stool finally has been assembled.

7. Clean off the surplus glue with a chisel or waste moistened in hot water as explained in Article 224.

228. Procedure for Gluing a Cabinet. 1. Plane, scrape, and sand the two sides which were glued as explained in Article 227, and fit the back, bottom, and front rails in place. It is easier to finish the sides before gluing the entire cabinet, because they can be clamped flat on the bench. Clamp without gluing to test accuracy of construction.

Fig. 11. Measuring diagonals.

2. Glue, as explained before, with one side flat on the bench. Place the cabinet in the natural position and apply clamps, being careful to protect the finished sides with small blocks, preferably of softwood.

3. Test for squareness with a framing square and by measuring the diagonals (Fig. 11). Adjust any inaccuracy by moving the clamps so that they are close against the sides at one end, and away from them at the opposite end. This is the same principle as is shown in Figure 9.

4. If the error cannot be corrected by any movement of the clamps, another clamp may be fastened diagonally on the corners having the longest diagonal, and tightened until the diagonals are even. A stick of the correct length also may be placed between the corners having the shortest diagonal.

5. Clean off the surplus glue as explained in Article 224, steps 9 and 11.

229. Procedure for Gluing a Drawer.   1. Fit the pieces together without glue, and have clamps and blocks ready. All the inside surfaces of the drawer should be finished and sanded.

2. Glue the dovetails first, and then the rear piece.

3. Place a piece of paper over the dovetails so as to prevent the blocks from sticking to the sides. The blocks should be fairly heavy and as long as the width of the sides. One or two clamps are necessary at the front and rear, depending upon the depth of the drawer.

4. Measure the diagonals very carefully, and insert a stick if necessary as explained in Article 228.

5. Place the drawer on a flat surface to make sure it is level. If two corners are high, adjust the clamps until it is level. In extreme cases, clamp the drawer to the flat surface, or place weights on it until all four corners touch.

6. Clean off all surplus glue, and set the drawer away to dry.

7. The bottom is slid into the groove and fastened to the underside of the back with brads or screws. In case of shrinkage, these screws can be removed and the bottom pushed farther toward the front. Some people prefer to glue the bottom to the front of the drawer (Fig. 171, p. 267).

230. Procedure for Gluing a Chair. 1. Glue the back and front separately, and set them away to dry.

2. After cleaning and sanding, fit the side rails and stretchers, if any, in place.

3. Apply glue to the mortises and tenons as explained in Article 227, and clamp them together, using blocks to protect the finished surfaces from being marred by the clamps.

4. Measure the diagonals very carefully, and adjust the clamps until they are even.

5. Clean off all surplus glue, both inside and outside. Blocks are usually glued and screwed to the inside corners to strengthen the joints.

231. Procedure for Gluing Doweled Joints and Segments. 1. Point all the dowels a little so that they will enter their corresponding holes easier. Also cut a small V groove along the side of each dowel so that the air and glue may escape when the dowel is driven into its hole (Art. 178).

2. Put glue in one set of holes with a small brush or stick. Dip one end of each dowel in the glue and drive it in place with a hammer. Wipe off surplus glue with a piece of dry waste or rag.

3. Put glue in the other set of holes, on the projecting ends of the dowels, and on the edges of the wood to be joined together.

Fig. 12. Gluing segments.

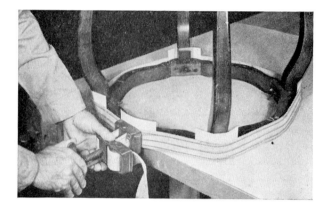

Fig. 13. Using a canvas belt clamp on a table with semicircular rails.

4. Clamp as explained in Article 227, if the work is straight.

5. If segments or curved pieces are to be clamped, a strong rope or strip of leather is wound twice around the work and twisted by means of a short piece of dowel rod, until the tightening of the rope brings the joints together (Fig. 12). It is advisable to use sash cord, because of its strength.

Special clamps, called "column clamps," consisting of an iron chain and screw, are recommended for this type of gluing job. Place small pieces of wood between the chain and the finished surfaces. An improvement over this clamp is the canvas belt clamp (Fig. 13). This type of clamp is not likely to mar the wood. This clamp is also manufactured with a steel band.

Fig. 14. Gluing irregular shape.

6. Legs may be glued to a turned column by clamping a hand screw firmly to each leg near the joint. This hand screw affords a hold for two other hand screws, which force the leg tightly against the column (Fig. 51, p. 213).

7. Glue one leg at a time, and allow it to dry before attempting to glue the next one. Fasten the column in a vise during the gluing process.

8. Irregular shapes are glued much in the same manner, except that the blocks must be shaped to fit the curves (Figs. 10 and 14).

232. Starved Glue Joints.* Many failures in glued wood products are caused by "starved" joints, or joints in which the film of glue between the wood surfaces is not continuous. Starved joints are readily identified by broken joints showing little or no wood failure or with little or no glue visible. Such joints according to the Forest Products Laboratory, are not necessarily the result of a lack of glue spread on the wood; heavy spreads are as likely to produce them under ordinary commercial conditions as light spreads. They are caused rather by the application of pressure to the joint while the glue is too fluid. Starved joints are more likely to occur with glues of low viscosity, such as warm animal glue, than with casein, vegetable, and other thick glues. Starved joints have also been observed with some of the thermosetting synthetic resin glues when short assembly periods and heavy pressures are combined with thin glue mixtures. Such thin mixtures may result from use of the glue too soon after mixing.

Some woods are more susceptible to the production of starved joints than others. Birch, maple, red oak, and ash, which have open pores, absorb glue in such considerable amounts that they often leave the joints starved. Basswood and yellow poplar also take up a great deal of glue, but weak joints are not very noticeable in these woods because the woods themselves are weak. Other woods with smaller cells do not seem to be so subject to starved joints.

In some cases starved joints may result from the use of wood containing too much moisture at the time of gluing. This has been observed frequently in the use of phenol-resin film glues and is likely to occur whenever wet wood is glued.

To avoid starved joints it is necessary to mix a glue solution thick or to allow it to thicken in the pot or on the wood before pressure is applied. When it is necessary to glue under conditions that might produce starved joints, the use of light pressure is advantageous.

Hot glue applied to an edge, however, should never be left exposed to thicken into a gelatin mass. When this happens, remove the glue with a dampened cloth and make a second application.

---

* Source: U. S. Department of Agriculture, Forest Products Laboratory, Technical Note, No. 193, Dec., 1952.

233. Occurrence and Removal of Glue Stains and Spots.* Caustic soda in glue, whether added to the glue as such or formed by chemical action during mixing, produces stains on certain species of wood, notably the oaks, maple, cherry, elm, ash, birch, and beech. Some glues stain the wood more than others, those that contain the most alkali usually being the most injurious. Generally speaking, a tendency to stain may be expected with starch, casein, or soybean glues. Animal and synthetic resin glues as ordinarily formulated usually give no trouble with staining, although any dark-colored glue may show through a thin, porous veneer of light-colored wood. The staining effect of the alkaline glues is caused by the action of the alkali on certain constituents in the wood. While no method has yet been found to prevent the reaction, precautions may be taken that will reduce the troublesome discoloration.

Other conditions being equal, a thick glue will penetrate less and stain less than a thin glue that will be squeezed more readily through the pores of the wood. For this reason, the quantity of water that is used in the glue might be reduced or "fillers," such as wood flour, added if staining is feared.

The alkali from the glue line will penetrate more readily through wet veneer than through dry veneer. It is important, therefore, that thin veneer be re-dried before gluing and that the gluing operation be carried out promptly after the veneer has cooled in order to prevent the veneer re-absorbing moisture from the air. After the stock has been spread with glue it should be placed under pressure promptly, the schedule being so arranged as to avoid long assembly periods.

Stains caused by alkali can be removed by moistening with a solution of sodium sulphite (one part sodium sulphite to 12 parts of water), followed by sponging with a solution of oxalic acid (also mixed in the concentration of one part of oxalic acid to 12 parts of water). The acid should be thoroughly washed from the wood afterward or it may affect the finish. Oxalic acid is poisonous and must be used with appropriate care.

Generally, it is good practice to let glue dry before removing any surplus that can be observed outside the joints. When removing it with a damp rag while still wet, one only spreads it over a wider area, and in so doing invites more difficulties when stain is applied.

* Source: U. S. Department of Agriculture, Forest Products Laboratory, Technical Note, No. 146, Feb., 1953.

REVIEW QUESTIONS, CHAPTER 7

Possible score 35 points

Your score . . . . . .

PART I. COMPLETION QUESTIONS. Complete the following statements:

1. Woodworking glues are either of natural origin or of the . . . . type.
2. The latter are of more recent development and are the products of modern
   . . . .
3. Glue made from bones, sinews, and other waste parts of cattle is called
   . . . .
4. Before this glue can be used it must be thoroughly soaked in . . . .
5. This glue should not be heated above a temperature of . . . . degrees.
6. Vegetable starch glue is made by grinding the wood of the . . . .
   . . . .
7. Casein glue is made from the curds of . . . .
8. Synthetic resin glues are classified either as thermosetting or . . . .
9. Resorcinol-resin glues are made in liquid form to which is added a . . . .
10. Polyvinyl-resin emulsion glue is often referred to as . . . .

PART II. TRUE-FALSE QUESTIONS. Indicate, by encircling T or F, whether the following statements are true or false.

11. When gluing with hot animal glue, the room temperature can be below 60 deg.	T	F
12. Animal glue can be reheated over and over before it looses its strength.	T	F
13. When assembling with hot glue, allow for good ventilation by opening doors and windows.	T	F
14. To prevent glued boards from buckling, the bar clamps are placed alternately on both sides of the boards.	T	F
15. After finishing the assembly of a bookcase or similar project, it should again be tested for squareness.	T	F
16. When gluing up a chair, the front and back are glued up separately, and set aside to dry.	T	F
17. When gluing up segments or curved pieces, it is best to use a chain column clamp.	T	F
18. A "starved" glue joint is a joint in which the film of glue between the wood surfaces is not continuous.	T	F
19. Starch, casein, and soybean glues have a tendency to stain the wood.	T	F
20. It is good practice to remove any surplus glue before it hardens with a damp cloth.	T	F

PART III. MULTIPLE-CHOICE QUESTIONS. Select, by encircling the correct letter, the answer which completes each statement:

21. One of the following is not a natural glue:
    A. Animal glue
    B. Urea-resin glue
    C. Casein glue
    D. Soybean glue
22. Vegetable starch glue is made from:
    A. The cassava bush
    B. Soybeans
    C. Animal waste
    D. Beef blood
23. When gluing up flat boards one of the following is not needed:
    A. Column clamps
    B. Bar clamps
    C. Hand screws
24. Present day column clamps are made with:
    A. A chain
    B. A canvas belt
    C. Heavy rope
25. Synthetic resin glues are made of all but one of the following:
    A. Coal
    B. Air
    C. Curds of skimmed milk
    D. Natural gas

PART IV. MATCHING QUESTIONS. Match the terms to the left with the descriptions to the right by placing the correct letter in the parentheses:

26. (   ) Woodworking glues
27. (   ) Flake animal glue
28. (   ) Cassava bush
29. (   ) Casein glue
30. (   ) Synthetic resin glues
31. (   ) Glue extenders
32. (   ) Phenolresin glues
33. (   ) Starved glue joints
34. (   ) Caustic soda
35. (   ) Solution of sodium
            sulphite

A. Requires soaking in water.
B. Is water resistant and can be used below 70 degrees temperatures.
C. Are either of natural or synthetic origin.
D. Added to glue to keep the cost down.
E. Likely to cause stains in certain woods.
F. Wood surfaces where the glue film is not continuous.
G. Used as a remover of stains caused by alkali.
H. Basically made from coal, air, petroleum, and water.
I. Mainly used for plywood production.
J. Should be wiped off before glue dries.
K. The base material for vegetable starch glue.
L. Sold in handy squeeze bottles.

CHAPTER 8

Metal Fastenings and Cabinet Hardware

Although wood very frequently is fastened with glue, it is also fastened together with nails, screws, and bolts. Different kinds of hardware as hinges, locks, door bolts, catches, casters, drawer pulls and knobs, escutcheons are used on movable parts as doors, table leaves, drawers.

236. Nails are used in house framing, roofing, interior trim, box making, upholstery, and for many other purposes. They are, therefore, made in many shapes and of different materials as steel wire, iron, brass, copper, etc. Some of the most common nails used in the woodworking industry are common wire nails, box nails, casing nails, finishing nails or brads, cut nails, and tacks (Fig. 1).

1. Common wire nails are made with a large, flat head in lengths from 1 to 6 in. Larger sizes are usually called spikes. The length of common wire nails is generally given by the word "penny" instead of in inches.

2. The penny system originated in England, but there is some difference of opinion as to its original meaning. Some claim that the word penny meant pound and that it referred to the weight of 1000 nails. Therefore, 1000 nails weighing six pounds were called sixpenny nails. At any rate, the

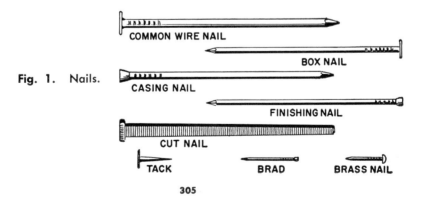

Fig. 1. Nails.

COMMON WIRE NAIL

BOX NAIL

CASING NAIL

FINISHING NAIL

CUT NAIL

TACK   BRAD   BRASS NAIL

relation of the length in inches to the penny system is as follows:

2-penny nail is 1 in. long	8-penny nail is 2½ in. long
3-penny nail is 1¼ in. long	9-penny nail is 2¾ in. long
4-penny nail is 1½ in. long	10-penny nail is 3 in. long
5-penny nail is 1¾ in. long	12-penny nail is 3¼ in. long
6-penny nail is 2 in. long	16-penny nail is 3½ in. long
7-penny nail is 2¼ in. long	20-penny nail is 4 in. long

3. Each length of common wire nails is made from a standard thickness of wire. In colonial days, nails were forged from iron and were therefore scarce and expensive. In modern times wire nails are made on a machine, which straightens the wire as it is fed from a roll, cuts it to length, forms the point and head, and ejects it from the machine.

4. Common wire nails are sold by the 100-lb. keg and are used mostly in house carpentry and in rough construction work.

5. Box nails are made like common wire nails, but are thinner than wire nails of the same length. To make them hold better, box nails are sometimes barbed or coated with resin or cement.

6. Casing nails have the same wire gauge as box nails. They are used for interior trim and can be set below the surface of the wood, because they have a small head.

7. Brads or finishing nails are made in lengths from ⅜ to 3 in. They are used like casing nails and have a very small head. The same length of brad is obtainable in different thicknesses. They are packed in 1-lb. cardboard boxes on which both length and thickness are marked, as for example 1¼ in. by 16 or 1¼ in. by 18. The last number refers to the thickness of the wire or wire gauge. *The higher the number, the thinner the nail.* An 18-gauge nail is about 1/20 in. thick; a 12-gauge nail is about 1/10 in. thick.

8. Cut nails are sliced from a wedge-shaped iron plate. They have a blunt end and a small head. They are used in nailing flooring, because they have a rough surface and therefore hold well. They should always be driven so that their wider sides are parallel to the grain otherwise their wedge-shaped form might split the wood.

9. Carpet tacks also are made of iron. They have a sharp point and a large head. They are used primarily in upholstery work and are made in lengths from 3/16 to 18/16 in. Their size is indicated in ounces. An 8-oz. tack, for example, is ½ in. long. Like penny, ounce is an old term which originally meant the weight of 1000 tacks. Because workmen are in the habit of putting such nails in their mouths, they are sterilized by dipping them in muriatic acid. This gives them a blue color.

10. Shingle nails, plaster-board nails, and felt-roofing nails are short nails with very large heads.

11. Brass, copper, and galvanized iron nails are used on work which is exposed to the weather and therefore likely to be damaged by rust.

237. Rules for Driving Nails. 1. Glue, grease, or dirt on the face of a hammer will cause it to glance off when striking a nail. Clean it with a piece of fine sandpaper.

2. Nails driven in a line following the grain may cause the wood to split. The best way is to stagger them.

3. When driving thin nails in hardwood, it is recommended first to bore holes for them. As a bit, use the same size nail as the one to be driven, cut off its head, and hold it in the chuck of a hand drill (Fig. 2).

4. Always clinch a nail with the grain, because its point can then be driven in between the wood fibers. This cannot be done if the nail is bent across the grain.

5. If the point of a nail comes outside the surface, drive it back with a nail set until its head projects enough above the wood to be pulled out with a hammer.

6. A nail has a tendency to follow the grain of the wood. Blunting its point with a hammer helps to drive it in a straight line.

7. Place a block under the head of a claw hammer to protect the surface of the wood when pulling a nail (Fig. 3).

Fig. 2. Boring hole in hardwood with nail.

Fig. 3. Pulling nail with claw hammer.

238. Screws for fastening wood are superior to nails, because they hold better, look better, and can be removed easily and without damage to the wood. Like nails, screws are made in many different shapes and sizes and of different materials as brass, soft steel, and iron. Screws are also brass or nickel plated, or galvanized. The most common screws are: flathead, roundhead, oval-countersunk head, Phillips head, lag screws, drive screws, screw eyes, screw hooks, and cup hooks (Fig. 4).

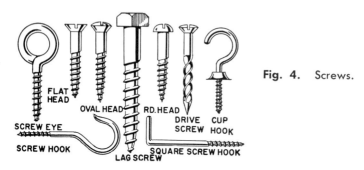

Fig. 4. Screws.

1. Screws are made in lengths from ¼ to 4 in. and in screw gauges from 2 to 18. The screw gauge for screws runs opposite to that for nails — *the higher the number, the thicker the screw.* For example, No. 5 is about ⅛ in. thick and No. 14 is almost ¼ in. thick. Screws are packed in cardboard boxes which hold one gross each. The length and screw gauge are marked on the box as for instance, 1¼ by 9 (Fig. 5).

SIZE IN INCHES	GAUGE NUMBERS												
¼	2		4										
⅜	2	3	4	5	6								
½	2	3	4	5	6	7	8						
⅝	2	3	4	5	6	7	8						
¾			4	5	6	7	8	9	10	12			
⅞			4	5	6	7	8	9	10	12			
1			4	5	6	7	8	9	10	12	14		
1¼			4	5	6	7	8	9	10	12	14	16	
1½					6	7	8	9	10	12	14	16	18
1¾							8	9	10	12	14	16	
2							8	9	10	12	14	16	18
2¼									10	12	14		
2½							8	9	10	12	14	16	18
3									10	12	14	16	18
3½									10	12	14	16	18
4											14	16	18

Fig. 5. Sizes of flat, round, and oval head screws.

2. Flat-head and round-head screws are the most commonly used. Flat-head steel screws are bright, and round-head screws generally are blue. In places where screws might rust, brass, brass-plated, nickel-plated, or galvanized-iron screws are used.

3. Phillips head screws have a flat or oval head with two slots at right angles to each other, but not extending to the edge of the screw head (Fig. 6). They can be driven only with a special screw driver, but faster and easier than ordinary screws and with less slipping of the screw driver.

4. Lag screws are made of iron. They have a square head like a bolt and are from ¼ to 1 in. thick and from 1 to 16 in. long (Fig. 4). They are used mostly in construction work and for expansion bolts (see Art. 240, step 8).

Fig. 6. Phillips head screw.

5. Drive screws have a very steep thread and can, therefore, be driven with a hammer instead of a screw driver. They are used instead of nails on such jobs as fastening galvanized iron sheets, etc. (Fig. 4).

6. Screw hooks, screw eyes, and cup hooks are made of steel, brass, and galvanized iron (Fig. 4). They are manufactured in many sizes and are used principally in the household for hanging pictures, curtains, kitchen utensils, keys, etc.

239. Rules for Driving Screws. 1. When two boards are to be fastened together with screws, a hole of the same diameter as the shank of the screw must be bored through one, and a smaller hole, equal to the root diameter of the screw, must be bored part way into the other. The root diameter of a screw is the thickness of the central part around which the threads are cut. The sizes of holes for different screw gauges are given in Figure 7.

2. In hardwoods the small hole or pilot hole must be bored as deep as the screw enters; in softwoods it may be bored to half this depth or it may even be omitted. The large hole must be big enough to permit the screw to be pushed through with the fingers. Its upper end must be countersunk when flathead or oval-countersunk screws are used.

GAUGE NO. OF SCREW	4	5	6	7	8	9	10	11	12
DIA. OF FIRST HOLE	$\frac{1}{8}$	$\frac{1}{8}$	$\frac{5}{32}$	$\frac{5}{32}$	$\frac{3}{16}$	$\frac{3}{16}$	$\frac{3}{16}$	$\frac{7}{32}$	$\frac{7}{32}$
DIA. OF SECOND HOLE	$\frac{3}{32}$	$\frac{3}{32}$	$\frac{1}{8}$	$\frac{1}{8}$	$\frac{5}{32}$	$\frac{5}{32}$	$\frac{5}{32}$	$\frac{5}{32}$	$\frac{5}{32}$

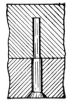

Fig. 7. Table showing size of holes in inches to be bored for screws of various gauges.

3. Soap or wax rubbed on the threads of a screw reduces friction and makes it much easier to drive. It therefore also reduces the danger of "twisting off," which means that the screw breaks when too much force is applied to drive it in place. It always breaks at the point where the threads end, and the threaded part remains embedded in the wood. Such broken parts are almost impossible to remove without greatly damaging the surface.

4. As brass screws are softer than steel screws, they twist off more easily. It is, therefore, a good plan to drive a steel screw of the same size first, especially in hardwoods, then remove it and drive the brass screw. In this way the steel screw cuts the threads in the wood for the brass screw.

5. It is important to use a screw driver that fits the slot in the screw and whose sides and end are flat and square. A screw driver that is too thin or has rounded edges constantly "climbs" out of the slot and damages it so that the screw becomes more and more difficult to drive and ruins its appearance (Fig. 8).

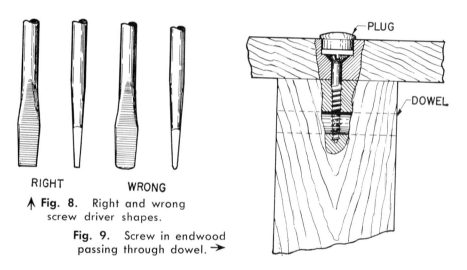

RIGHT   WRONG

↑ **Fig. 8.**   Right and wrong screw driver shapes.

Fig. 9.   Screw in endwood passing through dowel. ➤

6. As screws do not hold well in endwood, it is sometimes advisable to glue a dowel into the wood a short distance from the end. Driving the screw through this dowel makes the joint very strong (Fig. 9).

7. If a screw is to be concealed in the wood, first bore a shallow hole equal to the diameter of the head, then bore the regular screw hole and drive the screw in place. Now cut a plug with a plug cutter from the same kind of wood, and glue it into the hole above the screw. When dry, plane and smooth it level with the surrounding surface. Plugs with rounded heads may be bought in hardware stores (Fig. 9).

240. Bolts are used in woodwork where great strength is required as when timbers are bolted together, in draw-bolt joints (Fig. 43, p. 210), or when wood is fastened to metal or masonry.

1. Bolts differ from screws in that they do not taper to a point, but are of the same diameter from one end to the other. A head is made on one end of a bolt. The other end is threaded for a nut, which is usually square or hexagonal.

2. Washers or metal plates are usually placed between the work being clamped and the head and nut of the bolt. When great pressure is not required, a wing nut (Fig. 10), which can be screwed off or on by hand, is sometimes used.

3. Threads on bolts are not nearly as steep as those on wood screws. They are cut by hand with a steel die, by machine on an engine lathe, or on a special thread-cutting machine.

4. Bolts are made in different lengths and diameters and in many different forms according to the work they are to do. The ones most commonly used by the woodworker are stove bolts, iron bolts, carriage bolts, expansion bolts, and toggle bolts.

5. Stove bolts are small, cheaply made bolts from ⅜ to 6 in. long and from ⅛ to ½ in. in diameter. They have either round or flat heads, slotted for a screw driver, and a square nut (Fig. 10).

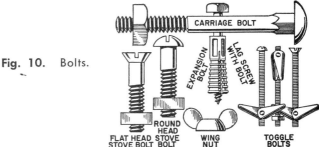

Fig. 10.   Bolts.

6. Iron bolts are from ³⁄₁₆ to ¾ in. in diameter and from 1 to 16 in. long. They have square heads and nuts and are used for draw-bolt joints and in other construction work.

7. Carriage bolts are also made of iron and in the same sizes as the iron bolts. They have a large rounded head with a square part just below it. They are especially useful for wood, because when they are driven into the holes bored for them, the square part will dig into the wood and prevent the bolt from turning. Carriage bolts have a square nut (Fig. 10).

8. Expansion bolts are used in brick, stone, and concrete. They consist of two parts, a lag screw and a shield (Fig. 10). The shield is a split, cast-iron cylinder threaded on the inside for the lag screw, and corrugated on the outside so that it will hold in brick or concrete when expanded. When timbers or machines are to be fastened to masonry, holes to fit the shields are first drilled with a star drill. When the lag screw then is driven into the shield, its two halves expand in the hole. Shields are made in sizes corresponding to diameters of lag screws.

9. Toggle bolts are used to fasten wood or metal to hollow partitions and hollow-tile walls. The bolt is a stove bolt with a special nut made of two pieces of bent sheet iron hinged together (Fig. 10). When the hole is made in the thin wall of hollow tile, the two wings of the nut are folded together, and the bolt is inserted in the wall. As soon as it is through the hole, a spring spreads the wings of the nut apart. Another type of toggle bolt has just a single bent-iron nut which is heavier in one end than in the other. When it is pushed through the hole the heavy end drops down at right angles to the bolt (Fig. 11).

Fig. 11. Toggle bolt.

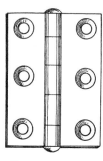

Fig. 12. Fast-joint butt hinge.

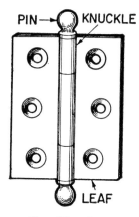

Fig. 13. Butt hinge.

241. Hinges are used a great deal both in cabinetwork and in carpentry. They are, therefore, made in many different shapes and of different materials as iron, galvanized iron, brass, brass plated and nickel plated.

1. The most common hinges used in cabinetwork are: butt hinges, chest hinges, desk hinges, continuous hinges, screen hinges, pivot hinges, invisible hinges, and card-table hinges.

2. The butt hinge is the type most frequently used. It is made in different lengths and widths and has either a riveted pin (fast-joint) (Fig. 12) or a

removable pin (loose-pin). A butt hinge always has two rectangular leaves joined together with a pin. The round, central part of the hinge, through which the pin passes, is called the knuckle (Fig. 13). The width of butt hinges is measured across both leaves in the open position. Butt hinges are used on doors, boxes, table leaves (see rule joint, Art. 218).

When loose-pin butt hinges are used on a door, the door can be removed by simply taking out the pins.

3. The chest hinge is a butt hinge with one leaf bent at right angles in the center (Fig. 14).

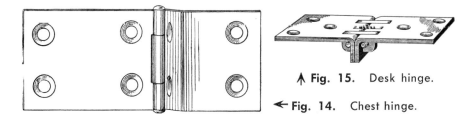

↑ **Fig. 15.** Desk hinge.

← **Fig. 14.** Chest hinge.

4. The desk hinge is also a butt hinge used for hinging the lid of writing desks or secretaries. It is always made of brass (Fig. 15).

5. The continuous hinge is another butt hinge sold by the foot of length. It is always used for hinging the lids on pianos (Fig. 16).

6. The screen or double-acting hinge (Fig. 17), has three knuckles and can, as its name implies, open both ways.

7. The pivot or pin hinge (Fig. 17) consists of two flat, narrow, rectangular pieces of iron. One of them has a pin which fits into a hole in the other. The part having the pin is screwed into the ends of the door, and the other part into the frame. Two hinges are needed for each door, one on top and one on the bottom. Pivot hinges, which are invisible, are used on cabinet doors and also on doors that open both ways, as for example between the kitchen and the dining room.

8. Invisible hinges, also named Soss hinges after the inventor (Fig. 16), are used principally on small cabinet doors. They are mortised into the edge of the door and the door frame. They are quite easy to apply, but are not very strong, because they are cast.

9. Card-table hinges are narrow brass hinges riveted together (Fig. 17). They are set into the edges of the two leaves of a card table.

10. Besides the butt hinge, a carpenter also uses a surface hinge, cupboard hinge, spring hinge, strap hinge, T hinge, and hinge hasp.

11. The surface hinge is shaped to give it a more decorative appearance. It is used on boxes and small doors and is generally brass or nickel plated

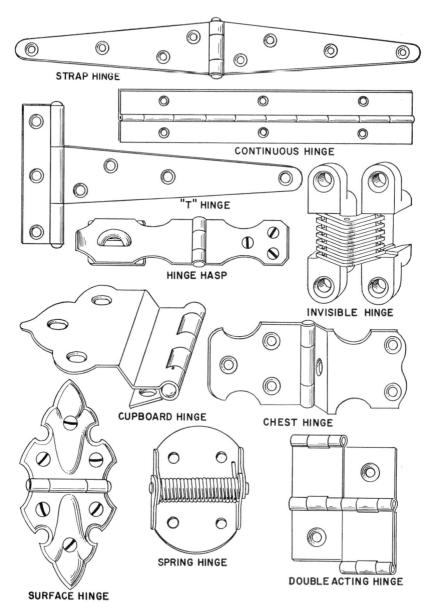

STRAP HINGE

CONTINUOUS HINGE

"T" HINGE

HINGE HASP

INVISIBLE HINGE

CUPBOARD HINGE

CHEST HINGE

SURFACE HINGE

SPRING HINGE

DOUBLE ACTING HINGE

Fig. 16. Hinges.

(Fig. 16). A surface hinge is simply screwed to the wood surface without cutting any recess for it.

12. One leaf of the cupboard hinge is like a butt hinge and is fastened to the framework of the cupboard. The other is offset or bent over the edge of the door and shaped (Fig. 16). Cupboard doors usually have a rabbeted edge.

13. The spring hinge is used on lightweight doors which are to close automatically, such as screen doors. It has a coil spring wound around the pin (Fig. 16).

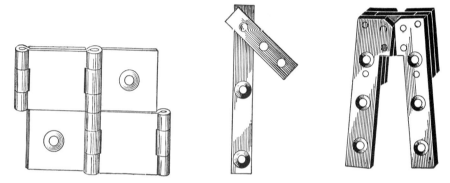

Fig. 17.   Left, double-acting hinge; center, pivot or pin hinge;
right, card-table hinge.

14. The strap hinge (Fig. 16) has long tapered leaves and is used mainly on rough work such as cellar or garage doors or large toolboxes.

15. The T hinge is used in the same way as the strap hinge. One of its leaves is like a butt hinge and the other like a strap hinge. Both of these hinges are made of plain and galvanized iron (Fig. 16).

16. The hinge hasp (Fig. 16) has two parts — a square plate to which a heavy wire loop is riveted, and a hinge, one leaf of which has screw holes and the other a slot that fits over the wire loop. The hasp is a locking device used with a padlock. The leaf which is screwed to the wood is covered by the slotted leaf, so that the screws cannot be removed when the hasp is locked. Hasps are used in the same type of work as strap and T hinges and are generally galvanized for outdoor use.

The cupboard, spring, strap, and T hinges, as well as the hasp, are all surface hinges.

242. Modern Cabinet Hardware.* Because cabinet hardware serves a functional as well as a beautifying purpose, the proper selection of design

---

* Source: "Advanced Course in Hardware Retailing," The National Retail Hardware Association, 1957, pp. 11–24.

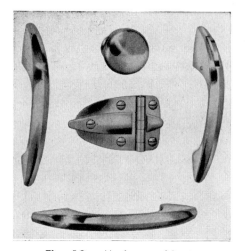

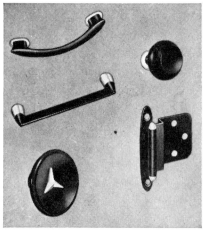

Fig. 18. Modern cabinet   Fig. 19. Contemporary cabinet
         hardware.   hardware.

is most important. For rooms with a modern but conservative feeling, modern designs as shown in Figure 18 are appropriate. In the kitchen and bathroom, particularly on painted surfaces, chromium platings are recommended. On natural wood cabinets and for use in other parts of the home, polished brass finish is more appropriate.

To fit in with contemporary furnishings, the patterns shown in Figure 19 are recommended. The most popular finishes are black with gold trim and copper finishes with black accents.

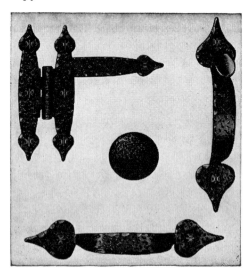

Fig. 20. Colonial and early
American cabinet hardware.

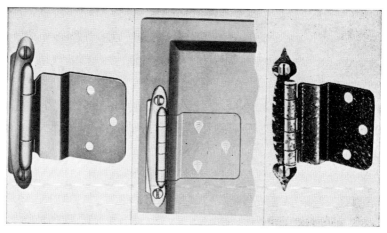

Fig. 21. Semiconcealed hinges.

For rooms with a Colonial or Early American flavor, the patterns shown in Figure 20 are most desirable.

Hinges. The semiconcealed hinges shown in Figure 21 show only the small leaf and joint when the door is closed and are the most popular types of cabinet hinges on the market today. They are available for both overlapping (lip) cabinet doors and flush cabinet doors. Most popular are the semiconcealed hinge for ⅜-in. lip doors and the semiconcealed hinge for ¾-in. flush doors. They are also available for special applications for lip doors in ½-, ⅝-, and ¾-in. insets and for panel type doors (Fig. 22).

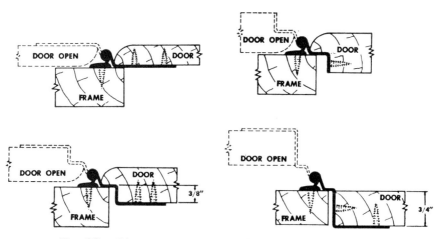

Fig. 22. Diagrammatic views of semiconcealed hinges.

Fig. 23. Concealed hinges installed.

Figure 23 shows two types of concealed hinges for flush overlap doors. They are designed for doors which completely overlap the frame of the cabinet (Fig. 24). The hinges shown can be used with or without mortising the door, although neater installation will result when the door is mortised on top and bottom.

243. Procedure for Hinging a Door.   1. When hinging a paneled door,

Fig. 24.   Cabinet doors hung with flush door concealed hinges.

it is the custom to place the hinges so that the upper one is just below the upper rail and the lower one just above the lower rail (Fig. 25). When hinging the lid of a box or chest, the hinges should be placed so that the distance from the hinges to the end of the box is equal to the length of the hinge.

2. Before the hinges can be attached, the door must be fitted to the frame. First plane the edge which is to be hinged, and then square the top of the door with that edge. If it is a large, paneled door, the ends of the stiles, called the "horns," are first sawed off.

3. The next step is to plane the door to width and finally saw and plane the lower edge until it fits in the frame. It is best to make a rather close fit to begin with, for it is easy to plane off more later on if necessary.

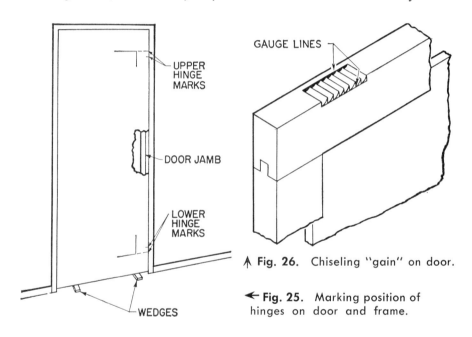

GAUGE LINES

UPPER HINGE MARKS

DOOR JAMB

LOWER HINGE MARKS

↟ **Fig. 26.** Chiseling "gain" on door.

← **Fig. 25.** Marking position of hinges on door and frame.

WEDGES

4. Now place the door in its opening so that its upper edge is tight against the frame. This may be done by driving wedges under it. Mark the position of the hinges both on the door and on the frame (Fig. 25).

5. Remove the door, and square lines across its edge from the points marked on its face. Do likewise on the frame.

6. Set the butt gauge equal to the width of the leaves, not including the knuckle, which should project beyond the face of the door and frame in order to permit the door to swing freely. Mark the width on both door and frame.

7. When hinging a cabinet door, set the butt gauge to half the thickness of the "knuckle," and mark lines on the face of the door and frame. On larger doors, only the thickness of the leaf is marked.

8. Chisel the outline or "gain" of the hinge very carefully, making a small V cut on the inside of the lines marked. Make a series of shallow chisel cuts within the V cut, and remove the surplus wood by chiseling carefully across the grain with the bevel side of the chisel up (Figs. 26, p. 203, and 61, p. 218). The recess may be finished with a router plane. Hinge gains also may be cut with a portable router (Fig. 102, p. 108).

9. Place the hinges in position, and bore for the screws with a bradawl or small bit (Art. 239). If a loose-pin hinge is used, take the hinge apart and screw each part to the door and frame respectively. Place the door in position, and insert the pin.

10. If there is a crack between the edge of the door and the frame, the recesses or gains cut for the hinges are not deep enough. If the edge of the door and frame come too close together, so that the door springs back when an attempt is made to close it, the gains are too deep. This defect can be rectified by removing the hinges, and placing a piece of cardboard in the gain or recess.

244. Cabinet locks are used on drawers, doors, desks, chests, and boxes. They are made in several different types and sizes and are either of brass or iron or partly iron and partly brass.

1. The principal parts of a lock are the lock box, the bolt, and the selvage. The lock box contains the tumblers, levers, springs, bolt, and other parts of the mechanism. The bolt is an iron bar which is moved in and out of the lock box with a key. It passes through the edge of the lock which is called the selvage.

When sizes of locks are given, the distance from the selvage to the key pin or center of cylinder is always included.

2. Some locks are furnished with a metal plate, called the strike, which corresponds in size and shape to the selvage and is fastened to the frame

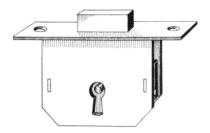

Fig. 27. Mortise lock.

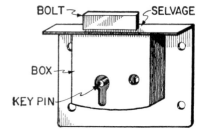

Fig. 28. Rim lock.

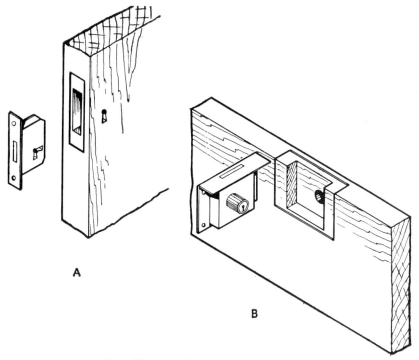

Fig. 29. Mortise lock set in wood.

of the door. It adds to the security of the lock, because it protects the wood from wear and it cannot easily be pried loose.

3. There are two kinds of cabinet locks — the mortise lock (Fig. 27) and the rim lock (Fig. 28). The mortise lock is completely set into the wood (A, Fig. 29). Some rim locks have no selvage and are screwed to the wood without cutting any recess. Others have to be recessed both for lock box and selvage (B, Fig. 29).

4. Keys are of two general kinds, barrel keys which are round and fit over a key pin, and flat keys which fit into cylinder locks (Fig. 30). Cylinder locks always are rim locks except on house doors, which have mortise locks with detachable cylinders.

5. Locks for desks, boxes, chests, and pianos are constructed to withstand an upward pull. The bolts on such locks therefore have hooklike projections, which are forced out by a spring, and engage the strike when in the locked position (Fig. 31). Some have bolts which move sideways and engage prongs on a strike which enters the lock (Fig. 32).

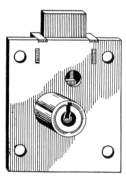

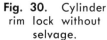

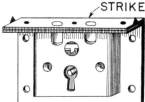

Fig. 32.   Chest lock.

Fig. 31.   Mortise lock with strike for a box.

Fig. 30.   Cylinder rim lock without selvage.

245. Procedure for Attaching Locks.   1. Measure the distance from the selvage to the key pin, and lay it off on the center line or above the center line as the case may be. Bore a hole slightly larger in diameter than the barrel of the key. *Note that the key pin is not always in the center of the lock box* (Fig. 28).

2. If a mortise lock is used, bore and chisel the mortise for the lock box in the center or toward the rear edge of the wood, so that sufficient material remains in front of the lock on which to fasten the escutcheon.

3. Place the lock in the mortise, and mark around the edges of the selvage. Then remove the lock, chisel the recess for the selvage, bore for screws with a bradawl, and screw the lock in position.

4. Finish the keyhole with a keyhole saw or coping saw (Figs. 38 and 40, pp. 28 and 29).

5. The procedure in fastening a rim lock is the same as for a mortise lock, except that the recess for the lock is chiseled on the inside edge of the drawer or door.

6. The strikes for chest, desk, or box locks are always provided with little points on the reverse side which help in locating their position (Fig. 32). Place the strike over the lock, and lock it. Close the lid, and press or pound on it with the hand. The marks of the points can then be seen, and the strike is easily located.

7. The position of the strikes for drawer or door locks can be located as follows. Turn the key so that the bolt is in the locked position. Put a little white paint or other coloring material on the edge of the bolt. Turn the key so that the bolt is again drawn into the lock.

Close the door or drawer, and turn the key a few times as if to lock it.

Some of the coloring material on the edge of the bolt will then be transferred to the frame, so that it will be easy to locate the strike.

Escutcheons or key plates usually are fastened over the keyhole with brass pins (Fig. 33). When thread escutcheons (Fig. 33) are to be used, the keyhole must be enlarged. They should fit very tightly, or they will come loose.

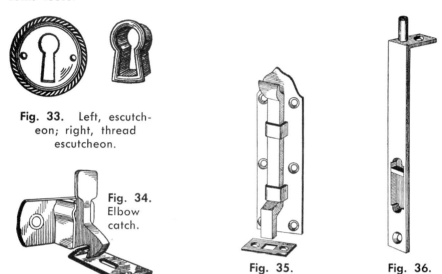

Fig. 33. Left, escutcheon; right, thread escutcheon.

Fig. 34. Elbow catch.

Fig. 35. Door bolt.

Fig. 36. Flush bolt.

246. Catches and door bolts are locking devices of a more informal nature than locks. They are used in such places as the left-hand door of double doors, tilt-top tables, or small single or double doors which need not be locked with a key. The following are the most commonly used bolts and catches in cabinetwork.

1. *Elbow catches* (Fig. 34) may be used on left-hand cupboard or bookcase doors. The catch is simply screwed to the underside of the center shelf, and the catch to the inside of the left-hand door.

2. *Door bolts* (Fig. 35) are screwed to the inside of left-hand bookcase doors near the top and bottom of the door, so that the bolt locks into the frame around the doors. Sometimes only one bolt is used on a door. Door bolts are sometimes fitted with a steel spring, which automatically keeps the bolt in the locked position. They are usually furnished with a strike plate. A hole must be chiseled or bored in the frame for the bolt.

3. *A flush bolt* (Fig. 36) is the neatest type of door bolt. It is fastened to the edge of the left-hand door and must be set flush with the wood. Flush bolts are sold in different widths according to the thickness of the wood.

The strike plate is set flush with the doorframe, and a hole is bored for the bolt.

4. *Ball catches* (Fig. 37) or friction catches consist of small brass cylinders with a steel spring bearing against a steel ball. They are used on small doors such as those on a phonograph or a radio cabinet, and are usually fitted into the upper or lower edges of the door. They are manufactured in diameters of ¼, 5⁄16, and 3⁄8 in., and all that is necessary to do to attach them is to bore a hole of the proper diameter in the edge of the door. The strike, which is beveled on one edge, is set into the frame flush with the wood. The beveled side should be placed toward the front.

5. *A table catch* (Fig. 38) is in reality a small spring lock, the bolt of which is moved in or out by means of a spring and a knob. A table catch is used for locking the top of a tilt-top table in a horizontal position. It is screwed to the underside of the table top. The strike plate is fastened to the wooden block to which the top is hinged. It is set flush with the wood and a recess chiseled for the bolt.

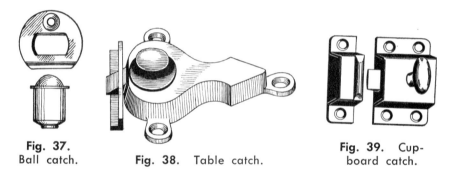

Fig. 37.
Ball catch.   **Fig. 38.** Table catch.   **Fig. 39.** Cupboard catch.

6. *A cupboard catch* (Fig. 39) is a small lock on a kitchen cabinet which is opened with a knob instead of a key. It is closed automatically by a coil spring which pushes against the bolt. A spring lock has a beveled bolt that slips easily into the strike.

Fig. 40. Cabinet door friction catch.

7. *The friction catch* with polyethylene rollers (Fig. 40) is installed particularly on flush cabinet doors. This catch has self-aligning arms and positive gripping action.

8. *A push-button catch* as shown in Figure 41 is made with a retracting bolt that automatically engages the strike attached to the cabinet frame or shelf until released by pressure on the "push button." The main advantage of this type of catch is its positive locking feature which holds the door securely in place even if it is warped. The handle of this catch can be supplied to match pulls, knobs, and hinges of the cabinet.

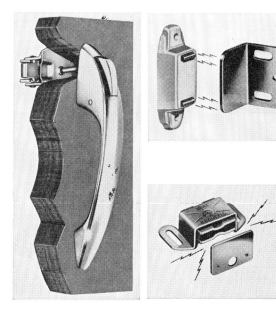

Fig. 41. Left, push-button cabinet catch; right, **Figs. 42** and **43,** magnetic catches.

Fig. 44. Colonial magnetic bar latch.

9. *Magnetic Cabinet Catches.* Starting out, more or less, as a novelty type of cabinet catch, magnetic catches have been improved in design and reduced in cost to where they are now a very practical item. The type that has a pull of 8 to 10 pounds should prove satisfactory for the average cabinet door. Figure 42 shows a magnetic catch that is attached to the door, whereas the strike is fastened to the cabinet or to the underside of a shelf. In Figure 43 the procedure is reversed; the catch is fastened to the cabinet frame or underneath the shelf, and the strike is

attached to the door. Either way assures full contact between pole pieces and strikes. The application of magnetic power to a Colonial pattern bar latch is illustrated in Figure 44.

247. Procedure for Attaching Casters, Glides, Chair Tips, Drawer Pulls, and Knobs.   1. Casters are used on heavy pieces of furniture to make them more mobile. They are generally made with a stem and a socket. The socket has a ring of teeth at its lower extremity, while its upper end is slit for a short distance and pressed to a smaller diameter. The wheels of casters are made of steel, brass, wood, fiber, rubber, or felt (Fig. 45).

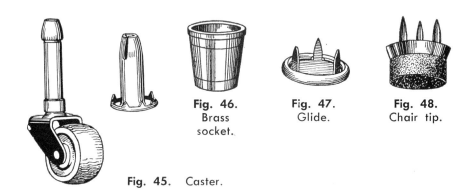

Fig. 46.
Brass
socket.

Fig. 47.
Glide.

Fig. 48.
Chair tip.

Fig. 45.   Caster.

2. To attach the caster, bore a hole in the end of the leg so that the socket fits snugly, but not tight enough to split the wood when the socket is driven in place. The ring of teeth must be driven into the end wood. The stem of the caster has a little enlargement on the upper end. A tap with a hammer will force it through the narrow end of the socket, which will again spring together and prevent the stem from slipping out.

3. Some casters are provided with a brass socket (Fig. 46) which fits over the end of the leg. Caster rings and sockets may also be bought separately and fitted over legs of furniture. They are made both square and round, and furnished in various sizes. They are decorative and prevent the wood from splitting.

4. *Glides* are hardened, polished, cup-formed pieces of steel used instead of casters (Fig. 47). They are provided with steel points and are fastened to the legs of furniture simply by driving them into the wood with a hammer.

5. *Chair tips* (Fig. 48) are similar to glides except that they are made of soft material, such as rubber, felt, or leather. They are attached to chair legs either by screws, nails, or steel points.

6. *Drawer pulls and knobs* are made in a great variety of patterns to conform to the furniture designs of the different historical periods. They

Fig. 49.
Furniture
knob.

Fig. 50.
Furniture
handle.

are fitted with machine screws about ³⁄₁₆ in. in diameter and 1 in. long which screw into holes, bored and tapped in the pull itself. These screws have a round, slotted head with a small washer soldered to it (Figs. 49 and 50).

7. *Cabinet Knobs.* Knobs are often used on small cabinet doors and drawers where pulls would seem too large. They are available in all sizes, large and small, and in designs to suit most every style preference. Concave knobs have become very popular, and are available with back plates to

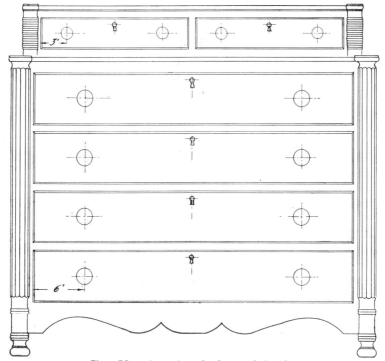

Fig. 51. Locating locks and knobs.

protect the finish of the wood from finger marks and scratches. When used as a replacement, the back plate also serves to cover up any old screw holes or marks that might otherwise mar the appearance of the installation. Sometimes knobs are placed in the center of the cabinet door for decorative purposes, as shown in Figure 52.

8. After locating their position on a drawer or door, as the case may be, bore holes of the same diameter as the screw right through the wood. Place the pull in position, insert the screws from the inside of the door or drawer, and tighten them with a screw driver.

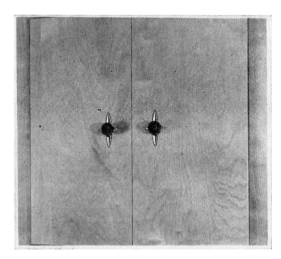

Fig. 52. Decorative door knobs.

9. No definite rules can be given for the location of pulls and knobs, except that they are always placed on the horizontal center line of drawers, and usually above the center of a cabinet door. On a chest of drawers, one is placed directly below the other; i.e., the same distance from the ends of the drawer (Fig. 51).

248. Procedure for Fastening a Table Top to a Frame.   In fastening a table top, provision should be made for the swelling or shrinkage of the wood. The following methods are in general use.

1. Holes are bored through the rails at an angle. The boring is done from the upper edge of the rail with a gimlet or twist bit, and a recess is cut on the inside of the rail with a gouge so as to make room for the head of the screw (A, Fig. 53).

2. A hole large enough for the head of the screw may also be bored part way through the rail with an auger bit, after which the remainder is bored with a gimlet or twist bit and the screw inserted (B, Fig. 53).

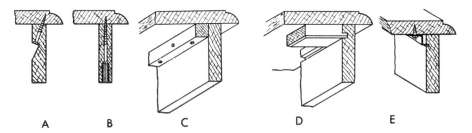

Fig. 53. Methods of fastening a table top.

3. Strips of wood, called "cleats," about ¾ to ⅞ in. square, may be screwed to both frame and top. Holes are first bored and countersunk from two adjoining sides at right angles to each other. The cleats are then screwed to the inside surface of the rails flush with or a trifle below their upper edges (C, Fig. 53).

4. The top is placed face down on the bench, the frame centered on it and then fastened to it with screws driven through the holes previously bored and countersunk. Protect the finished surface of the top by placing a newspaper, a piece of cardboard, or a couple of small boards on the bench top.

5. Another method is to cut a groove on the inside of the rails before they are glued to the legs. Wooden blocks, rabbeted on the end so that they fit

Fig. 54. Undersink pop-up refuse unit and towel dryer.

into the groove, are then screwed to the top at intervals (D, Fig. 53). This method permits of considerable movement of the top.

6. A modification of the wooden block is the table-top fastener, which is a small piece of iron bent at right angles. One end fits into a slit cut on the inside of the rails with a circular saw, and the other end is screwed to the top (E, Fig. 53).

249. Probably no other type of hardware is more popular than the so-called *storage in motion built-ins*. These built-ins are primarily designed for the comfort and convenience of the average housewife who spends a great deal of her time in the kitchen.

Figure 54 shows the pop-up refuse unit conveniently placed under the sink. The particular model shown here consists of chromium plated container with aluminum insert. The entire unit fastens to the inside of the undersink doors. Made for either right or left doors, it has a lid that pops up automatically and closes as the sink door is closed.

Shown also in this illustration and in Figure 55 is a towel dryer with three sliding bars. Notice how the door has been hung with flush door pin hinges.

In cabinets of this type some provision is made for the quick drying of wet towels. This can be done by making a series of vertical saw cuts in the door or by means of louvers. Provision must be made for air to circulate.

Pots and pans are readily stored on sliding holders as shown in Figure 56.

Fig. 55. Towel dryer.   **Fig. 56.** Sliding pan holder.

Fig. 58. Sliding flour sifter or sugar dispenser.

Fig. 57. Using swing out mixer shelf.

The ideal shelf for an electric mixer is by means of the mixer shelf shown in Figure 57. Cabinets can be so constructed to serve as storage of shelf and mixer at the same time.

Shelves of this kind can also be installed to hold typewriters, sewing machines, and portable phonographs.

For added convenience in the mixing area one often finds a sliding flour sifter or sugar dispenser (Fig. 58). These units can be fastened on the underside of the bottom shelf of a wall cabinet, or they can be mounted inside.

In kitchens where the wall cabinets form a right inside angle there is created in the corner a "dead space" area which is difficult to use for handy storage. For these areas manufacturers have developed the so-called "Lazy Susan," or full circle revolving shelves (Fig. 59). These units consist of two brackets, a post and usually three shelves. For additional storage convenience there are cup shelves, knife holders, spice shelves, utility shelves, lid holders, waxed paper and paper towel dispensers, and drawer liners for bread and pastry storage.

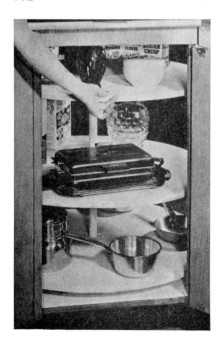

Fig. 59. Full-circle revolving shelves.

REVIEW QUESTIONS, CHAPTER 8

Possible score 55 points

Your score . . . . . .

PART I. COMPLETION QUESTIONS. Complete the following statements:

1. The length of nails is generally indicated by the word . . . .
2. Box nails are made like common nails but are . . . . than common nails.
3. In order to make them hold better, common nails are sometimes coated with . . . . or . . . .
4. Casing nails have the same wire gauge as . . . .
5. Nails sliced from a wedge-shaped iron plate are called . . . .
6. Brass, copper, and galvanized iron nails are used on work which is exposed to . . . .
7. In screw gauges, the higher the gauge number, the . . . . the screw.
8. Flathead screws are bright, round-head screws are generally . . . .
9. . . . . or . . . . rubbed on threads of a screw reduces friction.
10. To fasten wood or metal to hollow partitions and hollow tile walls, one best uses . . . .
11. Invisible hinges are named after the inventor whose name was . . . .

12. When hanging a door, the surplus length on the stiles, called .... is first cut off.
13. The shallow opening cut in the stile to hold a hinge is called ....
14. To make heavy pieces of furniture more mobile, ... are used in the legs.
15. To make dead space in kitchen corners useful, manufacturers have developed the so-called ....
16. Kitchen cabinet doors are generally hung with a surface type or .... hinge.
17. Cabinet catches are generally available in two major types, the push-button type and the .... type.
18. Generally, hinges consist of two leaves and one ....
19. To provide protection to floors and give easy sliding action, ... are used on chair and table legs.
20. When fastening hardwood with screws, one drills a shank hole and a smaller ....

PART II. TRUE-FALSE QUESTIONS. Indicate, by encircling T or F, whether the following statements are true or false.

21. A 2-penny nail is one inch long.	T	F
22. A 3-penny nail is three inches long.	T	F
23. Box nails are thicker than common nails.	T	F
24. Cut nails are primarily used in laying wood floors.	T	F
25. When pulling nails, it is good practice to place a piece of wood under the hammer head.	T	F
26. The gauge number of a flat-head screw indicates the length of the screw.	T	F
27. Phillips' head screws can be driven with an ordinary screw driver.	T	F
28. Butt hinges have either riveted or loose pins.	T	F
29. Flush door pin hinges are particularly popular in modern kitchen construction.	T	F
30. The only way to fasten table tops is by means of iron table-top fasteners.	T	F
31. A popular type of hardware is the so-called "storage in motion built-ins."	T	F
32. The selection of proper hardware is an important part of a construction project.	T	F
33. For kitchen and bathroom use, chromium plated hardware is the least practical and most difficult to take care of.	T	F
34. When hanging kitchen doors with semiconcealed hinges, it is always necessary to cut rabbets in the door edges.	T	F
35. A "push-button" cabinet catch is a combination of door handle and catch.	T	F
36. On most homes, cylindrical type locks have largely replaced conventional mortise locks.	T	F
37. Regular door hinges usually consist of two leaves, a pin and a plug.	T	F
38. Common nails range in length from 1 to 6 inches.	T	F
39. The gauge numbers of flat-head wood screws range from 2 to 34.	T	F
40. Furniture glides are cup-shaped pieces of steel fastened to the legs of furniture.	T	F

PART III. MULTIPLE-CHOICE QUESTIONS. Select, by encircling the correct letter, the answer which completes each statement:

41. The length of a 5-penny nail is:
    A. 1¼ in.
    B. 2 in.
    C. 1¾ in.
    D. 3 in.

42. All but one of the following screws can be driven with a common screw driver:
    A. Round-head screw
    B. Phillips' head screw
    C. Oval-head screw
    D. Flat-head screw

43. Nails shorter than one inch are referred to as:
    A. Brads
    B. Tacks
    C. Casing nails
    D. Escutcheon pins

44. When fastening a hinge leaf to a door, it is first necessary to cut a:
    A. Rabbet
    B. Groove
    C. Mortise
    D. Gain

45. In modern home construction, the locking device in doors is by means of a:
    A. Rim lock
    B. Cylindrical lock
    C. Mortise lock
    D. Cylinder rim lock

PART IV. MATCHING QUESTIONS. Match the terms to the left with the descriptions to the right by placing the correct letter in the parentheses:

46. ( ) Penny system
47. ( ) Cut nails
48. ( ) Expansion bolts
49. ( ) Pin
50. ( ) Flush door pin hinges
51. ( ) Strike
52. ( ) Lazy Susan
53. ( ) Cylindrical locks
54. ( ) Leaf
55. ( ) Pre-packaging

A. Used as fasteners in brick, stone, and concrete.
B. Primarily used on kitchen cabinet doors.
C. One of the parts of a door hinge.
D. The method used to designate the length of nails.
E. Now more popular than mortise locks.
F. The modern method of selling many hardware items.
G. Nails primarily used for flooring purposes.
H. Consists of two brackets, a post and shelves.
I. That part of a hinge that holds the leaves together.
J. A metal plate usually furnished with door locks.
K. One of the parts of a caster.

9

Wood Turning

The wood-turning lathe is a link between machine and hand tools, combining the art and skill of handwork with the speed and power of the machine. Wood turning as a trade, however, has practically disappeared, because all kinds of turned work can be produced on the modern turning machine much more rapidly and accurately than is possible with the human hands.

252. History. The art of wood turning is so old that detailed knowledge of its beginnings has been lost in antiquity. The most primitive lathe, called the bow lathe, is said to have been invented in Egypt and used there and in other Eastern lands long before the Christian era.

The bow lathe is rotated by the string of a bow wrapped around the work being turned (Fig. 1). The bow is held in one hand and the tool in the other. Strangely enough this primitive lathe is still used in parts of Asia and Africa.

The next step in the development was the pole lathe in which a string wrapped around the work being turned was still used. One end of this string was tied to a flexible pole, bolted to the ceiling, and the other to a treadle (Fig. 2). When the treadle was pressed down to the floor, the pole would bend and the work revolve toward the turner. When the treadle was released, the pole would straighten out and rotate the work backwards. When using this lathe or the bow lathe, the wood turner was able to cut only while the work revolved toward him, which was only half the time.

Later on, the treadle was connected by a crankshaft to a large wheel,

Fig. 1. Bow lathe invented in Egypt about 740 B.C.

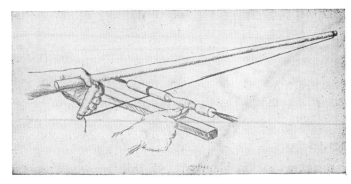

Fig. 2. Pole lathe. String tied to pole and to treadle.

which in turn was connected by a rope to a smaller wheel which rotated the lathe spindle. The same mechanical movement is used on a spinning wheel and a sewing machine, producing a continuous rotary movement (Fig. 3). This type of lathe was used until about fifty years ago, when the electric motor came into general use.

In some localities, however, where labor was cheap, lathes were some-

Fig. 3. Treadle connected by crankshaft to large wheel which is connected to small wheel with rope.

times rotated by a helper turning the "great wheel." This wheel was 6 ft. in diameter, bolted to the floor and connected by a belt to a cone pulley on the lathe (Fig. 4). These old lathes were made entirely of wood, except for the metal spindles which held the work being turned.

Fig. 4. Great wheel lathe.

Fig. 5. Modern motor-head wood-turning lathe.

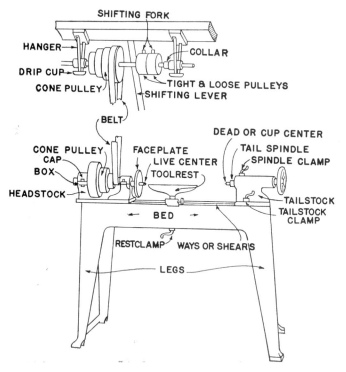

Fig. 6. Wood-turning lathe with counter-shaft.

During the sixteenth and seventeenth centuries, wood turning was practiced as a hobby by kings, queens, princes, and nobles of high rank. The costly inlaid lathes used by them, as well as examples of their work, can be found in many European museums.

Although not practiced by kings and princesses, wood turning today continues to be one of the most interesting activities in the school laboratory and the home workshop. When executed carefully and kept within good taste, wood turning adds a pleasing touch to a piece of furniture (Fig. 5, p. 486).

253. The Wood-Turning Lathe. The modern lathe is made entirely of iron and steel. Its principal parts are: the bed, the headstock, the tailstock, and the tool post.

The bed, which is supported on cast-iron legs, is a substantial casting resembling two parallel I beams. The bed of smaller lathes is fastened directly to a bench, bringing it to a height of 36 in. above the floor. The upper part of the bed is called the "ways" or "shears" and has a flat, smooth surface.

The headstock is bolted to the left end of the bed and contains the driving mechanism of the lathe. On direct-motor-driven or motor-head lathes, a hollow shaft is the rotor of the motor (Fig. 5). On older types this shaft is driven by a step-cone pulley keyed to it. The cone pulley in turn is belt driven either from a countershaft (Fig. 6) or from a motor placed below the lathe (Fig. 7).

The hollow spindle in the headstock is threaded on both ends. The end to the right or front has a right thread and is used for faceplates and screw chucks. The end to the left or rear has a left thread to which an aluminum

Fig. 7. Underbelted speed lathe.

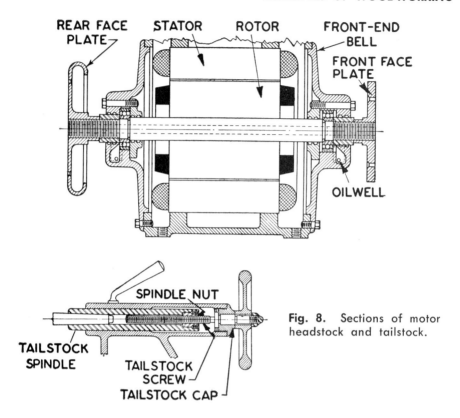

REAR FACE PLATE STATOR ROTOR FRONT-END BELL FRONT FACE PLATE OILWELL

SPINDLE NUT

TAILSTOCK SPINDLE TAILSTOCK SCREW TAILSTOCK CAP

Fig. 8. Sections of motor headstock and tailstock.

faceplate with a smooth rounded edge is fastened (Fig. 8). This faceplate may be used as a regular faceplate for turning work which is too large to fit over the ways, but it is used more for stopping the lathe with the hand after the power has been shut off.

The live center (A, Fig. 9) is tapered to fit into the front end of the hollow shaft or spindle. Twice the distance from the point of the center to the ways is called the "swing of the lathe" and is the greatest diameter to which stock can be turned.

The tailstock consists of a casting, which can be clamped to the lathe bed by means of a lever at any point between the headstock and the end of the bed. It contains the dead center, which, like the live center, fits into a hollow spindle. This spindle can be moved in a horizontal direction by means of a screw, which is turned by the handwheel at the right. When it is desired to remove the dead center, the spindle is moved into the tailstock until the end of the dead center comes in contact with the internal screw and can go no farther. Continued turning of the handwheel moves the spindle farther to the right, and the dead center is pushed out. The spindle may be clamped in any desired position by means of a lever (Fig. 8).

The tool post, like the tailstock, may be clamped at any point on the lathe bed. It consists of a socket which holds the T rest. The turning tools are held directly on the T rest, which can be moved up or down in the socket and fastened by means of a lever at any point.

A tool rest is a T-shaped casting with a short, round shaft. They are made in various lengths, some having two shafts and requiring two tool posts.

254. Lathe-Holding Tools. Several tools or devices for holding stock while it is being turned are used with every lathe. The most common of these are: lathe centers, faceplates, screw chucks, drill pads, and steady rests.

Lathe centers hold the work between the headstock and the tailstock. This is called spindle turning, because the centers are held in the spindles. The center in the headstock spindle is called the "live" center, because it rotates the stock. It has a central point and two or four steel spurs or prongs, which are driven into one end of the stock (A, Fig. 9).

The other end is supported on the dead center which fits into the tailstock spindle and does not revolve. There are two types of dead centers, the cone center and the cup center (B and C, Fig. 9). The cone center is tapered to a point; the cup center has a thin, circular steel edge around a thinner central point, and is less likely to split thin stock. As the dead centers do not revolve, the end of the stock which turns on them must be oiled, soaped, or waxed to prevent burning through friction. All lathe centers are tapered to fit corresponding tapers in the two hollow spindles.

Faceplates are cast-steel disks with a threaded hub which screws onto the headstock or "live" spindle. They are made in several diameters according to the size of the lathe and the diameter and weight of the stock they have to support. Several holes are bored and countersunk in them for flat-

A

Fig. 9. Lathe centers. A, Live center; B, cup center; C, cone center.

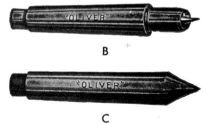

B

C

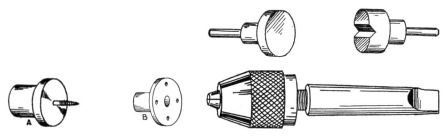

Fig. 10. A, Screw chuck;   **Fig. 11.** Drill chuck and drill pads.
          B, faceplate.

head screws (B, Fig. 10). Circular disks, bowls, pulleys, etc., are fastened to faceplates for turning. Faceplate work is supported on the headstock only.

Screw chucks are small faceplates with a single screw in the center (A, Fig. 10). They are used for holding smaller work such as napkin rings, boxes, pin trays, bases for candlesticks, etc.

Drill chucks are held on a tapered center which fits into either the headstock or tailstock spindle. They have three jaws and a sleeve and can be used only for straight-shank machine drills (Fig. 11).

Drill pads are used for supporting or centering turned work while boring it in the lathe (Fig. 11). Like drill chucks, drill pads are also held on a tapered center and may be used in either spindle. The drill chuck, drill pad, and work to be bored are brought close together. The lathe is then started and the tailstock spindle is gradually advanced until the drill enters the wood to the required depth.

Steady rests are devices for supporting thin stock between centers and preventing it from vibrating. They are made in different forms, some sup-

Fig. 12. Steady rest.

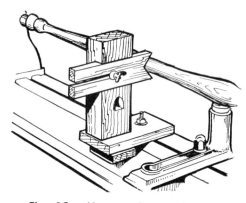

Fig. 13. Homemade steady rest.

Fig. 14. Stand-
ard set of
wood-turning
chisels. Square-
nose chisel is
missing.

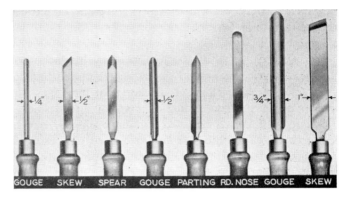

porting the wood at two points and others at three points (Fig. 12). Steady rests may also be made entirely of wood as shown in Figure 13.

255. Wood-Turning Tools. The common wood-turning tools are gouges, chisels, dividers, and calipers. Gouges and chisels are longer and thicker than similar bench tools. They are made in different widths and have long, sturdy handles. They have no shoulder, because they are not driven into the wood like hand chisels (Figs. 14 and 15).

Gouges are beveled on the outside or convex side, and the length of the bevel is about twice the thickness of the tool. The cutting end of wood-turning gouges is also rounded, because square corners would catch in the wood.

Skew chisels are beveled on one or both sides, and are ground to an angle of 60 deg. with one edge of the chisels. Skew chisels, beveled on both sides, are used for cutting and smoothing. Skew chisels, ground on only one side, are scraping tools. They are either right or left, depending upon which side the bevel is ground.

Diamond or spear-point chisels also are beveled on only one side, but

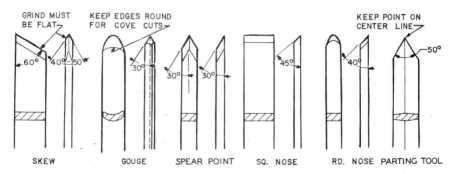

Fig. 15. Grinding angles for wood-turning tools.

they have two bevels which meet in a point in the center. One of these chisels, therefore, may be said to combine the right and left skew chisels in one.

Parting or cut-off tools also have two bevels which meet in a central point, but these bevels are ground on the edges of the tool instead of the sides. The center of these chisels is thicker than the edges, so that they will not bind or overheat when cutting off parts of turned stock.

Square-nose chisels are like ordinary chisels, but have a longer and heavier blade. They are scraping tools used only on straight surfaces.

Round-nose chisels also are scraping tools, with only one bevel. They are like ordinary chisels except that their cutting edge is round. They are used on concave surfaces.

Beading tools are scraping tools having only one bevel. This bevel is ground to concave shapes, so that beads of various sizes may be made.

Dividers are used to step off measurements and mark circles on faceplate work (Fig. 16-A). Spring dividers have two sharp-pointed legs. They can be set to distance by a screw and nut working against a steel spring.

Inside and outside calipers are constructed like the dividers, but are used for measuring inside and outside diameters of turned work (Fig. 16, B and C).

The sharpening of turning tools is fully explained in Chapter 4, Articles 134 to 140 inclusive.

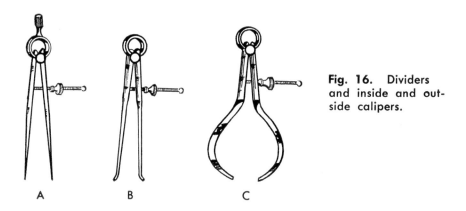

Fig. 16. Dividers and inside and outside calipers.

A   B   C

256. Safety Rules. Although the lathe is not a dangerous machine to operate, accidents may happen either through carelessness or ignorance. To guard against such accidents, the following safety rules are given:

1. Fasten the stock securely between centers and to faceplates, because stock thrown from a lathe strikes with tremendous force.

2. Examine the stock for cracks and flaws, and test all glue joints before fastening stock in the lathe. Cracked or poorly glued stock may come apart when run at high speed.

3. Tighten the clamps on the tool post and tailstock, and always revolve the stock by hand to see that it has enough clearance before turning on the power.

4. Do not run the lathe at too high speed, especially before the stock is rounded off, as it may cause excessive vibration and be thrown from the lathe. After rounding, stock less than 3 in. in diameter may be run at the highest speed. Stock over 6 in. in diameter should be run at the slowest speed, and stock from 3 to 6 in. at medium speeds.

5. Clamp the tool rest as close as possible to the work, and use only sharp tools. Dull tools are always dangerous.

6. Wear no loose or ragged clothes, roll up your sleeves and tuck in your necktie, or better remove it. Loose clothing can very easily be caught by the revolving stock and cause a serious accident.

7. Move the tool post out of the way when sanding, so that your fingers will not be caught between it and the stock.

8. Do not forget to oil the end running on the dead center, because friction will cause the wood to burn, and then the exact center will be lost.

9. Do not screw a faceplate part way onto the spindle and then turn on the power, because that will cause it to jam up against the shoulder of the spindle and make it very difficult to remove.

10. Do not allow anybody to stand near the lathe while you are turning as your attention may be distracted.

11. Before placing a faceplate on the threaded shaft, place a leather or thin cardboard washer against the shaft collar. This washer makes the removal of the faceplate from the shaft much easier.

257. Cutting Versus Scraping Method of Wood Turning. The cutting method is the oldest, fastest, and cleanest method of turning, but it is rather difficult to learn, and requires much practice and patience. All flat and rounded surfaces are smoothed with the skew chisel and all hollows are cut with the gouge. In this way smooth surfaces are produced which require little sanding.

The scraping method is the newer and more accurate method of turning, used principally in the patternmaking trade. All flat and convex surfaces are produced with the right and left skews, the square-nose and the spear-point chisel, and all hollows with the round-nose chisel. This method is learned quickly, but it is not as fast, nor are the surfaces as smooth as those produced by the cutting method. More sanding, therefore, is necessary.

The professional wood turner uses the cutting method only. For centuries the cutting method has been handed down from one generation of wood turners to the next. It, therefore, is so well established that many teachers will not even consider any other method, although they will allow scraping tools to be used on faceplate work because these tools are safer and more appropriate for this type of work.

The patternmaker uses the scraping method exclusively, because his work must of necessity be very exact. Moreover, as turning is only a part of his trade, he need not spend so much time on learning it.

As stated previously, turned furniture parts now are produced almost entirely on automatic turning machines. Wood turning as a trade, therefore, may be said to be almost extinct.

Since this trade practically has disappeared, it does not seem logical to the author to cling any longer to the old, outmoded traditions of wood turning, but rather to employ the easier learned scraping method, which, after all, is the only method of turning used in industry today. Moreover, wood turning is only an aid to cabinetmaking or a hobby for the amateur and, therefore, only of minor importance.

To the opponents of the scraping method, the following questions are addressed:

1. If it is right to use scraping tools for faceplate work, why is it wrong to use them for spindle turning?

2. If the scraping method is all right for the patternmaker, why isn't it all right for the cabinetmaker?

3. Since the student is not going to be a wood turner, why not let him use the easier and more quickly learned scraping method?

4. If good work can be produced with less spoilage and in a shorter learning time, why object to the scraping method?

In summarizing let us say that both methods have their advantages. Both have their place in the commercial, school, and home workshop. Some woodworkers will scrape because they know of no other method. Others will use the cutting method if only for the personal satisfaction they derive from it. The choice is pretty much up to the individual.

Spindle Turning

Spindle turning includes all turning operations on stock that is held between the live and dead centers. These are: straight and taper turning, shoulder cuts, hollows, rounds, beads, and split turning.

258. Procedure for Centering and Clamping Stock in the Lathe. 1. Saw the stock to dimensions, having the ends square to the sides.

2. On square or rectangular stock, draw diagonals on both ends. The center of the piece lies in the point of intersection.

On irregularly shaped stock, the center may be found as follows: Set a pair of dividers to approximately half the thickness of the piece. Hold one

Fig. 17. Finding centers of square and irregular-shaped stock.

 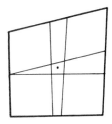

of the legs of the divider against one of the edges, and scratch a line parallel to it. Repeat on the other three edges. The center is now readily determined (Fig. 17).

3. If the lumber is hard, it is well to make a saw cut on the two diagonals on one end (Fig. 18), and to bore a small hole in the center of both this and the other end (Fig. 19), so that the live and dead centers may enter the wood more readily.

4. Remove the live center from the headstock of the lathe by pushing it out with an iron rod, which can be inserted from the opposite end of the headstock. This rod is part of the regular equipment of the lathe, and is usually found hanging on a lug on one of the legs.

Fig. 18. Sawing on diagonals.   **Fig. 19.** Boring for centers.

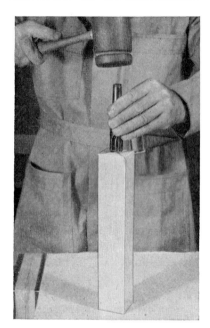

Fig. 20. Driving live center into end of stock.

5. Drive the live center into that end of the wood on which the diagonals were sawed, so that the prongs enter a saw cut. *Use a mallet* when driving on the center, because a steel hammer will upset (widen) the end of it so that it will not fit into the tapered spindle (Fig. 20). Do not drive the wood onto the live center while it is in the lathe, as the blows of the hammer will injure the bearings.

6. Drip machine oil on the other end of the wood, holding it in a vertical position, and allowing the oil to soak in. Soap or wax may also be used and will not discolor the wood.

7. Place the live center in the headstock spindle without removing the wood from it, and then slide the tailstock along the bed until its dead center enters the hole bored for it in the wood.

8. Clamp the tailstock in this position and turn the handwheel until the dead center presses against the wood. Then clamp the spindle to prevent it from moving backward. The cone center should not enter more than $\frac{3}{16}$ in. into the endwood otherwise it will cause excessive friction and burn the wood.

9. Adjust the tool rest so that it is about $\frac{1}{8}$ in. away from the edge that is nearest to it when the wood is revolved. Clamp it firmly to the lathe bed. Also adjust it to the correct height. This varies somewhat with the height of the person, but is *never below the lathe centers*. It is generally from $\frac{1}{8}$ to $\frac{1}{4}$ in. above the centers.

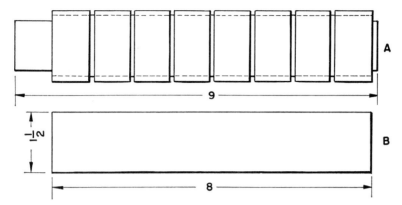

Fig. 21. Method of turning plain cylinder. A. Rough cylinder. B. Finished cylinder.

10. Revolve the wood by hand to make sure that it has sufficient clearance. See that all the clamps are tight and that no tools are in the way.

259. Procedure for Turning a Plain Cylinder (Fig. 21). 1. Start the lathe so that the stock does not revolve too fast causing the lathe to vibrate, which it is very likely to do before the stock has been rounded off. Excessive speed may even cause it to fly out of the lathe and injure someone.

2. Use the gouge for the first cut. Grasp the handle near the end with the right hand, and hold the blade firmly against the T rest with the left hand, so that the palm of the hand near the wrist and the little finger are in contact with the T rest (Fig. 22). Hold the handle well down and roll the gouge a little toward the right. This will throw the shavings away from you. Some turners hold the gouge in the manner illustrated in Figure 36. It is claimed that this method is faster and allows greater freedom of movement.

Fig. 22. Cutting with gouge.

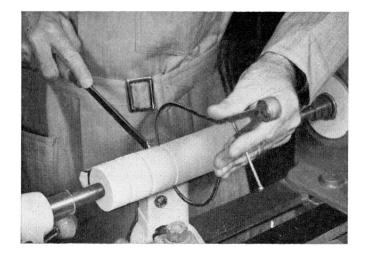

Fig. 23. Cutting to size with parting tool.

3. Start cutting a couple of inches from the dead center, moving the gouge away from you toward the dead center. Then start the next cut a couple of inches farther to the left, and so on until only an inch or so is left. Roll the gouge toward you, and move it toward the live center to round off the last part of the stock. Do not begin the cuts at the ends of the stock, because the gouge may catch in the wood and cause it to be thrown from the lathe. When too long a cut is taken while rounding off the corners, large chips are likely to fly off and injure the operator.

4. Move the gouge freely from one end of the piece to another until it is perfectly cylindrical and a little larger in size than actually needed.

5. Stop the lathe and move the T rest closer to the wood being turned.

Fig. 24. Smoothing with square-nose chisel.

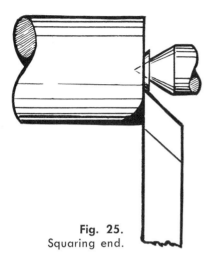

Fig. 25.
Squaring end.

Fig. 26. Testing for
squareness.

6. Set the outside calipers to about ⅟₃₂ in. more than the finished diameter of the piece. Grasp the parting tool in the right hand and the calipers in the left (Fig. 23). Cut into the wood with the parting tool while holding the calipers in the groove being cut until they slip over the cylinder. Make cuts about 1 in. apart throughout the full length of the cylinder with the parting tool (Fig. 23).

7. *Using the scraping method,* smooth the cylinder with a square-nose chisel as shown in Figure 24. Run the lathe at high speed, and hold the chisel flat on the tool rest with the beveled side down. Cut down to the bottom of the grooves made with the parting tool until the cylinder is smooth and of the same diameter throughout.

8. Square the end that runs on the dead center, with the parting tool or with the point or toe of a skew chisel held flat on the tool rest (Fig. 25). Test for squareness by placing the edge of the tool or a try square across the end (Fig. 26).

9. Finally measure the length of the cylinder from the squared end and cut down at this point with the parting tool until only ¼ in. of stock remains. This may then be cut through with the toe of the skew chisel. Hold the chisel in the right hand and catch the cylinder with the left when the wood separates (Fig. 27).

10. *Using the cutting method,* smooth the cylinder with a ¾-in. skew chisel, holding it at an angle of 60 deg. to the surface and cutting with the

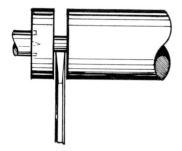

Fig. 27. Cutting to length.

Fig. 28. Smoothing a cylinder.

middle of the edge (Fig. 28). Move the chisel either to the left or the right, but never start a cut at the end.

11. The end of the stock running on the dead center is squared with the point of the skew chisel when its edge is held on the tool rest. Hold the handle of the chisel toward the right so that the bevel will be parallel to the endwood. Raising the handle forces the point or toe of the chisel into the stock (Figs. 29 and 30).

12. The stock is cut to length by first making a perpendicular cut with the toe of the skew chisel. A slanting cut is then made on the waste side of the stock meeting the perpendicular or square cut (Fig. 30). Slanting cuts may be made either with the toe or heel of the skew chisel. Continue in this way, alternating slanting and perpendicular cuts until only ¼ in. of stock remains. Finish the cut as explained in step 9.

260. Procedure for Making Shoulder Cuts. 1. Turn a plain cylinder as described in the preceding article to make the exercise shown in Figure 31.

2. Place a rule on the T rest, and lay off the dimensions from the drawing without moving the rule. Then hold a pencil point against one mark

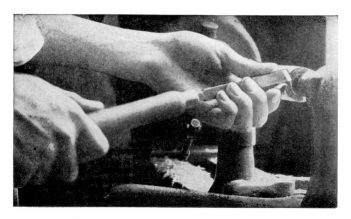

Fig. 29. Squaring end with skew chisel.

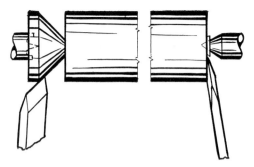

Fig. 30. Squaring one end of stock and cutting other to length.

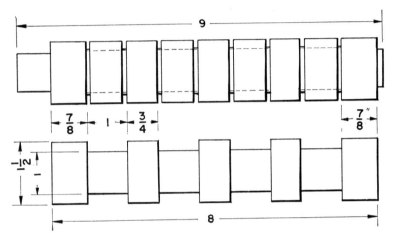

Fig. 31. Steps in making shoulder cuts.

Fig. 32. Laying out dimensions.

after the other, steady it on the T rest, and revolve the cylinder at slow speed, so that a line is marked all around its circumference (Fig. 32).

3. *Using the scraping method,* set the calipers to 1½₂ in., and cut down to this diameter with the parting tool on each side of the ¾-in. and ⅞-in. spaces (Fig. 23).

4. Run the lathe at high speed and, using a sharp ¾-in. chisel, cut the 1-in. spaces down to the bottom of the cuts made by the parting tool.

5. Finish the ends of the shoulders as shown in Figure 25, and touch up the cuts just made, taking very fine shavings.

6. *Using the cutting method,* make the shoulder cuts as explained in Article 259, step 11, and as shown in Figure 30.

7. Remove the waste stock between the shoulders with a ¼-in. gouge (Fig. 33), and smooth with a ½-in. skew chisel.

8. Finish the ends and cut to length as described in steps 10 and 11, Article 259.

Fig. 33. Cutting between shoulders with a gouge.

261. Procedure for Making Taper Cuts. 1. Consult the drawing (Fig. 34) and turn a plain cylinder large enough for this exercise.

2. Lay it out as described in the previous article, step 2, and mark lines all around it as in Figure 32.

3. *Using the scraping method,* cut down with the parting tool as shown in the drawing, and then turn the ends to finished dimensions with a square-nose chisel.

4. Rough out the tapered parts with a gouge, and smooth with a right

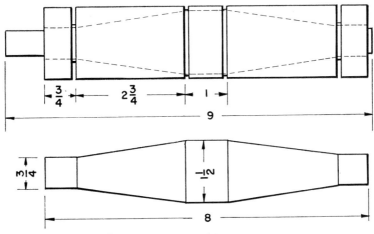

Fig. 34. Steps in making taper cuts.

and left skew chisel or with a square-nose chisel. Test the flatness of the taper cuts with a try square. There must be no hollows or bumps.

5. Square the ends, and cut to length as explained in Article 259.

6. *Using the cutting method,* turn both end and taper sections to a little more than finished dimensions with a gouge. Then smooth with a skew chisel as shown in Figure 28.

7. Square the ends and cut to length as explained in Article 259.

262. Procedure for Making Concave Cuts. 1. Consult the drawing in Figure 35, and turn a cylinder of the proper size for this exercise.

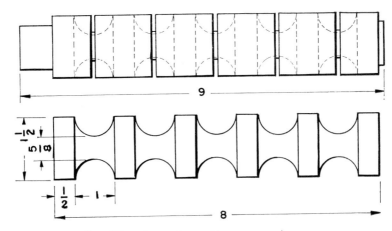

Fig. 35. Steps in making concave cuts.

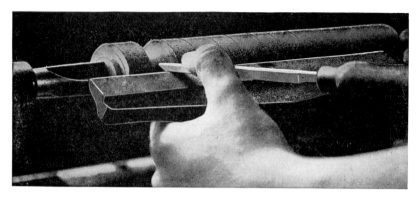

Fig. 36.   Making concave cuts with a round-nose chisel.

2. Lay out the cylinder according to Figure 35, and mark it as in Figure 32.

3. *Using the scraping method,* cut down with the parting tool in the center of the 1-in. spaces. Set the caliper to $^{11}/_{16}$ in., and hold them in the left hand while cutting with the parting tool held in the right hand as shown in Figure 23.

4. Use a ½-in. round-nose chisel for making the concave cuts. Hold it level and perfectly flat on the tool rest (Fig. 36), and begin the cuts a little inside the lines marked. Move the chisel from side to side and gradually work down to the bottom of the cuts made with the parting tool. The finished cuts must be semicircular in shape. Test them with a template made of cardboard or sheet metal.

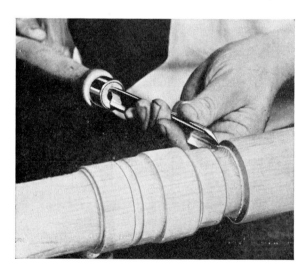

Fig. 37.   Starting a concave cut.

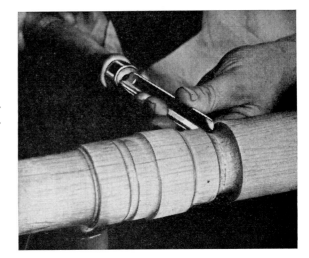

Fig. 38. Making con-
cave cut.

5. Cut the stock to length and square the ends as explained in Article 259.

6. *Using the cutting method,* lay out and mark the cylinder as before. Then make the concave cuts with a ¼-in. gouge. Hold the gouge on its side at the beginning of the cut (Fig. 37), and start cutting with the center of the edge, gradually rolling the gouge over on its back as the cut progresses (Fig. 38).

7. Cut from each side toward the center. In this way the cuts will be smooth, but do not attempt to cut past the center. Cut only a little at a time until the correct depth and curvature have been obtained. Test with calipers and templates.

8. Cut to length and square the ends as explained in Article 259.

263. Procedure for Making Convex Cuts. 1. Turn a plain cylinder 9 in. long and 1\%6 in. in diameter.

2. Lay it out and mark it according to the drawing in A, Figure 39.

3. *Using the scraping method,* make shallow V cuts with the spear-point chisel on all the lines marked.

4. Then round off the corners with the spear-point or right and left skew chisels.

5. Cylinder *B* in Figure 39 is first cut down with the parting tool, after which the square corners are rounded off as in step 4.

6. Cut both cylinders to length, and square their ends as explained in Article 259.

7. Beads, from ⅛ to ⅝ in., may also be made with special scraping tools called "beading tools." They are ground to the correct curve and are

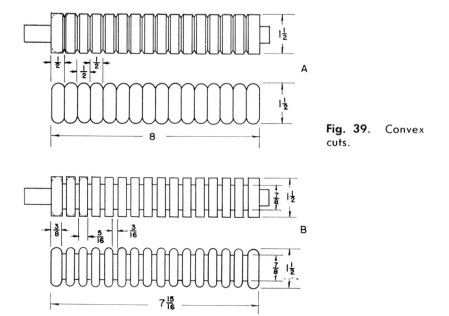

Fig. 39. Convex cuts.

held level and flat on the tool rest like roundnose or any other scraping chisel.

8. *Using the cutting method,* make the V cuts on cylinder *A* with the toe or heel of the skew chisel as shown in the left view in Figure 40.

9. Round the corners with the heel of a skew chisel, starting the cut near the center of the bead and rolling the chisel to right and left (Fig. 41).

10. Cut the openings between the beads on cylinder *B* with the parting tool, and then round them as explained above.

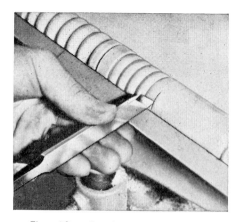

Fig. 40. Starting convex cuts.

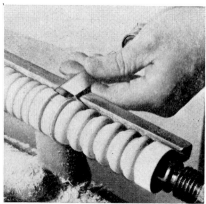

Fig. 41. Turning beads.

11. Cut both cylinders to length and square their ends as explained in Article 259.

264. Procedure for Turning Legs With Square Parts. Turned legs and stretchers for chairs, tables, or stools often have square or rectangular sections, which are mortised to join the tenons on rails and stretchers. Beginners usually have difficulty in turning such legs without chipping off the corners of the square parts.

1. Plane the stock to finished dimensions and cut the legs to exact length, because the marks of the lathe centers will not show, as one end of the legs will stand on the floor and the other will be covered by a table top or upholstery.

2. The legs should be planed to finish dimensions before turning, because it is very difficult to plane the small squared sections and get them all alike after the legs have been turned.

3. Place the legs side by side as in Figure 42, lay out the rectangular parts, and square lines across and around each leg at these points.

4. Center each leg very carefully in the lathe, and check by making a light cut, with a gouge or parting tool, on the turned part at each end of the leg. If one or two corners are not touched by the tool it means that the leg is not centered correctly. Make the necessary adjustments until the tool cuts the same amount on all four corners, as the square parts otherwise will not be centered with the turned parts.

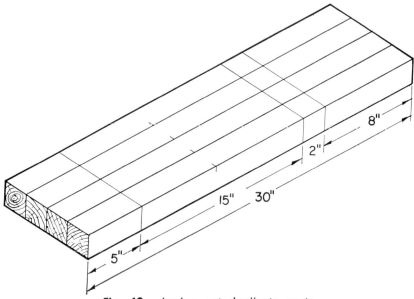

Fig. 42. Laying out duplicate parts.

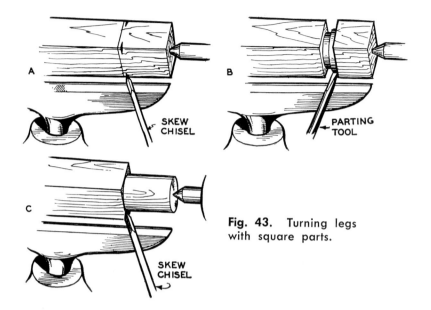

Fig. 43. Turning legs with square parts.

5. *Using the scraping method,* make a cut with a sharp parting tool just outside the square part. As an added precaution, the corners may first be nicked with the toe of the skew chisel (Fig. 43) or given a small saw cut with a backsaw. Make two or three more cuts with the parting tool as in *B* so that there will be room for rounding the parts to be turned with a gouge.

6. Leave a narrow flat piece on each side of the leg, because this will be removed when the leg is smoothed with a square-nose chisel (Art. 259). In this way the parts to be turned will be rounded to full size.

7. The corners of the rectangular parts are now rounded. It is best to measure the distance of the rounding — usually from ¼ to ⅜ in. — and square lines all around the leg at these points. Use a right and left skew chisel, hold it flat on the tool rest, and move the handle back and forth.

8. Then lay out the parts to be turned, and follow the directions given in the preceding articles.

9. *Using the cutting method,* nick the legs with the skew chisel as in *A,* Figure 43, round the parts to be turned with a gouge, and square the ends of the square parts with the skew chisel as in *C.* The square corners are rounded with a small gouge or skew chisel as in Figure 41.

265. Procedure for Turning Duplicate Parts. This is one of the most difficult things for the beginner to do, usually because he does not go about it in a logical and systematic manner.

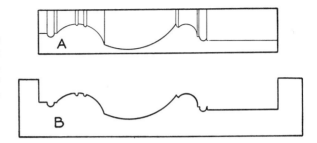

Fig. 44. (A) Full-size layout and measuring board; (B) template, which may be cut into convenient lengths.

1. The first thing to do is to make a full-size measuring stick by laying out the most important lengthwise dimensions on a thin piece of wood (A, Fig. 44). The edge of this stick corresponds to the center line of the turning. Mark also the most important diameters on the stick.

2. Cut all pieces to thickness, width, and length at the same time, center them carefully, and round them off to a little more than the largest diameter.

3. Place the measuring stick on the stock in the lathe, lay out the measurements, and mark lines all around at these points (Fig. 45).

4. Set the calipers to the largest diameter needed, plus ⅟₁₆ in., and cut to size with a parting tool. Then cut to the next largest diameter, and so on. Sometimes different parts of the turning have the same diameter. When that is the case, it is logical to cut them at the same time.

5. Then turn the "sized" parts of the cylinder to shape. To obtain the greatest accuracy, make a template of cardboard or sheet metal to fit over the turned parts (B, Fig. 44). It is generally easier to use a template that is cut into several smaller parts.

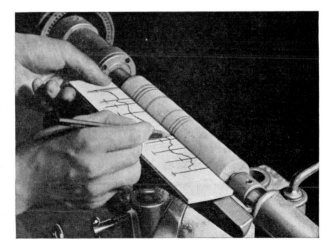

Fig. 45. Transferring dimensions from measuring board to cylinder.

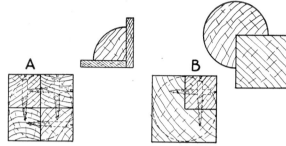

Fig. 47. Split turnings. (A) Quarters; (B) three quarters.

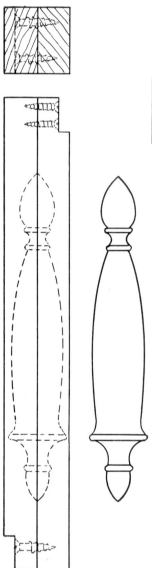

Fig. 46. Split turning.

266. Procedure for Doing Split Turning. Split turnings or semicircular turned pieces are used to decorate flat surfaces, such as the legs or panels of a cabinet. This method of decoration, which originated during the Jacobean period (1603–1688), is used extensively on modern reproductions, often in combination with moldings (Fig. 46).

1. Split work is turned between centers like any other piece of spindle turning. The stock is prepared and held together in the following way:

2. Cut 2 pieces of lumber about 4 in. longer than the finished dimensions of the split turning. Their width should be about ¼ in. more than the greatest width shown in the drawing, and their thickness should be equal to a little more than half their width.

3. Plane the faces of these two pieces, so that they will make a perfect joint when placed together.

4. They are fastened together in several ways. One of the safest is to glue them with a piece of paper in the joint. For extra security, insert a screw in each end as shown in Figure 46.

5. The stock is now mounted in the lathe, and turned as if it were a solid piece. It follows that the design is laid out in the center of the piece since there are 2 in. to spare on each end.

6. Cut the two ends away with a backsaw, and not with the parting tool. Sand the ends of the turned pieces smooth by hand.

7. The turned pieces may be separated by inserting the sharp blade of a ¾-in. paring chisel in the joint at one end. A light tap will usually cause the paper to split. Scrape and sand away the remaining paper and glue.

8. Quarter and three-quarter columns are sometimes used on chests of drawers, mirror frames, and other pieces of furniture. Quarter columns are first glued up in two halves as explained in previous steps. When dry, this piece is then cut in halves at right angles to the first cut, after which the pieces are planed and glued again as in A, Figure 47. Square the glued-up stock to dimensions and turn as a solid piece.

9. The three-quarter section is made by cutting a rabbet as shown in B. Another piece is cut to fit this rabbet and is glued to it with a piece of paper in the joint.

Faceplate Work

In faceplate work the stock is fastened to a faceplate or screw chuck, which is screwed to the headstock spindle and supported entirely on that.

267. Procedure for Fastening Stock to a Faceplate or Screw Chuck. As in spindle turning, it is of the greatest importance to mount stock in the lathe so that it can be operated with safety.

1. Examine stock carefully for cracks and strength of glued joints. Then, with a pair of dividers, mark a circle a little larger in diameter than the finished dimension is to be, and saw it on a band saw or with a turning saw.

2. The faceplate can be accurately centered by marking a circle on the stock, equal to its diameter, using the same center as before. If the wood is hard, holes should be marked and bored, so that the screws will not twist off when they are inserted (Art. 239). If this should happen, it would be necessary to replace the stock in most cases. About No. 12 screws should be used and soap or wax should be put on the threads.

3. Push the live center out of the spindle with an iron rod supplied for that purpose, and screw the faceplate onto the live or headstock spindle. It is best to place a leather or cardboard washer over the spindle, and to turn the faceplate on slowly, so that it will not jam against the shoulder, because then it will be hard to remove. *Never start the motor until the faceplate is fully screwed on the spindle.*

4. Screw chucks are fastened to the stock with a single central screw of the same diameter as the hole in the chuck. Fold a piece of fine sandpaper,

with the abrasive side out, to place between the chuck and the wood. This is to prevent slipping, which is likely to occur since the screw chuck has only one screw.

5. The side or end of the wood to be fastened to a faceplate or screw chuck must be flat and smooth.

A significant disadvantage of the method described above is that a number of screw holes will show in the bottom of the turned work. To avoid these screw holes, many wood turners first glue an auxiliary block to the stock to be turned. Just prior to clamping the two pieces together, place a piece of paper between the two glue surfaces. The principle used here is the same as the one used in making split turnings. After the stock has been turned to its proper size and shape it is removed from the waste stock by placing the cutting edge of a sharp chisel on the glue joint. A light tap will cause the paper to split, thereby separating the two pieces.

268. Procedure for Turning a Disk. 1. Screw the stock to the faceplate, and mount it in the lathe as described in the preceding article.

2. Adjust the T rest so that it is parallel to the face of the disk and at right angles to the lathe bed. It should be placed at a height a little below the center of the stock and only about ¼ in. away from it.

3. See that the disk revolves freely, and start the lathe at its slowest speed.

4. Remove enough of the material from the edge to make the disk circular This will diminish the vibration caused by uneven centering. The cutting is done with the toe of a skew chisel (Fig. 48) which is held at right angles to the face of the disk. The cut should be stopped about ⅛ in. from the rear face of the disk, as the wood is liable to split if the cut is extended all the way across the edge of the disk.

5. If the face of the disk is rough, or much material has to be removed,

Fig. 48. Cutting edge of disk.

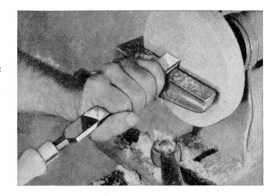

Fig. 49. Smoothing face of disk.

first use a round-nose chisel holding it flat upon the T rest and at right angles to the disk. Move the chisel across the face of the disk from the edge nearest the operator to the center and back again.

6. Smooth the face of the disk with a square-nose chisel (Fig. 49), and test for flatness with a try square (Fig. 50). This is called "facing off."

7. Mark the diameter of the disk by setting a pair of dividers or a pencil compass to a distance equal to the radius. Place one leg on the center, and scribe the circle with the other while the stock is revolving (Fig. 51).

Another way is to set the dividers to the required diameter. Rest one leg of the dividers on the T rest, and place it in contact with the stock while it is revolving. Bring the other leg of the dividers gradually in contact with the stock (Fig. 52). If two circles are marked, shift the dividers so that the points come in contact with the stock halfway between the two circles. When only one circle is marked, the dividers are held centrally. This method

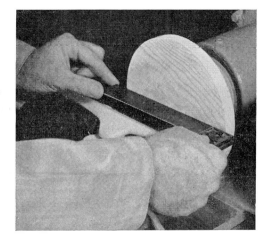

Fig. 50. Testing face of disk for flatness.

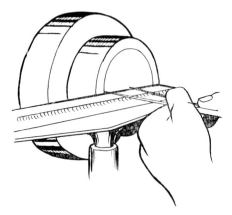
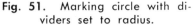

Fig. 51. Marking circle with dividers set to radius.

Fig. 52. Marking diameter with dividers.

is more exact, and especially useful for smaller diameters and when the center is cut away. It is very quickly mastered.

8. Reduce the disk to the required diameter as explained in step 6.

Then clamp the T rest parallel to the lathe bed and to the edge of the disk, and with the square-nose chisel remove the thin piece of material left on the rear edge of the disk.

9. Test for squareness by holding the stock of a try square against the face of the disk and the blade over its edge.

10. Convex and concave shapes are worked out very easily with the round-nose chisel, held flat on the tool rest and used as in spindle turning (Fig. 53).

Fig. 53. Finishing curves.

Fig. 54. Cutting a hole.

11. A hole to fit a turned tenon may very easily be cut with the toe of a skew chisel held perpendicular to the face of the disk (Fig. 54). The center of the hole may be cut away either with the skew chisel or round-nose chisel.

269. Procedure for Doing Chuck Turning. A chuck is an appliance in which work may be held securely while it is being turned in a lathe. Chucks are made in several different types and of different materials, as steel, brass, or wood. The type to be described in the following consists of a turned disk of wood fastened to a faceplate or a screw chuck. The wood turner makes these chucks easily and quickly as he needs them for the work he is doing. They are used for holding such turned objects as lamp bases, trays, bowls, boxes, rings, etc.

A lamp base is made as follows:

1. Get out the stock for the base, plane one side, cut it round, and screw it to the faceplate as explained in Article 268, steps 1 to 3.

2. Reduce it to the thickness and diameter required. Then cut a shallow recess in its face about ¹⁄₁₆ in. deep and extending within an inch of its outer edge. This is the lower surface of the base, and the depression is cut to make it stand well.

3. Bore a ¼-in. or a ⅜-in. hole from the side of the base to its center, as shown at A, Figure 55. This hole is for the electric wires. Sand the edge and lower surface of the base, and remove it from the faceplate.

4. Turn a disk from a piece of softwood at least 1 in. larger in diameter

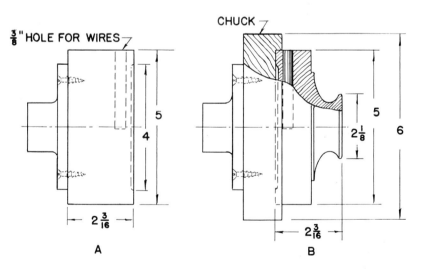

Fig. 55. Lamp base. A, Base turned to size; B, base chucked and turned.

than the base, and not less than 1½ in. in thickness. This is to be the "chuck."

5. Caliper the diameter of the lamp base carefully, and mark a circle of this diameter on the disk with a pair of dividers (Fig. 51).

6. Cut a recess in the disk within the circle marked. This recess should be about ³⁄₁₆ in. deep. The lamp base should fit into it very tightly as shown at B, Figure 55. If the recess is a little too large, place a piece of paper over it, and force the base into it. If the thickness of the paper is not sufficient to hold the base firmly in the recess, face the disk off again and cut another recess.

7. Drive the base into the recess, so that its lower surface bears against the bottom of the recess. This operation is called "chucking." It is the only way in which the base can be accurately centered and turned from the opposite side.

8. If the base is chucked correctly, it will run true without any danger of coming loose. The turning may now be finished according to the drawing, after which the hole is bored to fit the tenon for the upright (Fig. 54).

In this case, the chuck was made by cutting a recess into it. This is called *outside chucking,* because the outside edge of the lamp base was held in the chuck. In other cases, chucks are made by turning a shoulder on the disk, on which the object to be turned is held or chucked.

9. *Plug chucking* means to turn a cylinder and drive it into a hole bored for it in a wooden disk or chuck. Turn a tenon on the cylinder as shown in Figure 56 while it is held between centers.

10. Then cut a hole for the tenon in the wooden disk using a roundnose and a skew chisel as explained in Article 268. It should be a very close fit, so that the tenon will have to be driven in with a mallet.

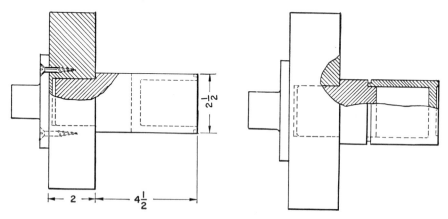

Fig. 56. Plug chucking.

Fig. 57. Turning end recess.

11. A box, as shown in Figure 57, may now be turned on the end of the cylinder. Deepen the hole with a round-nose chisel and smooth its sides with a skew chisel. As the hole gets deeper, the end of the tool rest may be turned into it to give better support to the turning tools.

12. Turn a rabbet for the lid on the edge of the box as shown by the dotted lines, then stain and finish it and cut it off with a parting tool.

13. A shoulder is now turned on the end of the chucked cylinder, over which the open end of the box fits (Fig. 57), while a shallow recess is turned in its bottom, so that it will stand well. This is called *inside chucking,* because the inner side of the box is held on the chuck.

14. The lid is turned and chucked as shown in Figure 58. First turn a recess to fit the rabbet on the top edge of the box. Try the fit frequently as the turning progresses, then hollow out the lid further and finally chuck and finish it.

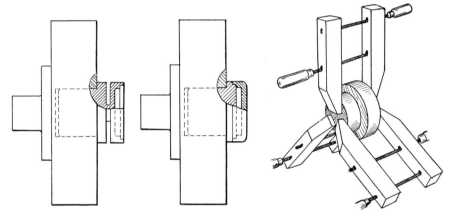

Fig. 58. Turning and chucking lid of box.

Fig. 59. Gluing to waste stock.

15. When turning objects as trays, plates, and boxes, which cannot be screwed to a faceplate or screw chuck without marring a finished surface, the stock may be glued to a disk turned on a faceplate. Spread glue on the disk, then glue a piece of heavy paper to it, and mark the diameter of the stock to be turned with a pencil. Finally, spread glue on one side of the stock, center it on the paper, and clamp it with three or more hand screws as in Figure 59. This is called *gluing to waste stock.*

16. When the turning has been completed, the object may be removed by driving a sharp chisel or a plane iron into the joint. This will cause the paper to split, so that the turned object can easily be separated from the disk. Scrape off glue and paper and sand smooth by hand.

270. Procedure for Sanding in the Lathe on a Spindle.   Where a sanding machine is not available, spindles of different diameters may be turned, covered with sandpaper, and used very effectively in sanding concave surfaces.

1. Turn the spindle according to directions given in Article 259. It should be somewhat smaller in diameter than the diameter of the curve to be sanded, generally from ¼ to ½ in., to allow for the thickness of the sandpaper and facility in working.

2. Fold a sheet of No. 1½ sandpaper around the cylinder, and cut away the surplus so that the ends of the sandpaper just meet when it is wrapped tightly around the cylinder.

3. Apply glue to the cylinder, wrap the sandpaper around it, and hold it in place by winding a string, or better, a piece of bandage around it. Set it away to dry (see also Art. 120, Figs. 119 and 120, p. 115).

4. Place the cylinder in the lathe, applying sufficient oil to the end running on the dead center, and remove the tool rest. Curves, such as those on table legs, are easily sanded by holding the pieces perpendicularly to the face of the cylinder, Figure 60, and moving them rapidly back and forth. If held too long in one place, ridges and hollows will result.

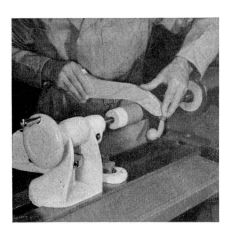 

Fig. 60.   Sanding leg on spindle.   **Fig. 61.**   Sanding end of leg.

5. When it is desired to sand a curve on the end wood of a leg to be doweled to a turned column, the leg to be sanded is steadied on the tool rest (Fig. 61). Move the leg from side to side to avoid burning the sandpaper and the wood.

271. Procedure for Sanding in the Lathe on a Disk.   A wheel or disk sander is useful for all convex surfaces. It is not recommended to sand flat surfaces on this "homemade" sander as the sides of the wheel very easily dig into the surface. It may be useful in sanding the ends of the legs of a table or stool, which does not stand evenly on all four legs.

1. From a 2-in plank, preferably softwood, cut out a circular disk, or wheel, of as large a diameter as the lathe will swing. Cut it as nearly round as possible with a handsaw or turning saw.

2. Screw a faceplate securely to the disk, and as nearly in the center as possible.

3. Turn the disk as explained in Article 268.

4. Apply glue to the disk, and glue the sandpaper in place. If the disk is larger in diameter than a sheet of sandpaper, place two pieces edge to edge.

5. Clamp the disk to a flat surface until the glue is dry. Trim the edges with a dull chisel or plane iron.

6. When the sanding wheel is to be used, the tool post should be removed from the lathe bed and a board clamped to it instead. This board should be thicker than the distance between the lathe bed and the edge of the wheel (Fig. 62).

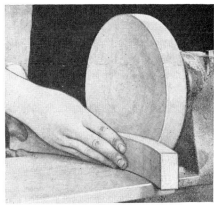

Fig. 62.   Sanding convex surfaces on sanding disk.

272. Procedure for Finishing and Polishing Turned Work.   It is a good deal easier to finish and polish work that is revolving in a lathe than it is to finish and polish flat surfaces of a piece of furniture.

1. A good polish can only be built up on a surface that is well sanded and free from any blemishes and defects. When sanding in the lathe, move the tool post out of the way so that the fingers will not be caught between it and the work.

2. Begin sanding with No. ½ sandpaper. For flat and rounded surfaces, use a quarter sheet folded once or twice. Move it quickly back and forth along the surface so as not to leave scratches. If moved slowly or held in

one spot, a series of fine rings will show on the surface. These rings are difficult to remove, but if left on the surface they will show much more when the polish is applied.

3. When sanding hollows, fold a quarter sheet into the desired shape and move it quickly from side to side. Beads are sanded with narrow strips of sandpaper held between thumb and forefingers of both hands.

4. Be careful not to round any sharp edges. Continue sanding with No. 2/0 sandpaper until the work is very smooth and free from scratches. It is then a good plan to wet the work with a brush dipped in clear water. Let it dry for an hour or two and then sand it again with No. 3/0 sandpaper.

5. The work is now ready for the stain, which should be allowed to dry a couple of hours. Be careful to apply it evenly and, if necessary, wipe the work with a piece of cotton waste to absorb any excess.

6. Rub the stained surface lightly with a piece of No. 3/0 steel wool, while the work is revolving slowly. Then apply a coat of thin shellac with a brush, and let it dry for two hours.

7. Rub this coat lightly with the steel wool, and apply the polish with a clean linen rag. The rag should be folded into a pad about 2 in. wide and 10 in. long. Thin shellac is applied to the middle of the rag with a brush, and a few drops of paraffin oil are placed on the work.

8. Run the lathe at its slowest speed, hold the ends of the rag with both hands, and move the rag slowly back and forth over the work with a light pressure. Keep moving the pad constantly, otherwise the shellac may pile up and form rings and ridges (Fig. 63).

9. If this should happen, apply a little denatured alcohol to the rag and

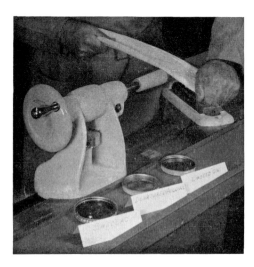

Fig. 63. French polishing on lathe.

a few more drops of paraffin oil to the work, because this helps to distribute the shellac more evenly.

10. When a good polish has been obtained, let the work dry overnight and apply a second coat the next day. If the pad is kept in a closed can or bottle it will not become hard and stiff, but remain soft and pliant.

This finishing process is generally known as French polishing.

REVIEW QUESTIONS, CHAPTER 9

Possible score 45 points

Your score . . . . . .

PART I. COMPLETION QUESTIONS.   Complete the following statements:

1. The most primitive lathe, called the bow lathe was invented in . . . .
2. The next type of lathe invented was the . . . .
3. That part of a modern lathe which contains the driving mechanism is called the . . . .
4. The two centers between which all spindle turning is done are called . . . . and . . . . centers.
5. Cast steel disks used in turning bowls and other round objects are called . . . .
6. The tool that prevents spindles from vibrating is called a . . . .
7. When measuring inside and outside diameters, one uses . . . .
8. There are two methods of wood turning: . . . . and . . . .
9. When turning a square piece of stock into a rough cylinder, the tool used is a . . . .
10. When a rough cylinder is to be turned into a true cylinder, one first makes a series of sizing cuts with the . . . .
11. In the cutting method a cylinder is made true and smooth with a . . . .
12. A cylinder which is thicker at one end than at the other end is called a . . . .
13. When using the cutting method, concave cuts are best made with a . . . .
14. Semicircular turned pieces used as decorations are called . . . .
15. When turning a bowl, the rough stock is first fastened to a piece of . . . .
16. When a hole needs to be cut in the turned base of a lamp, this hole is readily cut with a . . . .
17. The finishing method done on a slow moving lathe with shellac and oil is called . . . .
18. The modern wood-turning lathe is completely made of iron and . . . .
19. The T-shaped casting which fits into the tool post is called the . . . .
20. The round-nose and square-nose chisels are both . . . . tools as distinct from cutting tools.

PART II. TRUE-FALSE QUESTIONS. Indicate, by encircling T or F, whether the following statements are true or false.

21. Wood turning as a trade is still practiced extensively.   T   F
22. The primitive bow lathe is still used in parts of Asia and Africa.   T   F
23. A modern wood-turning lathe has a direct motor-head drive.   T   F
24. The dead center is tapered to fit into the front end of the hollow shaft of the headstock.   T   F
25. A screw chuck is a small faceplate with a single screw in the center.   T   F
26. Turning gouges are beveled on the inside or concave side.   T   F
27. Square-nose chisels are like ordinary chisels but have a longer and heavier blade.   T   F
28. Turning stock should be free of cracks and flaws.   T   F
29. When turning wood, roll up your sleeves, tuck in your tie, or better yet, remove it.   T   F
30. The experienced, professional wood turner turns by using the scraping method.   T   F

PART III. MULTIPLE-CHOICE QUESTIONS. Select, by encircling the correct letter, the answer which completes each statement:

31. When smoothing a cylinder with a skew chisel, the position of the top of the tool rest is:
    A. Above the top of the cylinder.
    B. Well below the center of the cylinder.
    C. At the center of the cylinder.
    D. Slightly below the top of the cylinder.
32. To make concave cuts in a cylinder by the scraping method, one best uses:
    A. The gouge.
    B. The spear-point chisel.
    C. The round-nose chisel.
    D. The skew chisel.
33. When finishing on the lathe, one uses all but one of the following:
    A. Shellac
    B. Turpentine
    C. Linseed oil
    D. Soft rag
34. Historically, which lathe was used earliest:
    A. Pole lathe
    B. Motor-head lathe
    C. Great wheel lathe
    D. Bow lathe
35. One of the following is not a scraping tool:
    A. Square-nose chisel
    B. Beading tools
    C. Gouge
    D. Round-nose chisel

PART IV. MATCHING QUESTIONS. Match the terms to the left with the descriptions to the right by placing the correct letter in the parentheses:

36. ( ) Bow lathe
37. ( ) Pole lathe
38. ( ) Great wheel lathe
39. ( ) Bed
40. ( ) Steady rest
41. ( ) Cutting method of wood turning
42. ( ) Parting tool
43. ( ) Concave cuts
44. ( ) Beads
45. ( ) Chucking

A. An early improvement over the bow lathe.
B. The main, supporting part of a lathe.
C. The oldest, fastest, and cleanest way to turn wood.
D. The most primitive of all lathes.
E. Made with a rolling movement of the gouge.
F. Small convex cuts, made with a sharp skew.
G. Required two men to operate.
H. A device that prevents turned work from vibrating.
I. A method of holding certain turned jobs in the lathe.
J. A long slender tool with bevels that meet at 50 deg.
K. A method of finishing on the lathe.

CHAPTER ⬛ 10

Surface Decoration

The most common ways of enriching or decorating a wood surface are by inlaying, veneering, carving, and painting.

While the majority of these processes require the highest type of skill and artistic ability, it is nevertheless possible to select some which, while comparatively simple to execute, are of sufficient artistic merit to greatly enhance the beauty as well as the intrinsic value of pieces of furniture.

Great care must be taken in decorating an object. This rule is of especial importance to beginners, who, in their eagerness and enthusiasm over the new work, often overdecorate the object, or select a design or type of decoration that is unsuitable for the work in hand.

It may be said in general that surface decoration should be simple and appropriate, and should be used sparingly. The beginner should not rely entirely on his own taste, but should be guided by a study of good designs. These are easily found in museums, exhibits, books, and art magazines. In them, numerous examples of both classic and modern decoration may be studied and the proper selection made.

275. General Suggestions for Decorations. 1. Furniture, such as tables, chairs, or cabinets for the kitchen, made of soft or inexpensive woods, should not be decorated by inlaying or carving. It would be more appropriate to paint these pieces. A border or edge painted in a darker or contrasting, harmonious color would be a suitable form of decoration.

2. Inlaying, veneering, carving, or reeding are best employed to decorate or enhance the beauty of pieces on which a good deal of labor has been expended, such as small decorative tables, cabinets, lamps, etc.

Inlaying should be done only on close-grained woods, such as maple, birch, walnut, mahogany, etc. A thin line of 1/16-in. satinwood is often appropriate as a border line on the front of a drawer, or on straight tapered legs. Inlaid border lines are also used along the edges of table tops of different shapes, on cabinet doors, mirror frames, serving trays, and similar pieces. Sometimes the corners of an inlaid top or door are made more prominent by the design of the border line itself or by inlaying special corner insets (Fig. 1). Occasionally an inset is placed in the center of a top, door, or tray having an inlaid border line.

The contrast in color between the inlay and the surface should not be

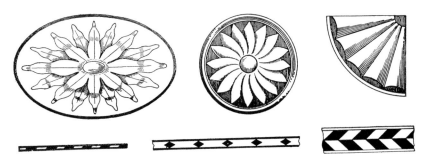

Fig. 1. Typical commercial designs of lines and insets.

too glaring, but it should be sufficiently well defined to make the inlay stand out clearly.

3. The purpose of veneering is to enhance the beauty of the wood surface. A fine line of inlay is often combined with the veneers to form or accentuate a border. Insets are rarely used with matched veneers, because such veneers are decorative enough.

4. In general, it is better not to use carving and inlaying on the same piece of furniture. Carving may be done on both close- and open-grain woods. Simple forms of carving, such as are illustrated in Figures 28 and 29 are sufficient.

5. Spiral reeding and straight reeding should not be used together on the same turned column, except when the turned parts thus decorated differ greatly in length and shape. For example, straight reeds may be carved on a long tapering part of a column, while spiral reeds may be carved on a short ball-shaped part of the same column.

6. Overlays, veined, and pierced work should generally follow the outline of the surface to be decorated. The minor parts of the design of this type of decoration, however, may differ greatly from the contour of the surface to which it is applied. The colors of two-toned work should not be strongly contrasting, but should rather be a light tone and a dark tone of the same color.

7. When using moldings, it is better to err in making them too small, rather than too large. Moldings should be smaller when made of fine-grain woods, such as mahogany or maple, and larger when made of coarse-grain woods, such as oak and ash.

Inlaying

Inlaying is often regarded by the amateur craftsman as a difficult process, quite beyond his powers, and only within the capability of the expert or specialist. This attitude of mind often arises owing to the fact that the person in question has never seen how inlaying is done and, therefore does not realize how comparatively simple and easy the process really is.

In general, inlaying may be explained as the process of cutting a shallow recess in one member into which another member of a different color or material is fitted and glued.

Material for inlay is made commercially in two forms: (1) lines or bands of varying widths, and (2) insets in numerous sizes, shapes, and designs (Fig. 1). Lines are generally used along the edges of a surface, as a border or frame, while insets are used in the center of a surface or sometimes in corners. While it is possible to make up lines of a simple pattern, it is rather difficult to make suitable insets. From a commercial point of view, it does not pay, as such material can be bought very cheaply from firms making a specialty of this work. Lines are made in pieces one yard long, from ⅟₂₈ to ⅟₁₆ in. thick, and vary in price according to width and design. Insets are sold by the piece, and also vary greatly in price according to their size and design. They are made of many small pieces of wood of different colors, carefully cut and glued together on a piece of brown paper. The beautiful shading, so characteristic of these pieces, is executed by placing them on edge in a shallow iron saucer filled with moist sand. When placed over a fire, the sand at the bottom of the saucer dries, and becomes so hot that the pieces are scorched on their lower edges.

276. Procedure for Inlaying Lines or Bands. 1. Make a tool for cutting the grooves by breaking a piece off an old hack-saw blade and grinding it on an emery wheel to the exact width of the line to be inlaid.

2. A bevel is ground on one side, after which it is sharpened just like a cabinet scraper (Art. 131).

3. Remove the spur or point from a marking gauge, and insert the piece

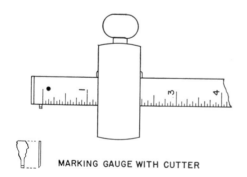

Fig. 2. Tool for cutting grooves for narrow bands of inlay.

MARKING GAUGE WITH CUTTER

CUTTER

Fig. 3. Cutting grooves with marking gauge.

of steel instead, so that its sharpened edge projects about 1/16 in. or less, depending upon the thickness of the band to be inlaid (Fig. 2).

4. Make a trial cut on a piece of waste wood to see if the groove is of the right width and depth.

The marking gauge is held and operated in the usual manner; i.e., away from the operator (Fig. 3). Consequently, the beveled piece of steel is placed so that it cuts like a cabinet scraper, with the flat side toward the front.

5. The inlay should fit so snugly that it must be forced into the groove (step 10). Therefore, if the groove is too wide, a little should be ground off the sides of the cutter until it cuts a groove of the exact width.

The above method is recommended especially for narrow lines. The cutter will cut both with and across the grain on hard, close-grain woods, as maple, birch, mohogany, or walnut., the smoothness of the cut depending upon the sharpness of the cutter. The slight roughness appearing at the edges of grooves cut across the grain is removed when the inlaid surface is scraped and sanded, as directed in step 11 following.

6. For wider lines it is better to use a scratch stock (Fig. 4). A scratch

Fig. 4. Scratch stock.

$\frac{1}{2}$ — VENEER

$\frac{1}{2}$

8

$1\frac{1}{2}$

4

$\frac{7}{8}$

VARIOUS CUTTERS

stock is a homemade tool consisting of two pieces of close-grained hardwood, from ⅜ to ½ in. thick, bolted together with stove bolts. A piece of veneer may be glued between the pieces in the handle, but that is not necessary or even convenient if cutters have to be changed frequently.

7. The cutter is made from a piece of broken saw blade filed or ground to shape on an emery wheel. It has square edges and is sharpened like a handscraper (Art. 132). The scratch stock is a useful tool for making small moldings, beads, flutes, grooves, etc.

8. Regulate any little unevenness in the corners with a sharp chisel, cut the lines to length, and miter them in the corners. This is best done with a very sharp chisel or dovetail saw.

9. Plane a piece of wood to about 2 or 3 in. wide and 12 in. long. Glue and nail two strips of hardwood to its upper surface and make two miter cuts as shown in Figure 5.

10. When the inlay lines have been cut to length and mitered, they are brushed with thin, hot, animal glue, or cold resin glue, and are forced into the grooves with a hammer, either by striking light blows on a block of wood laid over the inlay, or by running the hammer over the lines while exerting pressure on the head of the hammer. This must be done carefully so that the inlay will not be injured.

11. After drying about ten hours, the inlaid piece may be scraped with a very sharp cabinet scraper until all glue has been cleaned off and the lines are absolutely level with the surface. It is then ready for sanding and finishing.

Bands of inlay absorb some moisture from the glue which causes them to swell. As they cannot expand sideways in the narrow grooves, they swell in an upward direction. When the water evaporates, they again shrink to their

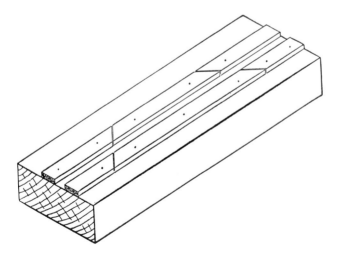

Fig. 5. Miter block for line inlay.

Fig. 6. Cutting grooves with portable router.

original thickness. It is, therefore, important to allow sufficient time before scraping them level with the surface. They will continue to shrink after a too early scraping, thus forming an unsightly hollow.

Grooves for line inlay can be cut very easily with a portable router (Fig. 6). This machine is furnished with a guide for both straight or curved work. The machine is fitted with a bit of the proper diameter and adjusted to the desired depth of cut. The guide is fastened at the correct distance and held against the edge of the piece while the groove is being cut.

277. Procedure for Inlaying Insets. 1. Insets sold by manufacturers of marquetry are about ⅛ in. in thickness. They are glued to a piece of brown wrapping paper and are set in the center of a piece of veneer in order to protect the edges. Cut away this surplus veneer with a sharp pocketknife by slicing it into narrow strips. After all of the strips have been carefully broken away, it will be found that bits of paper project all around the edges of the inset. This surplus paper is best removed by running a fine file, as for instance a saw file, lightly over the rear edge of the inset, which is the side to which the paper is glued.

2. When the edges have been cleaned, the inset is placed face down on the surface at the place where it is to be inlaid.

3. If the inset is elliptical, for example, and it is to be inlaid in the center of a tray or table, two center lines crossing each other at right angles are laid out both on the tray and on the inset. The inset is then placed face down so that the center lines coincide and its outline is traced on the surface with a sharp, hard pencil. As the inset may not be absolutely symmetrical, it is also well to mark it so that it will always be placed in the same position.

4. If the inset is diamond shaped, the straight lines forming the outline may be cut with a chisel, but if it is elliptical or circular, the outline, in the absence of special tools, can be cut with a sharp pocketknife or gouges of the proper curvature.

5. The wood within the outline is cut to a depth of about ⅛ in. with a router plane. Set the plane so that it cuts only a thin shaving until the desired depth, equal to the thickness of the inset, has been reached.

6. Fit the inset into the recess just cut. If it does not go in all the way around, mark the places to be cut with a sharp knife and remove the projections little by little until the inset fits into the recess.

7. Recesses for insets are cut very easily with a portable router. Do not cut quite up to the pencil line, but finish the outline of the recess with a gouge of the proper curvature.

8. Glue the inset in place *face down,* so that the brown paper faces up. Apply hot animal glue to the recess, press the inlay into it, and force out the surplus glue by rubbing a ¾-in. chisel over it for a few minutes until the glue has set and the inset is firmly embedded in the recess. Place a piece of cardboard over it, and clamp a board across the top overnight.

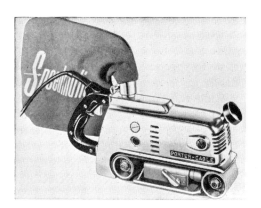

Fig. 7.   Portable belt sander.

9. After allowing about 10 hours for drying, the inset and surrounding surface are scraped with a cabinet scraper and are sanded smooth. This will remove the brown paper so that the colors and shading of the different pieces of wood, of which the inset is composed, appear in all their beauty. The paper can be sanded off very easily if a portable sander is available (Fig. 7). Be sure that the sanding belt is of very fine grit.

If an inset is glued in place with the papered side down, a good bond is not formed between it and the wood into which it is inlaid, because the paper is liable to split, causing the inset or parts of it to become loose.

278. Procedure for Cutting Straight Reeds. The beauty of a turned column, such as illustrated in Figure 8, may be greatly enhanced by reeding. A reed, in this sense, may be defined as a semicircular molding or bead; in architecture, it is known under the name "astragal." A reed is really very easily carved by hand, and the time and patience needed for its execution is fully repaid by the added beauty and intrinsic value of the piece of furniture thus decorated.

1. The first step in the process of reeding is to make a box having neither top nor bottom, but only the four sides which may be nailed together. The size of this box should be such that the piece to be reeded will fit easily within its four sides (Fig. 9).

2. The piece to be reeded is held in this box with a screw driven through each end of it into the holes left by the lathe centers.

3. Lay out vertical center lines on each end, and bore a ¾₆-in. hole for the screw in each of these lines, so that the part to be reeded will be nearly level with the top edges of the box.

Fig. 8. Beautiful example of reeding done by hand.

Fig. 9. Laying off reeds from paper strip.

4. Determine the number of reeds to be cut. Wrap a strip of paper around the thickest part of the column. Cut it so that the ends just meet, and divide it into the desired number of parts.

5. Wrap the paper around the column again, and lay off the divisions (Fig. 9).

6. Place the column so that one of these marks is approximately equidistant from both sides of the box. Set a marking gauge with the block against one of the sides and the point on the mark, and gauge a line

Fig. 10. Gauging reeds from division marks.

Fig. 11. Gauging division lines.

throughout the length to be reeded (Fig. 10). It is best to bring the point of the marking gauge all the way out, so that it can reach the smaller diameters of the column. If there is much difference in the diameters of the part to be reeded, a piece of wood, shaped to its outline, must be nailed to the side of the box so that the marking gauge can ride on that (Fig. 11).

7. Repeat at all the other marks of division, being careful to hold the block of the marking gauge against the same side of the box.

8. Wedge the column firmly against the sides of the box, and chisel a

Fig. 12. Chiseling "V" cuts.

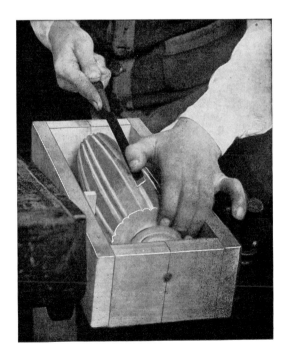

V cut on one of the gauge lines. A carver's veining tool or skew chisel, or an ordinary ½-in. paring chisel having beveled sides, may be used, for this work (Fig. 12). Be careful to see how the grain runs, taking small cuts and reversing the direction of the cut whenever necessary.

9. When the V cuts have been made sufficiently deep, the sharp edges are rounded, thus forming the beads or reeds.

10. These are further smoothed with scrapers and sandpaper.

11. Flutes may be laid out and cut in the same way, but it is more difficult to get them smooth and even.

Flutes on straight work may be cut with a scratch stock (Fig. 4).

12. Reeds and flutes are easily cut with a portable shaper. The piece to be reeded is placed between the lathe centers. A board is fastened to the lathe bed, and the shaper is screwed into the holder which is moved along this board (Fig. 13). The cutter is set to the level of the lathe centers and

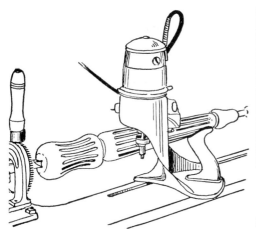

Fig. 14. Dividing disk.

Fig. 13. Cutting flutes.

held against the stock being reeded or fluted. A cogwheel attachment is fastened to the live spindle for the purpose of dividing the turned stock into the desired number of reeds equally spaced. Some lathes are equipped with a permanent dividing disk on the headstock (Fig. 14).

279. Procedure for Cutting Spiral Reeds. 1. Place the column to be reeded in the lathe. Wrap a strip of paper around it at each extremity of the part to be reeded, and divide the two strips into the same number of equal parts. If the diameters of the column are different, it follows that the divisions on one strip of paper will be larger than on the other.

2. Determine the pitch the reeds are to have. This is done according to the desire of the workman. The reed may go once around the column or

Fig. 15. Laying out spiral reeds.

only halfway. In either case, a straightedge is cut from a piece of cardboard or other flexible material, and is wrapped around the column so that each end of the cardboard touches one of the division points marked at each extremity of the column (Fig. 15).

3. Draw a pencil line along the edge of the cardboard as it winds around the column. Move the cardboard to the next pair of division points, and mark a line along its edge as previously done. Continue around the column in this way until all the reeds have been marked.

4. Chisel a V cut along these lines, as explained in Article 278, round off the sharp corners, and smooth the reeds with scraper and sandpaper.

It will be found that the shaping of spiral reeds is easier than the straight ones, because the cutting is done at an angle to the direction in which the grain runs. There is, therefore, less chance of the chisel following the grain rather than the line marked.

280. Procedure for Carving a Single Spiral on a Turned Cylinder. 1. Turn the cylinder to the required diameter, and determine the number of turns the spiral is to make. It is customary to make the length of each turn approximately equal to the diameter of the cylinder.

2. Divide the length of the cylinder into that number of equal parts, and mark a heavy line at these points while it is revolving in the lathe.

3. Divide each of these major parts into four equal parts, and mark lighter circles at these points, A, Figure 16.

4. Wrap a strip of paper around the cylinder and divide it into four equal parts. Mark these divisions on the cylinder, move the T rest close to it, and draw longitudinal lines along it at these points as in a, b, c, d, A, Figure 16.

5. Draw the spiral line, beginning at the left end of the cylinder on one of the longitudinal lines, for example a. Continue toward the right to where the next line b intersects the first circle, and so on. When the first heavy

circle is reached, the spiral should have made one complete turn around
the cylinder. Proceed in like manner until the end of the cylinder has been
reached. Do not let the spiral line begin or end too abruptly, but make it
more parallel to the turned beads at both ends.

6. The carving is done as follows: With a backsaw, make a shallow cut
about ½ in. deep, starting and stopping the cut about ½ in. from each end.

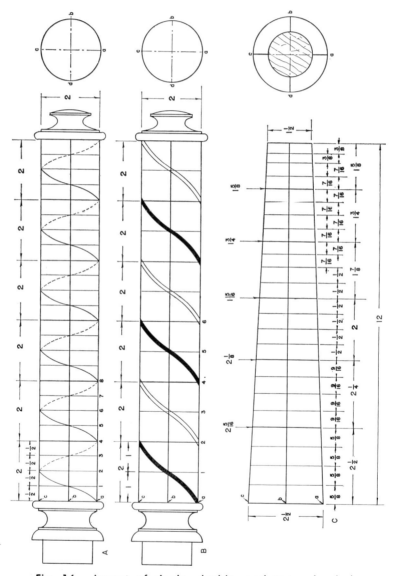

Fig. 16.   Layout of single, double, and tapered spirals.

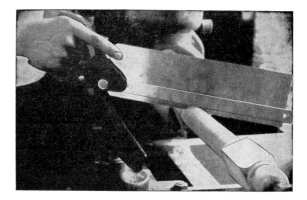

Fig. 17. Making saw
cut along spiral line.

Use a backsaw with a metal guide as in Figure 17, or clamp one of wood
to an ordinary backsaw. It is best to make this saw cut while the turning
is held between centers in the lathe.

Fig. 18. Chiseling V
cut for spiral.

7. Now clamp the leg on the bench top while making broad V cuts all
along the spiral with a ¾-in. chisel (Fig. 18). Finally shape the spiral with
rasp, files, and sandpaper.

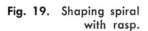

Fig. 19. Shaping spiral
with rasp.

Fig. 20. Finishing spiral with sandpaper. Note ends of spiral have been turned.

These operations, which are quite easy to do, are shown in Figures 19 and 20.

281. Procedure for Carving a Double Spiral on a Turned Cylinder. 1. When a double spiral is to be carved, proceed as explained in Article 280, steps 1 to 4, but divide each of the major divisions into two equal parts only (B, Fig. 16).

2. Draw the first spiral, indicated by the heavy black line, from *a* to

Fig. 21. Single and double spirals.

line *b* and circle 1, then to *c* and circle 2, and so on, until at line *a* and circle 4 one complete turn has been made.

3. The second spiral, shown by the fine lines, begins on the opposite side of the cylinder at line *c,* continues to line *d* and circle 1, and from there goes to line *a* and circle 2, and so on. For the sake of clearness, these spiral lines have been shown on only one side of the cylinder.

4. Figure 21 shows two double spirals. The one in the center, resembling two pieces of rope twisted together, is carved exactly as explained in Article 280, step 6.

5. The hollow double spiral at the right in Figure 21 is laid out as shown at B, in Figure 16. The spiral lines in this case form the ridge, and are ³⁄₁₆ in. wide. They may be laid out from a strip of heavy paper ³⁄₁₆ in. wide wrapped around the cylinder.

6. The sawing should be done on a line marked between the spiral lines starting at line *a* and circle 1, continuing to line *b* and circle 2, and so on. This line has not been shown in the drawing as it might prove to be confusing.

7. The spirals are worked out with chisel, rasp, file, and sandpaper. Spirals should not begin or end too abruptly.

282. Procedure for Laying Out Tapered Spirals.   1. Wrap a strip of paper around the cylinder, divide it into four equal parts and draw four longitudinal lines on the cylinder (Art. 280, step 4).

2. Measure the diameter at the largest end of the tapered cylinder, and lay off this distance along one of the horizontal lines.

3. Then measure the diameter at this point, and lay off this distance along the cylinder. Continue in this way until the small end of the cylinder has been reached.

4. Adjust the various lengths so that they diminish proportionally, and so that the sum of their lengths equals the total length of the tapered cylinder.

5. These major divisions are again divided into two or four parts according to whether a single or a double spiral is to be carved.

Spiral turning, which is of eastern origin, was introduced in Europe in the seventeenth century by Portuguese explorers. It is done commercially on special lathes and routers.

Simple Carving

Wood carving, even in its simplest forms, adds much to the beauty and distinction of a piece of furniture. As this art cannot be learned very readily from written instructions only, the easiest way for the beginner is probably to try to imitate some simple border or ornament such as those illustrated in

Figures 28 and 29. This, in most cases, will be found surprisingly easy, especially if an actual carving can be had for a model.

In selecting a carved ornament for a piece of cabinetwork, the student should consult books on historical ornament in order to have the carving of a form and type that is in keeping with the period of the piece of furniture which he is constructing.

Tools

The beginner needs only a few carving tools, such as a ½-in. skew chisel, two or three straight gouges of medium curvature, ⅛, ¼, and ⅜ in., a veining tool, and a parting or V tools (Fig. 67, p. 38).

283. Procedure for Cutting Beads. Beads, such as those shown on the legs of the table in Figure 22 and the stretcher in Figure 23 are made with a scratch stock, shown in Figure 4, and described in Article 276.

284. Procedure for Cutting Chamfers and Hollows. Stopped chamfers do not extend all the way along the edge of a board, and, therefore, cannot

Fig. 22. Beaded table leg.

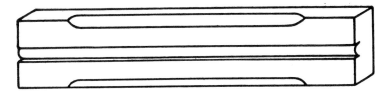

Fig. 23. Beaded and stop-chamfered stretcher.

be planed except on a portion in the center. They may be chiseled with a paring chisel. Cut the ends first, holding the bevel of the chisel down between the ends (Fig. 24). Next hold the chisel diagonally and the beveled side up (Fig. 24), but do not chisel quite down to the lines. Finish the part (Fig. 25). Smooth with block plane, scraper and sandpaper.

Stopped chamfers may be planed on the jointer by tilting the fence to 45 deg. and lowering both tables the same distance as shown in Figure 26.

Hollows are chamfers which have been curved with a gouge. First plane the chamfer, and then chisel the hollow in the center with a gouge of the proper diameter and curvature (Fig. 27). The sharp edges of the chamfer determine the width of the hollow. Chamfers and hollows also may be made with a scratch stock.

285. Procedure for Carving Borders. Other examples of carving made with the gouge only are illustrated in Figure 28 at *a, b, c,* and *d.*

1. The border at *a* is cut by first driving the gouge into the wood almost perpendicularly, and then taking a slanting cut, almost horizontally, into the first cut, so that a hollow is formed. This border is further embellished with a fine line cut on each side of it. This may be cut with a V tool, or it may in some cases be scratched with a marking gauge.

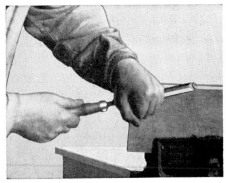

Fig. 24. Chiseling end of stopped chamfer.

Fig. 25. Finishing a chamfer.

Fig. 26. Planing stopped chamfer. Hand screws clamped to fence as stop blocks.

Fig. 27. Cutting hollow on edge with bent-shank gouge.

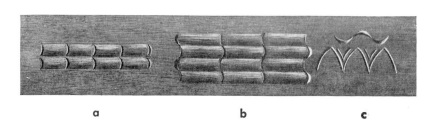

a   b   c

d

Fig. 28. Simple carved borders.

a   b

Fig. 29. Simple carving.

2. The border *b* is a variation of *a,* the only difference being the direction of the cut. While the two bands in *a* were cut in the same direction, each two adjoining bands in *b* are cut in opposite directions.

3. Borders *c* and *d,* although quite different in appearance, are cut in the same manner as *b;* i.e., one perpendicular cut and one slanting cut running into the first. The difference is that the slanting cuts in these borders are much steeper than in *b*.

4. The *strapwork* shown at *b,* Figure 29, is a very popular and quite simple form of wood carving. In this example, the outline has been cut with a V tool, after which the band between these outlines has been hollowed with a gouge.

It is more common in strapwork to leave the bands in relief and cut down the background to a depth of about ⅛ in. (Fig. 30). The usual pro-

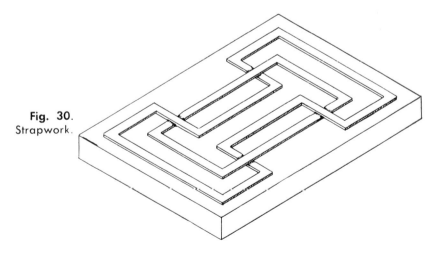

Fig. 30.
Strapwork.

Fig. 31. Acanthus leaf.

cedure is to cut the outline of the bands with a flat chisel held perpendicularly. A mallet is used to drive the chisel into the wood. Be careful not to undercut the bands because the edges are liable to crumble and break. Then make slanting cuts meeting the perpendicular cuts, gradually working toward the center of the background.

The router machine described in Article 116 is a very useful tool for cutting away the background.

5. A very effective and easy form of carving, made by a combination of perpendicular and slanting cuts as explained above, is shown at *a,* Figure 29.

6. The lower border at *c,* Figure 28, shows outline carving done with a V tool. While this appears the most simple and easiest of the types described, it takes quite a good deal of practice to be able to cut these fine lines so that they are of a uniform width and closely follow the curves or straight lines of the design.

7. Carvings, such as the acanthus leaves illustrated in Figure 31, are not difficult to make for the beginner, especially if he has a model from which to work. It is recommended first to outline the rib running through the center of the leaf, then shape the latter roughly, and finally cut and shape the small individual leaves.

Moldings

The appropriate use of moldings adds much to the beauty and character both of cabinetwork and interior woodwork. Like carving, it is the play of light and shadow over the uneven surface which attracts the eye to a molding. Moldings are therefore used to accentuate certain parts of a piece of furniture such as a cornice, a base, or a panel (see Fig. 128, p. 248).

Moldings are either plain or carved. They are made in a great variety of shapes, and are known by many names of Greek, French, Latin, and English origin. Some of the most common moldings are: the band, the sunk or raised fillet, the round shapes such as quarter, half round, and three-quarter round, the bead or astragal, the hollow shapes or cove moldings

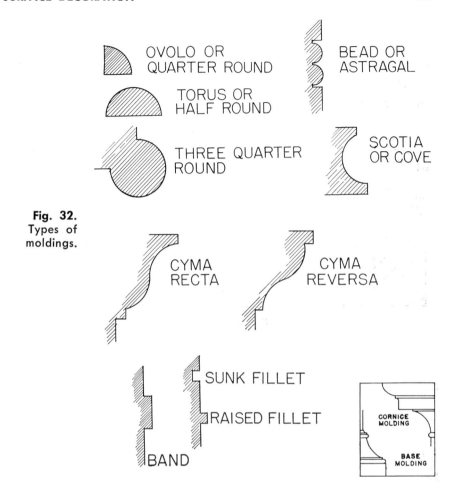

OVOLO OR
QUARTER ROUND

BEAD OR
ASTRAGAL

TORUS OR
HALF ROUND

THREE QUARTER
ROUND

SCOTIA
OR COVE

Fig. 32.
Types of
moldings.

CYMA
RECTA

CYMA
REVERSA

SUNK FILLET

RAISED FILLET

BAND

CORNICE
MOLDING

BASE
MOLDING

made in several degrees of curvature, and the combination round and hollow moldings called "cyma" moldings (Fig. 32).

286. Procedure for Making Moldings. Moldings are usually cut on the shaper or planed by hand with special molding planes or with a universal plane. Small moldings may be made entirely with the scratch stock (Fig. 4).

They also can be worked out roughly on a circular saw and smoothed with chisels, gouges, or scrapers. The method of procedure in the latter case is as follows:

1. Square the stock from which the molding is to be made, and lay out its profile on one end of the stock.

2. Make a number of saw cuts on the circular saw in the manner suggested in Figure 33. All square and flat surfaces of the molding can be

cut exactly in this way. All curved surfaces can be cut only approximately to shape.

3. The curved surfaces are now smoothed with sharp chisels and gouges, after which they are scraped with molding scrapers, whose edges are filed to conform to the shape of the molding.

4. The final smoothing is done with sandpaper folded over small pieces of wood, which are shaped to fit different sections of the molding. These pieces of wood, called "rubbers," should be at least 4 in. long.

Directions for mitering and applying moldings are given in Chapter 6, part V on miter joints.

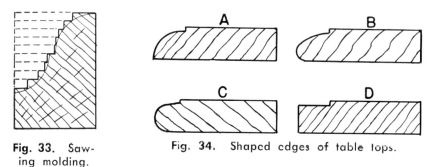

Fig. 33. Saw-
ing molding.

Fig. 34. Shaped edges of table tops.

287. Procedure for Shaping the Edges of Table Tops. In order to make a table or cabinet more attractive and interesting, the edges of the top may be shaped or molded in different ways.

1. The edges shown in A, B, and C, Figure 34, are all produced in the following manner: Cut a shallow rabbet, about $\frac{1}{16}$ in. deep and from $\frac{3}{4}$ to 1 in. wide, on the face of the top as shown in D, Figure 34. If a circular

Fig. 35. Cutting shallow
rabbet.

saw is available, this may be very easily done by making a single cut ⅟₁₆ in. deep. The rabbet otherwise may be planed with a rabbet plane (Art. 170).

2. The edge is now planed to the desired shape with a block plane. Clamp a piece of thin stock on the edge of the rabbet in order to prevent the plane from cutting into it. Test the edge frequently with a template made of cardboard or sheet metal while it is being planed.

3. A round top may be rabbeted as at D, on the circular saw by first making a form or cradle for it in which it can be rotated as in Figure 35. The form is clamped to the saw table, and the saw is started and brought up through it to the correct height.

4. After rounding the rabbeted edge, fold a quarter sheet of sandpaper in the middle, hold it in the palm of the hand, and sand until smooth. The sharp edge of the rabbet may be sanded by folding the sandpaper over a hand scraper.

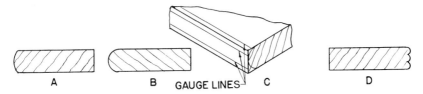

Fig. 36. Rounded and beaded table top edges.

5. The edges shown at A and B, Figure 36, are simply rounded with a jack plane according to lines marked with a pencil (C, Fig. 36). If the table is round, a circular plane or a spokeshave is used instead of a jack plane. These edges are smoothed with a file scraper and sandpaper. The beaded edge, D, Figure 36, is made with a scratch stock (Fig. 4) or a hand beader, which is a tool resembling a spokeshave.

288. Procedure for Doing Simple Veneering. 1. To veneer a surface means to glue a thin sheet, usually of another kind of wood, to it. This is done for two reasons, first, to strengthen the wood and, second, to make its surface more beautiful.

2. Wood is many times stronger when it is built up of several layers glued at right angles to each other, than when it is in one solid piece. Plywood is glued up in that way from several layers crossing each other, called "laminations." The modern waterproof glues make such fabricated wood practically indestructible (see Art. 223).

3. Veneer consists of thin sheets of wood, usually only ⅟₂₈ in. thick, which are sliced from a solid log on special machines. Depending upon its use, some veneer is plain and cut from common woods, and some is highly figured and cut from rare and costly woods.

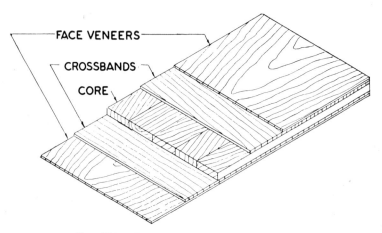

Fig. 37. Simple veneered construction.

4. The latter wood could not be used if cut into solid boards, because highly figured wood splits and warps more than straight-grained wood. It is, therefore, necessary to make a good foundation of plain, straight-grained boards on which to glue veneers. Such a foundation is called a "core."

5. The core for a table top should be glued up like an ordinary table top, but of narrow boards only from 2 to 3 in. wide. When dry, this core is planed flat and smooth on one side, then gauged on edges and ends and planed on the other side until it is smooth and of uniform thickness throughout.

6. Two pieces of plain, straight-grained veneer, called the "crossbands," are glued at right angles to the core, one on each side (Fig. 37). Use a cold-water glue, such as resin or casein glue, apply it to both sides of the

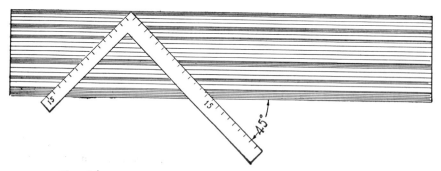

Fig. 38. Laying out 45-deg. angle on striped veneer.

core, and clamp the pieces in a veneer press. If the work is small enough, it may be clamped with hand screws between two boards.

Note that much veneering is still being done in the old way with animal glue, which requires a hot press or heated sheet-metal plates.

7. The work is now ready for the two outside pieces of veneers. The one to be glued to the bottom of the table top is called the "back veneer" and has plain grain. The other, to be glued to the top or face, is called the "face veneer" and is usually of a better grade of veneer, selected for its beauty, color, and grain. It is often cut to form various geometrical patterns. This is called "matching."

8. One of the most common forms of matching is the "diamond match." To make this match, select a piece of striped veneer and cut it at an angle of 45 deg. to its side (Fig. 38). This may be done by placing a steel square on the veneer so that the same number on the tongue and blade is over the edge. The angle will then be 45 deg. Use a veneer saw (Fig. 39) or a strong, sharp knife for cutting the veneer.

9. Place the piece of veneer, just cut, on the center lines which should be marked on the face of the top (Fig. 40). Turn the sheet of veneer over as in Figure 41, and cut the second piece of veneer. Then cut the third and

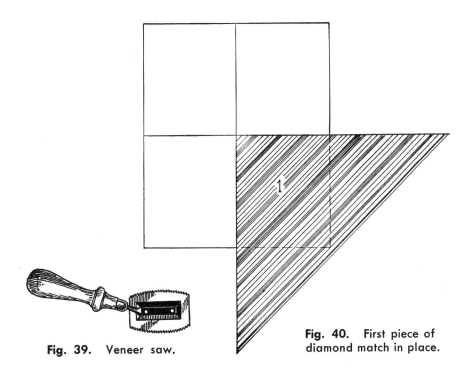

Fig. 39. Veneer saw.

Fig. 40. First piece of diamond match in place.

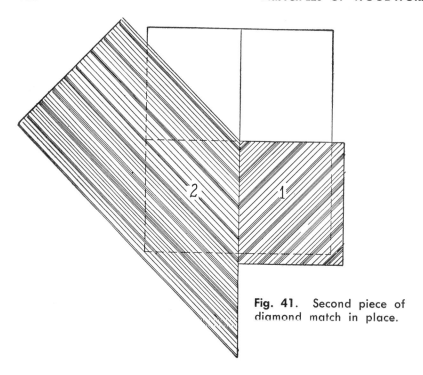

Fig. 41. Second piece of diamond match in place.

fourth pieces as shown in Figure 43. Another method of cutting a diamond match is shown in Figure 44.

10. It is now necessary to plane the sawed edges of the veneer, so that they will fit perfectly together. This is done by clamping them in a home-made clamp made of hardwood such as birch or maple. Note that the inside surfaces of the clamp are slightly rounded in order to hold the veneer tightly (Fig. 42).

11. Plane the edges to be glued along one of the center lines, then nail two of them (1 and 2) to a board, using veneer pins or fine brads. Drive them on a slant so that the two veneer edges will be brought as closely together as possible (Fig. 45). Reverse Numbers 2 and 4 and join to Numbers 1 and 3. If the veneer is too narrow for the pieces needed, waste pieces

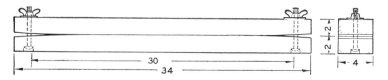

Fig. 42. Clamps for holding veneer while jointing.

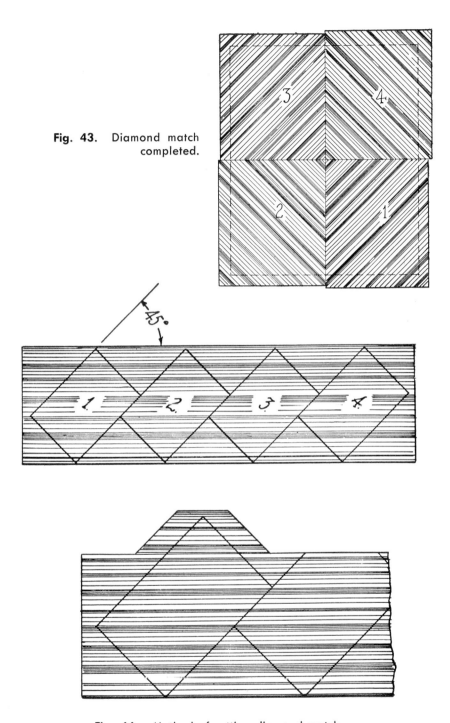

Fig. 43. Diamond match completed.

Fig. 44. Method of cutting diamond match.

Fig. 45. Taping veneers.

Fig. 46. Veneered stock in press. As the stock in this case was a little larger than the press, the projecting parts were clamped with C clamps.

may be joined to the edge with veneer tape as shown in the lower drawing. While in this position, glue a piece of veneer tape or ordinary gummed paper over the joint (Fig. 45). Plane and tape the other two veneers (3 and 4) in the same way.

12. The two taped pieces of veneer are then placed face to face and their edges are planed and taped. Be sure to plane these long edges square to the taped edges, and be careful not to chip them in the center. Tape the veneers on the face side only, because a piece of paper in a glued joint will not make a good bond.

13. Before gluing, the center lines should be squared over the edges in order to center the diamond match correctly. Each two joined edges must be directly above each center line. Put plenty

Fig. 47. Cutting veneer across the grain for a border.

of glue on the face side of the cross-banded core, but none on the veneer. Place the veneer in position and nail it with veneer pins (headless) or fine brads. Cut the heads of the brads off ¼ in. above the surface, place a couple of sheets of newspaper over the veneer, and then a piece of fir plywood, named the "caul," which is pressed down over the projecting brads.

14. Glue the back veneer at right angles to the crossbands, and then put the whole assembly in the veneer press and tighten it as much as possible. If the veneered surface is a little larger than the platen of the press, a few C clamps may be clamped along the edge as in Figure 46.

15. The veneered top should be left several hours in the press until perfectly dry. It is then squared in the same way as solid wood and the veneer tape removed by moistening it with water and gently scraping it off.

16. If it is desired to veneer the edges of the table top, cut strips of wood, a little wider than the thickness of the top, across the grain as in Figure 47. Tape them together, side by side, and glue them to the edges as in Figure 48.

Note that there are many variations of the diamond match and endless ways of combining veneers into beautiful and harmonious designs.

289. Procedure for Decorating by Overlays, Frets, or Veining. The chief object of these types of decoration is to relieve the monotony of a

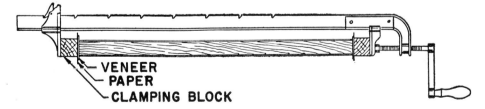

VENEER
PAPER
CLAMPING BLOCK

Fig. 48. Veneering edges.

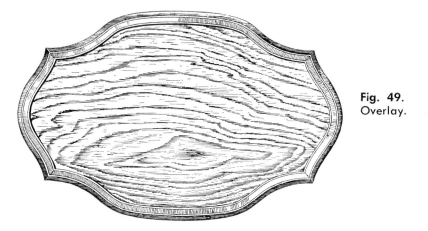

Fig. 49.
Overlay.

surface by a suitable design applied to it or outlined on it in two different shades of a color.

1. Overlays, as the name implies, are pieces of thin wood applied on top of a surface so as to form a raised part (Fig. 49). They should be made of selected grades of veneer with beautifully figured grain, and may be built up with plywood to various thicknesses. They are generally stained a lighter tone than the surface they decorate.

2. Frets are pierced overlays used especially as a decoration on panels. They are often stained darker than the panel to which they are glued. Both panel and fret should be finished before gluing. Glue should be applied very sparingly to the back of the fret, so that it will not be squeezed out on the panel.

Grilles are frets or latticework set in an open frame, as in doors of bookcases. They are sawed out of plywood.

3. Veining consists of a thin line of pleasing patterns, carved with a veining tool or a machine router, to decorate a plain surface (Fig. 50). As a method of decoration, it is almost identical with overlays.

Fig. 50.　Veined panel.

In some cases, the part within the line is stained a different shade from the part without the line, called "two toning," and in others the line itself is colored to make it stand out more clearly.

4. In the latter case, stain and fill the wood as described in Chapter 13, and clean the filler out of the line with a pointed stick.

5. Apply a sealing coat of shellac or lacquer, and sand smooth.

6. Apply the vein line color over the sealing coat with a fine-pointed artist's brush.

REVIEW QUESTIONS, CHAPTER 10

Possible score 45 points

Your score . . . . . .

PART I. COMPLETION QUESTIONS.   Complete the following statements:

1. In surface decoration, the beginner should be guided by a study of good
. . . .

2. Inlaying should be done only on . . . .

3. The purpose of veneering is to enhance the . . . . of the wood.

4. The process of cutting a shallow recess in one member into which another member of a different color or material is fitted and glued is called . . . .

5. Line inlays are from $\frac{1}{28}$ to . . . . in. thick.

6. Lines for inlays are readily cut by shaping a special cutter and fastening it in a . . . .

7. Grooves for line inlays can be cut easily with an electric . . . .

8. Insets for inlaying are glued in place with the brown paper . . . .
. . . .

9. The beauty of a turned column may be greatly enhanced by . . . .

10. In order to facilitate the making of flutes on the lathe, some lathes are provided with a . . . .

11. In addition to inlaying, furniture is often beautified by means of . . . .
. . . .

12. A popular design readily carved by the beginner is the . . . . leaf.

13. . . . . are used to accentuate certain parts of a piece of furniture such as a cornice, a base, or a panel.

14. The process of gluing a thin sheet of one kind of wood to another kind is called . . . .

15. Plywood is glued up from several crossed layers called . . . .

16. The thick, foundation layer of a piece of plywood is called the . . . .

17. To cut veneer, use a strong sharp knife or a . . . .

18. Four pieces of veneer, cut and glued at 45 degrees, form a . . . .
. . . . . .

19. The technique of applying a piece of thin wood on top of a surface so as to form a raised part is called . . . .

20. The thin layers of wood glued next to the core of plywood are called . . . .

PART II. TRUE-FALSE QUESTIONS. Indicate, by encircling T or F, whether the following statements are true or false.

21. Often wood surfaces are enriched or decorated by veneering, inlaying, carving, and painting.   T   F
22. The contrast between an inlay and the inlaid surface should be as high as possible.   T   F
23. Designs of inlay lines and insets can be bought commercially.   T   F
24. Bands of inlay absorb some moisture from the glue which causes them to shrink first and swell when dry.   T   F
25. To make spiral reeds it is necessary to make a careful layout.   T   F
26. Wood carving can be readily learned by following written instructions.   T   F
27. The acanthus leaf is seldom carved as an ornament on wood.   T   F
28. Some table top moldings can be partly completed on the circular saw.   T   F
29. The back veneer is always the good side of veneered plywood.   T   F
30. Frets are pierced overlays, used especially as a decoration on panels.   T   F

PART III. MULTIPLE-CHOICE QUESTIONS. Select, by encircling the correct letter, the answer which completes each statement:

31. One of the following woods is not satisfactory for inlaying:
    A. Sugar pine
    B. Maple
    C. Walnut
    D. Birch
32. Insets sold by manufacturers are as thick as:
    A. ¼ in.
    B. ⅛ in.
    C. ¹⁄₂₈ in.
    D. ½ in.
33. To do successful fluting on the lathe, the machine should have:
    A. Tool rest
    B. Steady rest
    C. Dividing head
    D. Assorted faceplates
34. One of the following is not a carving tool:
    A. Skew chisel
    B. Round-nose chisel
    C. Straight gouge
    D. Veining tool
35. In a piece of plywood, the two layers next to the outside are called:
    A. Core
    B. Face veneer
    C. Back veneer
    D. Crossbands

PART IV. MATCHING QUESTIONS. Match the terms to the left with the descriptions to the right by placing the correct letter in the parentheses:

36. (   ) Line inlays
37. (   ) Insets
38. (   ) A reed
39. (   ) Astragal
40. (   ) Stopped chamfers
41. (   ) Acanthus leaf
42. (   ) Torus
43. (   ) Ovolo
44. (   ) Laminations
45. (   ) Grilles

A. Are glued to a piece of brown paper to keep them together.
B. The architect's name for a reed.
C. A leaf design popular with wood carvers.
D. Made in pieces one yard long, $\frac{1}{16}$ in. to $\frac{1}{28}$ in. thick.
E. A quarter round molding.
F. The glued layers of plywood.
G. A semicircular molding or bead.
H. Latticework set in an open frame, as in doors of bookcases.
I. Flat cuts which do not extend all the way along the edge of a board.
J. A half-round molding.
K. Carvings with a veining tool.

11

Upholstery

The art of upholstery dates back to antiquity in Egypt and the Orient. In France, it reached a high degree of development during the reign of Louis XIV (1643–1715). In the same period of time, only loose cushions or pads were used in England, but when the monarchy was restored under Charles II (1660–1685), real upholstered furniture and fine woven fabrics made their appearance. The revocation of the Edict of Nantes in 1685 was a great factor in this development, because the French protestants, called "Huguenots," many of whom were skilled craftsmen, emigrated in large numbers to England to avoid religious persecution. The Edict of Nantes was a guaranty of religious freedom to French protestants.

Upholstery, like wood finishing, wood turning, and wood carving, is one of the trades that is closely related to cabinetmaking, and in some measure dependent upon the latter. It is, therefore, fitting that this book should give some attention at least to the most elementary processes of this art, a knowledge of which will be found useful and valuable in the making of chairs, stools, and similar articles of furniture.

292. New Upholstery Materials.* Upholstery today is still very much the art it has been for many years. A number of interesting changes, however, have taken place in recent years. Some of the more important ones are briefly discussed here. The upholstery craft continues to be a matter of

---

* Source: Thames, Gena, Reupholstering Chairs with Foam Rubber. Cornell Miscellaneous Bulletin, No. 20, 48 pp., 1954.

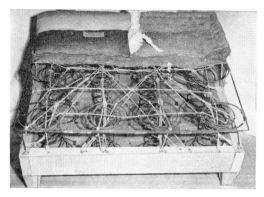

Fig. 1. Cut-away view showing tied springs.

Fig. 2. Jute webbing fastened to bottom. Springs are tied to webbing with string.

stretching webbing so that springs are supported properly; the technique of tying springs in place; the application over springs of various layers of materials for comfort and ease of rest; and finally the process of covering the unit to be upholstered with an attractive and long-wearing cover. Besides the usual jute fiber webbing, there now is on the market a webbing made of steel. Steel webbing has two distinct advantages over jute webbing. First, when properly installed it does not sag in the course of time; second, it eliminates tying of springs which is necessary with the old type of webbing (Figs. 1 and 2). Steel webbing is fastened to the frame with so-called "strong hold" (one way) nails or size 4 rosin-coated nails. It is, like other webbing, stretched tight with a special webbing stretcher. In many upholstery jobs coil springs are being replaced by so-called no-sag springs (Figs.

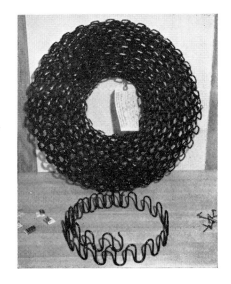

Fig. 3. No-sag springs.

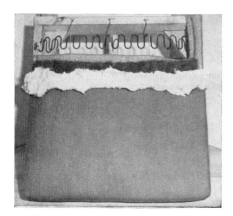

Fig. 4. Cut-away view show-   Fig. 5. Bottom view of no-sag
ing no-sag springs.   springs.

3, 4, and 5). These springs are self-supporting and eliminate a great deal of bulk and weight. They are fastened to the frame with metal clips (Fig. 6). Little springs between the large springs prevent excessive sideways movement. Often they are held in place with regular spring twine.

As a first covering over springs, an insulation cover of wire-woven burlap can be used. This type of burlap differs from plain burlap in that it need not be tied to the springs underneath.

Probably the greatest advance in upholstery has been made by the introduction of foam rubber as the material for making comfortable seats.

293. What Is Foam Rubber?* Briefly, it is the milk or sap of the rubber tree. Pure latex is collected on the rubber plantations, mostly of Southeast Asia, and shipped in liquid form to manufacturers all over the

* Source: National Rubber Bureau, "Convert to Comfort with Latex Foam," 21 pp., 1959.

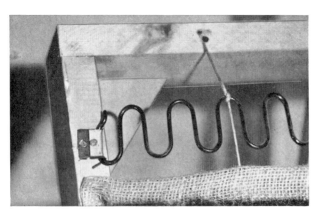

Fig. 6. No-sag
springs in place.

world, particularly those in the United States of America. At the manufacturing plants, certain chemicals are added to the latex to assist in the curing process as well as to help form the spongy structure.

After having been chemically treated, the latex is next whipped into a creamy froth. The addition of air plus some other ingredients cause the latex to foam. It is during this foaming process that the future texture or firmness of the finished material is being controlled. The extreme lightness of the finished product (85 to 95 per cent air) is in direct proportion to the amount of air that has been added in the mixing process. When this foamy mixture has reached the right consistency it is poured into metal molds of the desired shape and placed in giant ovens to "bake" under controlled heat and pressure.

After the curing process, the latex foam is removed from the ovens, stripped from the molds, washed to remove any impurities and finally dried. It is now ready to go on the market as a most versatile upholstery material.

Latex foam rubber is being successfully used wherever a cushion is needed. Besides in the transportation field and in many home furnishings, it has proved to be the ideal upholstery material in theaters, auditoriums, hotels, public buildings, hospitals, and many others.

There are five general types of latex for upholstery work (Fig. 7). Of these, plain sheet stock and cored utility stock can be adapted to many uses. Since latex foam is readily cut to size and form with scissors, these two types are more practical and more economical than special molded units. All types made come in different grades of density, from very soft to very firm.

Plain sheet stock (Fig. 7A) may be purchased in solid sheets and cut in any desired shape. Sheets are available in thicknesses ranging from ¼ in.

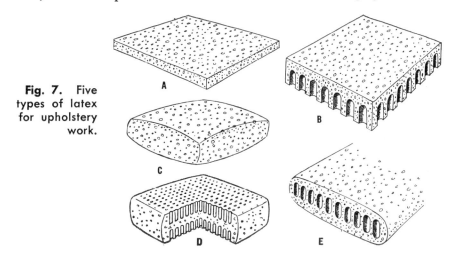

Fig. 7. Five types of latex for upholstery work.

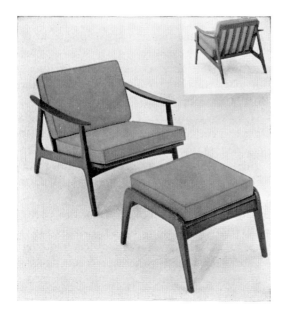

Fig. 8. Danish chairs and ottoman with reversible zippered cushions.

to 1¼ in. Wherever thin padding is desirable, such as over springs, seats, backs, and arms, sheet stock is most suitable.

Cored utility stock (Fig. 7B) is made with molded openings in one side and is recommended for applications where more depth and buoyancy is needed. It comes in thicknesses ranging from ¾ in. to 4½ in. Several grades of density are available. It can readily be cut and cemented into place.

Fully molded cushions (Fig. 7C) are full-depth units which have been molded ready-to-fit into furniture. They cover without further cutting or shaping. One can select from a variety of standard forms or have one's requirements made to individual specifications. Molded cushions are sold as solid foam, half-cored or cored through. Furniture manufacturers use these types a great deal in quantity production of identical chairs and other mass produced units.

Inner cushion units (Fig. 7D) are often used in installations where economy and cost is a factor. They can satisfactorily take the place of the more costly innerspring units in seats and reversible cushions (Fig. 8).

Utility inner cushions (Fig. 7E) are extra-long molded units, from which sections can be cut to suit a particular need. They have inside coring and are crowned one way only, namely across the width.

The equipment and tool requirements for work with foam rubber are quite simple and limited. A soft lead or wax pencil can be used for marking and laying out patterns. A pair of large scissors cuts this material to almost any shape.

When doing a reupholstery job over existing springs, it is advisable to protect the latex foam cushion from unnecessary rubbing and wear by first stretching over the springs a suitable insulating pad of burlap, jute, cotton, or sisal.

When applied over hard, solid surfaces, provisions should be made for proper ventilation. In a plywood base, for example, one should bore a number of evenly spaced holes to permit free passage of air. Metal bases should have a rust-resisting finish. Foam rubber should not be exposed to direct sunlight and heat. If so exposed, it will discolor, harden, and crumble. When latex foam is directly applied over jute webbing, it can be held in place with tape and rubber cement. Tacking tape serves as a means of forming a smooth edge and of securing the cushion to the base. It should be cemented on the foam for a distance of at least one inch. The proper cement must be applied to both the tape and the edges of the piece of foam rubber and allowed to dry long enough to become "tacky." Any cement left exposed should be dusted with powdered soapstone. Freshly cemented pieces must be permitted to set for several hours.

In the following article a short step-by-step procedure in doing a simple reupholstery job is presented. With the ever rising cost of having home repairs done by trained experts, the versatility of foam rubber is being readily adopted by the home craftsman and hobbyist.

294. Procedure for Reupholstering a Slip-Seat Chair. 1. Take the seat from the chair, and "strip" the worn cover (Fig. 9). Make any necessary repairs to the seat at this time.

2. Place the frame upside down on a piece of cored utility stock of foam rubber of the desired thickness. With a wax pencil, trace around the seat, adding ½ in. to all sides (Fig. 10).

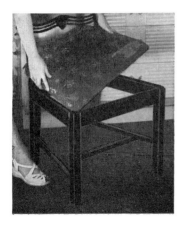

Fig. 10. Laying out size of seat.

Fig. 9. Removing worn seat.

Fig. 11. Cutting foam rubber.

Fig. 12. Trimming edges on cored side.

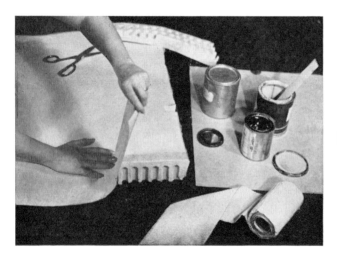

Fig. 13. Taping the edge.

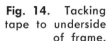

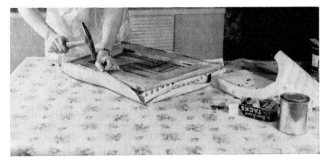

Fig. 14. Tacking tape to underside of frame.

Fig. 15. Tacking final covering in place.

3. Cut out the cushion and bevel the edges with a pair of scissors (Figs. 11 and 12).

4. Apply cement to both tape and edges to be covered. Permit the cement to dry until it becomes "tacky." Put tape in place as shown in Figure 13.

5. Place the seat upside down and fasten the edge to the frame with upholstery tacks (Fig. 14).

6. Lay out and cut the final covering material. Tack this in place with upholstery tacks (Fig. 15). If the final covering has a straight line or striped pattern, make sure that the lines of material run in the proper direction.

7. Replace the completed seat on the chair.

295. Procedure for Making a Plain Pad Seat. A pad seat is the simplest form of upholstery and, as the name implies, merely consists in making a pad or cushion on a wooden base (Fig. 16).

1. If the pad is to cover the entire board, except for a 1-in. margin along the edges, a line is marked accordingly all around the board.

2. Use tow, moss, or hair for the stuffing; pick it carefully so that it is free from lumps, and spread half of it evenly over the seat to about ½ in. from the line marked.

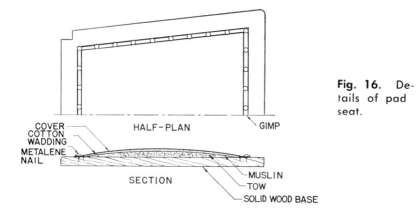

COVER
COTTON
WADDING
METALENE
NAIL

HALF-PLAN   GIMP

SECTION   MUSLIN
TOW
SOLID WOOD BASE

Fig. 16. Details of pad seat.

3. It is important that the stuffing does not slide on the wooden base. It may be held in place either by tacking it to the base or by coating the base with glue before spreading it.

4. Distribute the rest of the stuffing evenly over the first layer, and stretch and tack a piece of muslin over it. Fold the muslin over on itself, and begin tacking it from the center of the four edges, gradually working toward the corners.

5. Place a piece of cotton wadding over the muslin, and then tack the covering in place.

6. Begin tacking from the centers of the front, back, and sides, driving the tacks only partly home. This is called "slip tacking."

7. Restretch the cover by stroking it from side to side and from front to back. Pull out a few of the tacks at a time, and retack the cover firmly.

8. Make a gimp or narrow band of the same material as that of the covering. Gimps also may be bought ready made. Tack the gimp in place, so that it is even with the line marked. Use metalene nails on leather or imitation leather, and gimp tacks on a cloth covering. Space the tacks from 2 to 4 in. apart.

9. The gimp is mitered in the corners by folding a pleat on it.

Tow is made from the dried stems of flax plants, which go through various picking and refining processes. Tow is sold to the trade in different grades of fineness. Muslin, wadding, and imitation leather are all products of the cotton plant. Muslin is a thin cloth which is sold either bleached or unbleached. Wadding or cotton felt is a by-product of the ginning process. Imitation or artificial leather consists of a strong woven cloth, which is dyed to the color of the finished product. It is then covered with nitrocellulose, which is a liquid also made of cotton. This forms a very strong and durable material used for many other purposes besides upholstery, as, for instance, suitcases, bookbindings, novelties, and automobile interiors.

Moss is a plant which grows on the branches and trunks of trees. It grows abundantly in swampy regions in Louisiana, Florida, and South America.

Fresh moss is piled in small heaps kept moist with water. In the course of two or three months, the green covering rots away leaving only the black hairlike fiber. This is then dried, ginned, and baled. Moss is sold in different grades, according to the length of the drying time and the number of ginnings it has had.

Hair used in the upholstery trade is cut from the tails and manes of horses and from cattle and hogs. Most of it comes from South America, Texas, Montana, and Canada. It is sorted, sterilized, and permanently curled in a chemical bath.

296. Procedure for Making a Pad Seat With a Roll Edge. This type of seat differs from a plain pad seat in that the covering extends over its outer edges. A roll of stuffing must be made to cover the sharp wooden edges in order to prevent them from cutting through the cover. A roll edge is formed as follows:

1. Tack a piece of burlap, about 3 to 4 in. wide, close to the outer edges of the seat so that the burlap projects beyond the seat (Fig. 17). Sometimes a fold about ¼ in. wide is made on the edge of the burlap so that the tacks will hold better.

2. Use fine tow, hair, or moss for the stuffing. Place it along the edge and fold the burlap over it. Make the roll as hard and as even in size and shape as possible, and then tack the burlap in place (Fig. 18). If the burlap is cut straight, the lateral threads of the material will act as a guide in forming the roll. The size of the roll varies with different conditions. For ordinary work, such as a seat on a footstool, a role about 1 in. in diameter is suitable.

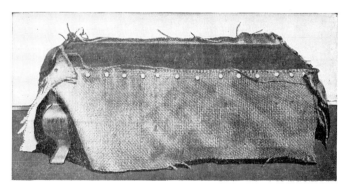

Fig. 17. Burlap for roll edge tacked to sides of seat.

Fig. 18. Roll edge formed.

3. Proceed with the upholstery as explained in Article 295, steps 2 to 4.

4. Sliptack the muslin to the sides of the seat, or in the case of a footstool, to the rails near their upper or lower edges. Restretch the muslin as explained in Article 295, step 7, until it is tight and smooth. Then tack it firmly in place folding the edge over on itself.

5. Place a piece of wadding over the muslin, and tack the covering and the gimp along the lower edges of the rails.

6. When the covering extends over the sides of the seat and is tacked to the lower edge of the rails as in the footstool, Figure 19, the corners must be folded or pleated in a certain way.

7. Stretch the covering well, and tack it along the lower edges of the rails to within 2 in. of the corners.

8. Fold the cover from the sides with the short rails over the front and rear corners, and tack it in place.

9. Cut away the surplus material at the corners, fold a pleat on the

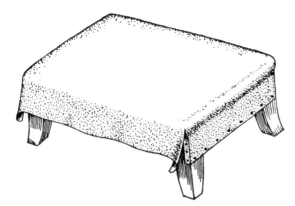

Fig. 19. Making pleats.

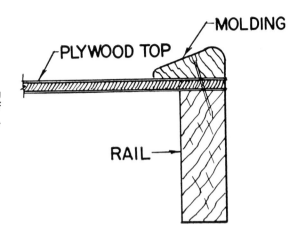

Fig. 20. Wood molding used in place of roll edge.

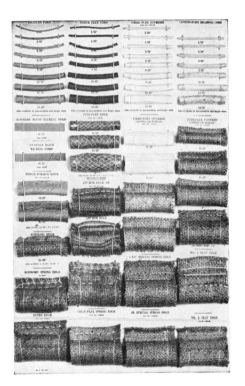

Fig. 21. Seaming cords and edgings.

front part of the covering, and fasten it with one tack so that it is even with the corner. Pleats on chairs are always laid to the rear.

10. The effect of a roll edge may be produced very simply by making a molding as shown in Figure 20, mitering it in the corners and nailing it along the edges.

Burlap is a coarse cloth, woven from the bast of the jute plant (Art. 365) which grows in India. It is used for a great many purposes, such as up-holstery, draperies, bags for sugar, potatoes, and other products, as a base for linoleum, etc. Burlap is made in different qualities or weights. The pieces are generally 40 in. wide and 100 yds. long.

Instead of making roll edges, edging can be purchased ready made. Figure 21 shows a display of seaming cords and edgings.

297. Procedure for Upholstering a Slip Seat. A slip seat fits tightly between the rails of a chair, bench, or stool. The seat, which may be up-holstered or woven over a wooden frame (Art. 298), generally fits into a rabbet cut on the inside edges of the rails. It may also be supported and fastened to blocks or cleats screwed to the rails.

1. The frame of the seat is made of four pieces of wood ¾ to ⅞ in. thick and about 2½ to 3 in. wide. They may be joined by end-lap joints (Art. 185), dowel joints (Art. 178), or slip joints (Art. 198). Slip joints are the strongest and, therefore, preferred.

2. Join the pieces to conform to the shape of the seat as square, rectangu-lar, or trapezoid. Allow from 1⁄16 to ⅛ in. for the covering on each of the outside edges of the frame, depending upon the thickness of the material. In other words, if the seat, for example, measures 12 by 18 in. within the rabbets, the finished outside dimensions of the frame should be 11⅞ by 17⅞ in. if 1⁄16 in. is allowed, and 11¾ by 17¾ in. if ⅛ in. is allowed.

3. After the frame has been glued, it should be smoothed with a plane. A chamfer, about 3⁄16 in. wide, should also be planed on the upper outside edges of the frame.

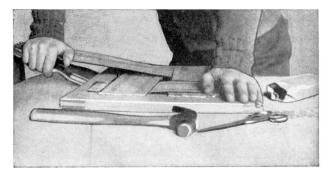

Fig. 22. Stretching webbing.

4. Begin the upholstery by nailing strips of webbing to the upper faces of the frame. For a chair-seat frame, two or three strips of webbing are used each way. Fold the webbing over about 1½ in. from the end so that the carpet tacks pass through two layers of webbing. Tack one end of a piece of webbing in the center of one of the rails and about 1 in. from its outer edge. Stretch the webbing over the opposite rail with the webbing stretcher (Fig. 22), and drive in three or four 10-oz. tacks. Release the stretcher, and cut the webbing with a pair of scissors about 1½ in. outside the tacks. Bend this end back over the tacks and fasten with a few more tacks. Fasten the other pieces of webbing in the same manner.

Pieces of webbing crossing each other should be interlaced for greater strength.

Like burlap, webbing is also made from jute fibers. Webbing is sold in rolls 72 yd. long. The standard widths are 3, 3½, and 4 in.

5. Cut a piece of burlap to about the size of the frame. Fold the edges over about ¾ in. all around, stretch and tack it to the face of the frame so that the webbing is covered. Use 4-oz. tacks.

6. Apply a layer of fine tow, or moss, about 2 in. thick, evenly over the face of the seat (Fig. 23). Pick it carefully with the fingers so that it becomes light and fluffy without any hard lumps.

7. Cut another piece of burlap a little larger than the frame, and stretch it over the layer of stuffing. Tack it temporarily to the edges of the frame without driving the tacks home. Now sew the burlap and stuffing to the webbing, using a long upholsterer's needle and twine (Fig. 24). First sew all around along the inside edges of the frame and then along the center. Have the stitches about 3 in. long come on top of the burlap, and pull them tight after completing the sewing. The stuffing and burlap are now held firmly, and

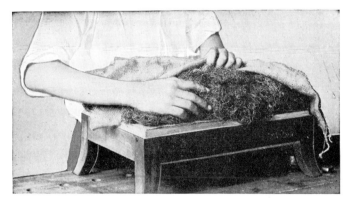

Fig. 23. Picking stuffing and placing it on frame.
Notice burlap tacked over webbing.

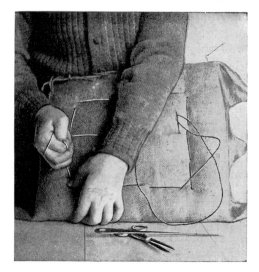

Fig. 24. Sewing stuffing to webbing.

the tacks temporarily holding the latter should be removed from the edge of the frame.

Thin three-ply veneer may be used instead of webbing. The processes in applying and sewing stuffing and burlap are the same. The upholsterer's needle is generally strong enough to go through thin three-ply veneer, but if the veneer should be too heavy for the needle, a few small holes may be quickly bored.

8. To form the edge of the seat, add some moss along the edge, shape it into a roll, pull the burlap over it, and tack the latter to the chamfered edge of the frame. Shape the edge of the seat so that it overhangs the edge of the frame a little and is of the same height as the part that was sewed to the webbing. When tacking the burlap to the frame, fold its edge toward the inside so that the outside is perfectly smooth.

9. Finish the corners last. If they have been cut to fit against the corner

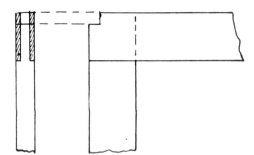

Fig. 25. Rear corner of chair-seat frame.

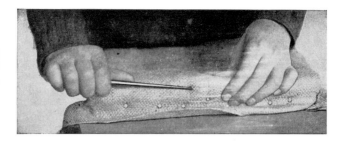

Fig. 26. Shaping edge with regulator.

of a chair leg (Fig. 25), as is often the case, the edge must, of course, conform to that shape. The sharp peen of an upholsterer's hammer is very helpful in forming such corners.

10. The shape of the edge is now improved and made sharper by manipulating the stuffing with the regulator (Fig. 26). It is then sewed with a curved needle, so that the stitches, each about ½ in. long, lie on top and below the edge, but do not pass over it (Fig. 27). The thread passes over the edge only in corners that fit around a square leg or post. This is done so as to make a sharper corner.

A curved needle is used instead of a straight one, because it goes in deeper and therefore pulls more material toward the edge.

11. A thin layer of moss or hair is next spread over the seat, so that it is made slightly higher in the center, sloping gently toward the edges (Fig. 28). A piece of muslin is stretched over this and fastened temporarily by

Fig. 27. Sewing edge with curved needle.

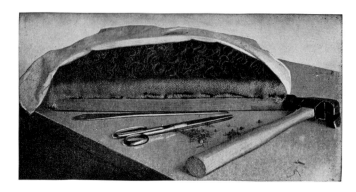

Fig. 28.
Stretching and
tacking muslin
to edge.

slip-tacking or with large pins or skewers which are stuck into the upholstery just above the wooden frame. The muslin is then tacked to the edge
of the frame, after which the pins are removed.

If the seat is to be covered with silk, damask, or other thin material, a
sheet of upholsterer's blue cotton wadding should be placed over the muslin
to prevent the hair from sticking through the covering fabric.

12. The covering is tacked to the underside of the frame.

13. A piece of black cambric tacked to the underside of the frame will
prevent dust from the upholstery material from falling to the floor.

Cambric is a cloth woven either of linen or cotton threads. Upholsterers
use a cambric made of cotton. It is made only in two colors, white and black.

When a slip seat is made flush with the rails of a chair, the sewed edge
may be omitted.

298. Procedure for Weaving a Fiber Seat.   Although rush weaving and
caning has nothing to do with upholstery in the strict sense of the word,
these processes are, nevertheless, used for the same purpose — the covering,
of a chair seat — and are, therefore, treated in the present chapter.

Woven seats for chairs, stools, and settees have been popular in this
country since the first New England settlements. These seats were called
"rush seats" or "flag seats," and were woven from a grasslike plant growing
to a height of from 2 to 4 ft. The soft, pliant stems of these plants were
dried and then twisted together to form the ropelike strands of the
rush weave.

Rush seats are still made in the same manner, but it requires some skill
to keep the strands properly twisted and of a uniform thickness. A newer
material called "art fiber," which consists of paper twisted into a rope of
uniform thickness, makes a strong and good-looking seat, and is much easier
to work with. This fiber is made in various thicknesses. A strand about ³⁄₁₆
in. or less in diameter is suitable for the weaving described in the following.

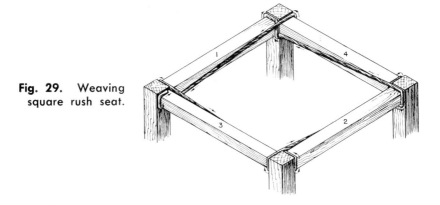

Fig. 29. Weaving square rush seat.

Fiber may be woven over the rails of a chair or stool, or over a loose frame to fit inside the rails of a chair. This loose frame is called a "slip seat." In any case, the outside sharp edges of the wood should be slightly rounded so as not to cut the fiber. On a fixed seat, the legs should extend as much above the rails as the thickness of the fiber (Fig. 29). On a slip seat, a block of the same thickness as the fiber should be glued to the top of the frame in each corner (Figs. 30 and 31). In both cases, the weaving should be flush on the edges with the legs or corner blocks. The rails should, therefore, set back from the corners for a distance equal to the thickness of the fiber. The weaving is done as follows:

1. Cut a few yards from the roll of fiber and tack one end of this to the underside of the rail numbered 1 (Fig. 29).

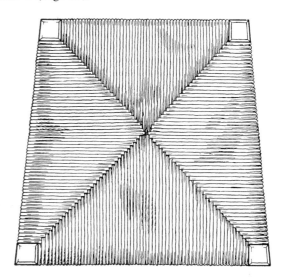

Fig. 30. Rush-woven slip seat.

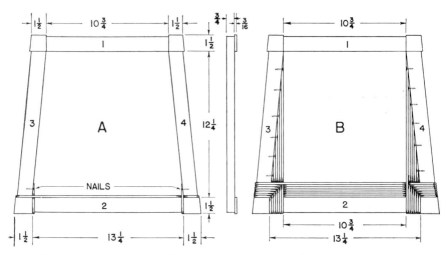

Fig. 31. Rush weave on slip seat. A, One strand woven and tacked in place. B, Front rail filled in.

2. Bring the length of fiber back and up over 1, under 2, back over 2, under 3, over 3, under 4, over 4, under 2, over 2, under 1, over 1, under 4, over 4, under 3, over 3, under 1, and so on until the seat is completed.

3. Keep each succeeding strand as close to the previous one as possible and be careful to pull them as tightly as you can.

4. This weave forms two diagonal lines which cross in the center on a square seat. Take care to get these lines straight. If necessary, hammer the fiber in place by driving on a block of wood held against any strand which is out of line.

5. Join a new length of fiber to the one with which you are weaving by tying a square or reef knot. This knot, of course, should always come on the lower side of the seat.

6. It is well to stuff pieces of soft paper in between the upper and lower strands of fiber so as to make the seat more solid.

7. When finishing the seat, use a sharpened dowel to force the strands apart in the center in order to make room for the last strands.

When the seat is wider at the front than at the rear, such as the chair seat shown in Figure 30, this extra width is filled in as follows: Tack the end of a strand of fiber to the inside edge of side rail No. 3 near the front corner (A, Fig. 31). Bring it under front rail No. 2, back over 2, under 3, over 3, under 4, over 4, under 2, over 2, and then nail it to the inside edge of side rail No. 4 near the front corner. Cut off the end above the nail, weave another strand and continue in this manner until the distance between the woven strands on the front rail equals that between the blocks on the

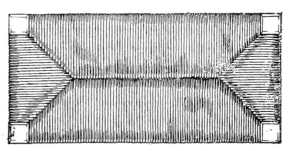

Fig. 32. Rectangular
rush-woven seat.

rear rail (B, Fig. 31). Then tack a strand to the underside of the rear rail
No. 1 and continue the weaving as explained above (Fig. 29).

When the seat is rectangular, such as that shown in Figure 32, the
weaving is done as explained above until the two short rails are completely
covered. The fiber is then woven back and forth between the two long rails
until these are also covered.

8. It is recommended to give rush seats a coat of glue sizing in order to
make them waterproof. They may then be varnished or lacquered as desired.

Fiber is made in many different colors. Follow manufacturer's directions
as to finishing.

299. Procedure for Weaving a Cane Seat. Cane is made from the bark
of a palm, which grows in the Philippines and other East Indian countries.
This bark is stripped from the trunk by machinery, after which it is cut
into narrow ribbons called "cane." Cane is graded according to the different widths into which it is cut, as superfine, fine-fine, fine, medium, coarse,
and binding.

1. The frame for a cane seat is made in the manner explained in
Article 297.

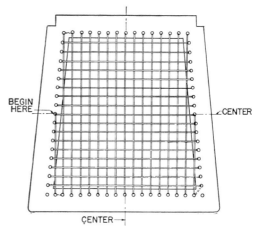

Fig. 33. Caning a chair
seat; two single strands
woven.

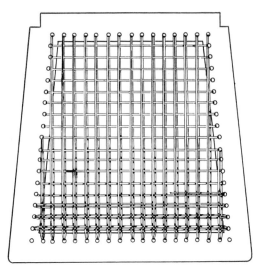

Fig. 34. Caning a chair seat; fourth strand being interlaced.

2. The holes for the cane are bored about ⅝ in. from the inside edges of the frame. For fine cane, the holes should be ⁵⁄₃₂ in. in diameter and spaced ½ in. center to center. For medium cane, the holes should be ³⁄₁₆ in. in diameter and spaced ⅝ in. center to center.

3. Mark a pencil line all around the frame ⅝ in. from its inside edges. Mark the center point of each member of the frame on this line, and lay out the centers of the holes from these points.

4. Notice that there are four holes more in the front rail than in the rear rail (Fig. 33). To overcome this difficulty, start the first strand of cane in the center hole in one of the sides, and bring it down through the second hole in the front rail. Then draw it up through the third hole in the front rail, and down through the corner hole in the rear rail, and so on, until a row of parallel strands is stretched between the front and rear rails (Fig. 33).

5. Now weave a similar row of strands between the two side rails. This row of strands will cross the first row at right angles (Fig. 33).

6. When a strand is used up, its end is looped around the weave running between the holes on the underside of the seat. A new strand is fastened in a similar way. A couple of round, wooden pegs, fitting into the holes of the frame, will serve to hold the cane during the weaving process.

7. After completing the weaving of the single strand between the sides, repeat the weaving between the front and rear rails, drawing the cane through the same set of holes. The single strand woven from side to side, therefore, passes between the two strands woven from front to rear.

8. A fourth strand is now woven from side to side, and interlaced between the first and third strands as shown in Figure 34.

9. The weaving is completed with two diagonal strands crossing each other at right angles (Fig. 35).

10. A piece of coarse cane, called "binding cane," is usually fastened along the edge of the weaving. Very fine cane is used to bind it.

An awl, a tool resembling an ice pick in shape, is useful in forcing the weaving together in the holes, so that new strands may be inserted.

Fig. 35. Section of completed weave.

300. Procedure for Applying Cane Webbing. Weaving cane by hand, as explained in Article 299, is a slow and tedious process. Caning is, therefore, often done with machine-woven cane, called "cane webbing."

Cane webbing is manufactured in widths of 10, 12, 14, 16, and 18 in., and is sold by the yard. Open-woven cane resembles the weaving done by hand. Cane webbing is quickly and easily applied, and it looks just as well as hand-woven cane.

1. Cut a groove ¼ in. wide by ⅜ in. deep along the inside edges of the seat frame to be caned. The distance from the edges to the groove should be about ⅝ in. If the grooves are straight, they may be cut on the circular saw, but if they are curved, they must be cut on a router or boring machine, using a router bit.

2. Cut the cane sheets, so that they are at least 1½ in. larger than the distance between the outside edges of the grooves. This will allow ¾ in. of cane on each side for driving into the grooves.

3. Soak the sheet of cane in water for at least one-half hour, and in the meantime prepare a board which will fit over the inside edges of the frame without covering any part of the grooves.

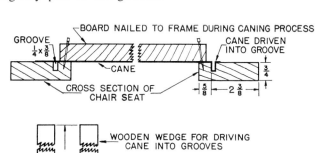

Fig. 36. Applying cane webbing.

4. Run hot glue into the grooves, and place the wet sheet of cane over the frame, so that it projects equally over the grooves on all four sides. Place the board over the cane, and fasten it with a fine brad to each of the rails (Fig. 36).

5. Drive the cane into the grooves with a wooden wedge, shaped like a ¾-in. cold chisel, but with a rounded point (Fig. 36).

6. Run more glue into the grooves and drive the splines in halfway. Splines made of rattan are used especially on curved grooves. On straight grooves, wooden splines may also be used.

7. Cut away the projecting ends of the cane before driving the splines in all the way. This may be done by running a sharp knife or chisel along the outside edges of the spline.

8. Drive the splines in all the way, using a small block of wood to protect them from being marred by the blows of the hammer.

9. When the cane dries, it will contract, thus making the seat very tight.

REVIEW QUESTIONS, CHAPTER 11

Possible score 35 points

Your score . . . . . .

PART I. COMPLETION QUESTIONS.   Complete the following statements:

1. Upholstery reached a very high degree of development under the reign of the French king . . . .
2. Besides a jute fiber webbing, there is now on the market a webbing made of . . . .
3. Instead of coil springs, upholsterers now often use so-called . . . . springs.
4. Probably the greatest recent advance in upholstery has been made by the introduction of . . . .
5. Basically, this material consists of the milk or sap of the . . . .
6. This material can be purchased in solid sheets, called . . . .
7. Probably the simplest form of an upholstery job consists of making a . . . .
8. Webbing is stretched with a special tool called . . . .
9. The final piece of material tacked to the underside of an upholstered chair is called . . . .
10. Cane, used for weaving seats, is made from the bark of a palm which grows in a number of East Indian countries particularly the . . . .

PART II. TRUE-FALSE QUESTIONS. Indicate, by encircling **T** or **F**, whether the following statements are true or false.

11. The art of upholstery dates back to antiquity in Egypt and the Orient.   T   F
12. The reign of the French king Louis XIV lasted from 1543–1615.   T   F
13. During the past fifty years no changes have been made in the art of upholstery.   T   F
14. Coil springs are the only type of springs used in upholstery.   T   F
15. Foam rubber, as an upholstery material, is of little or no value.   T   F
16. The lightness of foam rubber is in direct proportion to the amount of air that has been added in the mixing process.   T   F
17. Foam rubber, when exposed to direct sunlight, will discolor, harden, and crumble.   T   F
18. The making of slip seats is considered one of the more difficult upholstery jobs.   T   F
19. Rush weaving and caning used to be a popular method of covering chair seats.   T   F
20. Before using cane, it should be soaked properly.   T   F

PART III. MULTIPLE-CHOICE QUESTIONS. Select, by encircling the correct letter, the answer which completes each statement:

21. The greatest recent advance in upholstery was made with the introduction of:
    A. Coil springs
    B. Jute webbing
    C. Foam rubber
    D. Cane
22. One of the following is not used as a stuffing in upholstery:
    A. Hair
    B. Moss
    C. Cambric
    D. Tow
23. One of the following is an unnecessary tool when making foam rubber seat covers:
    A. Scissors
    B. Webbing stretcher
    C. Cement
    D. Tape
24. The first job in reupholstering a slip seat chair is:
    A. Cut the new cushion to size
    B. Attach final covering material
    C. Strip the worn cover
    D. Tape the edges
25. One of the following is not used when fastening springs in upholstery jobs:
    A. Tape
    B. Webbing stretcher
    C. Tacks
    D. Tack hammer

PART IV. MATCHING QUESTIONS. Match the terms to the left with the descriptions to the right by placing the correct letter in the parentheses:

26. (   ) Edict of Nantes
27. (   ) Steel webbing
28. (   ) Metal clips
29. (   ) Pure latex
30. (   ) Fully molded cushions
31. (   ) Ventilation
32. (   ) Slip tacking
33. (   ) Wadding
34. (   ) Cambric
35. (   ) Caning

A. Used in fastening no-sag springs.
B. Ready to use in furniture upholstery.
C. Guaranteed religious freedom to English protestants.
D. The procedure of driving tacks partly home.
E. Does not sag and eliminates tying of springs.
F. Cover underneath a chair.
G. Collected on the rubber plantations.
H. A method of making seats, using cane.
I. A by-product of the cotton ginning process.
J. Important in the use of foam rubber.
K. Guaranteed religious freedom to French protestants.

CHAPTER 12

Modern Coated Abrasives

When speaking of an abrasive we mean any hard, sharp material which wears away a softer, less resistant surface when the two are rubbed together. This term embraces sharpening stones, grinding wheels and the great variety of coated abrasives, often incorrectly referred to as sandpaper.

The first true abrasive of which there is any record is emery. The Old Testament refers to a stone called Shamir, another name for emery. It was used to shape and sharpen the crude, metal tools of those days.

Several centuries passed before an attempt was made to fit abrasive grains to a flexible backing. The Chinese crushed seashells and fixed these bits of shell to parchment. About two centuries ago, the Swiss began coating crushed glass on a paper backing. This practice continued for many years, though glass has neither the strength nor the sharpness to make a satisfactory abrasive. About one century ago glass was replaced by the more durable abrasives, flint and emery. These two minerals can be found in many parts of the world, and were for many years the only abrasives known.*

303. Types of Abrasives.** Abrasives fall into two convenient classifications, natural and electric furnace. Among the natural ones, one finds flint, garnet, and emery. The two electric furnace abrasives most commonly used in industry are silicon carbide and aluminum oxide.

Flint or flint quartz is found in many parts of this country but not all flint quartz is suitable for abrasive purpose. For example, gray flint used by the early American Indians in making arrow and spear heads, is unsatisfactory as an abrasive. The best types range from a dull grayish-white to faint pink and are mined from open pits in New Hampshire and Maryland (Fig. 1). At the manufacturing plant the large lumps are crushed into fine, sharp crystals. Flint lacks the hardness and durability of other abrasives. It is sold in sheets or handy packages primarily for the use of homeowners and hobbyists.

Garnet crystals are much sharper and harder than flint crystals (Fig. 2). This mineral actually belongs to the precious stone family, but as a gem

---

* Behr-Manning Co., "A Lecture Course on Coated Abrasives," pp. 7 and 8.
** *Ibid.*, pp. 9–17.

Fig. 1. Flint.

Fig. 2. Garnet.

it has little value because of flaws and impurities. This, however, does not affect its usefulness as an excellent abrasive.

Although there are seven known forms of garnet, only two have been used to any extent for coated abrasives. The best garnet, called Almandite, comes from the Adirondack Mountains in the state of New York.

Garnet crystals are found embedded in surrounding minerals, which are useless as abrasives and must first be separated. The process by which garnet is obtained is similar to the process of panning for gold. After the ore is blasted from the mountainside, it is crushed and passed over a series of vibrating "jigs" operated in water. The garnet, being heavier, settles down. Only about 5 to 7 per cent of garnet is present in the ore, which means that whole mountains must be removed and sorted out to supply the demand. When received at the manufacturing plant the individual pieces of garnet are about the size of a bean.

Abrasives are measured for hardness on a scale known as the Moh scale. On it diamonds are rated as 10, the highest possible rating. Garnet ranges from 6.5 to 7.5 which indicates that it is a fairly hard mineral. In addition to this hardness, garnet has a certain toughness which prevents the crystals from breaking down too quickly. As an abrasive it is far superior to flint.

Emery is a natural abrasive which for centuries has been mined in Turkey and 'Greece. It is a dead-black mineral, essentially a mixture of iron oxide (40 per cent) and corundum (60 per cent) (Fig. 3). This corundum is a natural aluminum oxide and forms the abrasive action of emery. Although iron oxide detracts from the efficiency of emery as an abrasive, it adds to its polishing action. With a grain shape which is somewhat round, the cutting action of emery is very slight, but it has great polishing potentials.

Silicon carbide is an electric-furnace abrasive first made in 1891. This material was discovered in an attempt to make artificial diamonds. When a mixture of silicon (sand) and carbon was heated in a miniature electric furnace, the experimenters succeeded in fusing a minute portion of this mixture, producing a few exceedingly hard and sharp crystals of a beautiful blue color (Fig. 4). They were found to be hard enough for the polishing of diamonds and gems.

In the present manufacturing process of silicon carbide, the two primary ingredients are coke, which supplies the carbon and sand containing silicon. This mixture of sand and coke is built up around a large electrode running the full length of the furnace, and is next walled up with uncemented firebrick. A small amount of sawdust added to the mixture assists in carrying off large amounts of inflammable gases. The sawdust also makes the mixture porous.

When the furnace is ready for firing, the electric current is turned on upward of 6000 amperes which surge through the electrode for 36 hours. The terrific heat, reaching a temperature as high as 5000 degrees Fahrenheit, creates a chemical reaction resulting in the formation of silicon carbide. After a 24-hour cooling period, the firebricks are removed and the outer crust of the furnace mixture torn out. The core of glistening bluish-black crystals is now exposed and next removed. Each furnace "run" produces a "pig" of crude abrasive weighing several tons.

Fig. 3. Emery.

Fig. 4. Silicon carbide.

Two outstanding characteristics of silicon carbide are its extreme hardness and sharpness. In hardness it is rated at 9.5 to 9.9 on the Moh scale, which makes it almost as hard as diamonds. It is, however, more brittle than aluminum oxide. This property limits its usefulness for certain types of work.

Aluminum oxide is made from a raw material called bauxite. This ore, which also produces metallic aluminum and alum, is a claylike substance found near the surface of the earth in many parts of the world. During the manufacturing process of aluminum oxide, bauxite is mixed with a small amount of coke and iron filings which act as reducing and purifying agents. This mixture is loaded into an electric furnace and heated to approximately 3500 degrees Fahrenheit. As more bauxite is added, a large "pig" is formed, the center of which yields about 50 per cent aluminum oxide. After proper cooling, this "pig" is removed and broken into lumps for easier handling (Fig. 5). Aluminum oxide as an abrasive is quite different from silicon carbide. Although not quite as hard and sharp, it has a toughness which makes it stand up under the most severe working conditions. In color, aluminum oxide is reddish brown. It is available on the market under such trade names as "Alundum," "Adalox," and "Metalite."

Fig. 5.   Aluminum oxide.

304. Abrasive Backings.* Abrasives are coated on several kinds and grades of backing, each one best suited for a particular job. The three most commonly used paper backings are: rope paper, kraft paper, and jute paper.

Rope paper, as the name indicates, is made from old rope, and has the strongest fiber of all paper backings. It is recommended for work that puts a severe strain on the abrasive product.

Kraft paper is made from wood pulp and is designed for use where the exceptional strength of rope paper is not necessary.

---

* *Ibid.,* pp. 19–21.

Jute paper, made from the jute plant is used as a backing for pouncing paper, that extremely fine abrasive used in the manufacture of felt hats.

Before paper can be accepted for use as a backing for coated abrasives, it must pass a number of rigid tests. It must meet standards pertaining to bursting strength, ply adhesion, folding qualities, density of fibers, tensile strength, stretch, tear resistance, surface finish, porosity, and uniformity of thickness. To meet these standards, special testing apparatus has been developed.

Cloth backings are used when certain operations require a coated abrasive with more strength or flexibility than paper backings. The two grades of cloth generally used are **jeans and drills.**

Both jeans and drills are of a special diagonal weave in which the lengthwise threads are of greater strength than those in the crosswise direction. This factor is especially desirable in endless belts, as it insures against sideway tearing and provides for greater resistance to stretch. Of the two types of cloth backing, jeans is the lighter of the two, and is used where the stresses are not so severe but greater flexibility is important.

Sometimes, in order to produce a satisfactory backing, cloth and paper are used in combination. Depending upon the work to be performed, the two are glued together.

305. Adhesives.* In the manufacture of coated abrasives, two types of adhesives are used primarily: *hide glue* and *synthetic resins.*** For all sorts of dry sanding, hide glue is well suited, but where sanding is done with water, it is necessary for the adhesive to be waterproof. Synthetic resins have now been developed which meet the demand for this type of work.

Hide glue used for coated abrasives must be of high quality and must pass a number of strict laboratory tests which include the following: grease content, viscosity, jelly, bacterial decomposition, and foam test.

Synthetic resins were developed for those operations which require the use of water or generate intensive heat. They stand up to the most severe treatment without melting or softening, and hold the abrasive grains firmly in place. Modified glues and resins were developed during the closing years of World War II. It was found that by adding certain extenders to these glues their resistance to heat and water was improved. Modified adhesives are noted for their exceptional grit anchorage, which results in longer coated abrasive life.

306. The Manufacture of Coated Abrasives.† The manufacturing process of coated abrasives includes, primarily, the following steps: (1) crush-

---

* Behr-Manning Co., "Coated Abrasives Today," p. 15.

** Note: For a more detailed discussion of different types of glue, see Chapter 7, pp. 287–290.

† Behr-Manning Co., "A Lecture Course on Coated Abrasives," pp. 23–35.

ing the abrasive material into suitable size, (2) preparing the cloth, (3) preparing the glue, (4) the actual making process, and (5) the finishing operations.

After arriving at the factory, the abrasive material, whether in lump or smaller form, is first crushed, by way of powerful jaw and roll crushers, into suitable sizes. This crushing process yields grits from the very coarsest to the very fine "flours." They are separated by passing the mixture over a series of vibrating screens of silk bolting cloth. These silk screens are especially handmade in Switzerland, where this art has been handed down from father to son for many generations. The various screens are distinguished by numbers which correspond to the grit size of the finished product. For instance, a garnet grain No. 1/2 (or No. 60) mesh has passed through a screen having 60 openings to the linear inch. This same grain size would not go through the next screen, No. 80, having 80 openings to the linear inch in each direction. Neither must the No. 60 screening contain any of the next coarser grit, No. 50, which has been separated by another screen (Fig. 6). The finest screen size is No. 220, which has, in addition to the silk strands, 48,400 openings per square inch.

The grading process for the very finest particles cannot be done by screens, but is accomplished by other methods. In one way these "flours" are graded by "sedimentation," in which the microscopic grains are classified according to the length of time they take to settle in water. Another method is "air flotation," in which the flour is blown by a fixed volume and speed of air. The size of the grain is determined by the distance it travels by air, the lightest flour being blown the farthest.

Fig. 6. A battery of silk grading machines.

Fig. 7. Cloth processing machine.

The cloth used as a backing must undergo a number of processes before it is ready for use. As it comes from the cotton mills the cloth is too porous and has too much stretch.

While the cloth is being stretched it is also dyed to its proper color. After drying, the pores of the cloth must be filled to prevent the glue coating from penetrating. Usually some inert material such as clay, starch, or talc is used with a mixture of glue.

The next step is the application of a thin coat of glue to the cloth. This is known as the "sizing coat," and will unite with the heavier glue coat that is applied later. After proper drying, the cloth is now ready for the making machines. Figure 7 shows the machine which processes the cloth.

Hide glues used in coated abrasives are received dry, coarsely ground, and

Fig. 8. Diagram of steps in manufacturing abrasives.

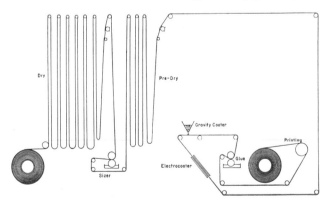

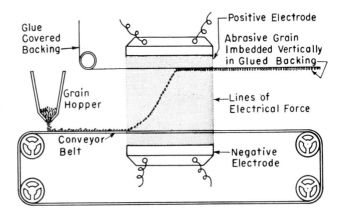

Fig. 9. Diagram of electro-coating method.

must be put into solution before they can be used. This is done by first soaking the glue in the proper amount of water and then heating it to the correct temperature.

With the abrasive grains graded, the adhesive in solution and the backing in readiness, the next step is the actual making of the product. The backing, whether paper, cloth or a combination of both, is first spliced, one huge roll to another so that stops will not be required once the "run" or "make" begins. The widths of backing vary from 27 in. up to 50 in.

Figures 8 and 9 show by diagrammatic sketches the course a roll of backing completes. The first step is the passing of the backing over printing rollers which print the trademark, brand name, grit and serial number on the backing. The ink dries in two seconds to prevent smudging. Next the adhesive is applied by calender rolls in carefully regulated amounts, varying in concentration and quantity with the size of the grains to be secured. At the next stage, the abrasive grain is applied, either by a gravity method or electrostatically. By these methods the amount of grain deposited on the glue covered sheet is controlled with great accuracy and can be varied from a very thin "open coat" to a dense "close coat."

Fig. 10.   Position of abrasive grains after passing through electrostatic field.

Electro coating is one of the most momentous developments in the abrasive industry and has its origin in one of the simplest physical experiments. It is the experiment of rubbing a comb or fountain pen barrel over one's sleeve, causing the articles to become charged and picking up bits of paper and holding them at right angles to the charged objects.

In Figure 9, an electrostatic field of 50,000 volts is built up between the positive and the negative electrode. As the conveyer belt carries the grains between the electrodes, they are raised on end and then, like tiny arrows, fly toward the upper electrode, end first. This occurs because they align themselves in the direction of the flow of electrical force. At the same time, all these particles separate themselves at equal distances one from another since they carry like charges (Fig. 10).

After the electrostatic process the product goes to the drying racks. It is then carried to the sizing machine. There, while not completely dry, a second and light solution of glue is applied. This second coat unites with the still wet original bond and serves to anchor the grain securely. Upon leaving the sizing machine, the goods are carried by the same racking system to the final drying room. When dried to the proper degree, the material is wound into huge "jumbo" rolls of thousands of yards each from which are cut the various shapes of the finished product. The types of coatings on these large rolls vary from one to the other, since each type has been manufactured to perform a specific job. Just how do coated abrasives do their work? It is generally assumed that they remove stock in the form of dust, but actually each grain on the sheet is a cutting tool much like a chisel or plane iron. By regulating the amounts of abrasive material placed on the backing, the grades of coated abrasives are either *closed coated* or *open coated* (Fig. 11). Closed coating means that the abrasive grains completely cover the surface of a backing. Many services require that the grain coating be dense in order

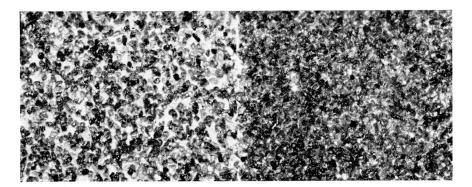

Fig. 11. Open and closed coated abrasive paper.

Fig. 12.   Sandpaper roll goods.

to lengthen the life of the abrasive. Closed coatings are particularly useful where the abraded material does not clog the spaces between individual grains.

Open coating means that the individual grains are spaced at predetermined distances from one another, leaving bare spaces of controlled area in the backing. Only about 50 to 70 per cent of the surface is covered with abrasive. This results in an increased flexibility and keeps the paper or cloth from "loading up" when sanding materials which are likely to clog the cutting edges of the grain before they have done their work.

Fig. 13.   Roll goods cut into sheets.

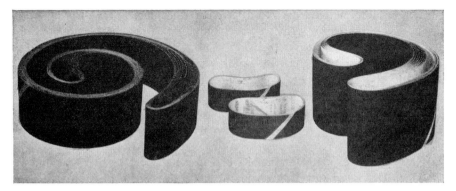

Fig. 14. Spliced belts.

The final stage in the manufacturing process consists of converting the huge "jumbo" rolls into sizes and shapes required by the consumers. Broadly speaking, there are three classes of finished goods:

1. *Roll goods,* which include material sold in full width or with edges trimmed; also, material slit into narrower width suitable for making belts, bands, drum covers and others (Fig. 12).

"Jumbo" rolls are cut into narrower width on special machines, called slitters. They are capable of cutting widths as narrow as ¼ inch.

2. *Sheet goods* include mainly paper and cloth backed goods intended for hand use (Fig. 13). The machine that cuts sheet goods is a combination slitter and fly knife, which cuts each sheet to the exact length.

3. *Specialties* include spliced belts, bands, cones, disks, and other goods not strictly in roll or sheet form (Figs. 14 and 15).

Belts are made by first cutting one end at a 45 degree angle and checking the edge against a straightedge. After cutting the other end to length at

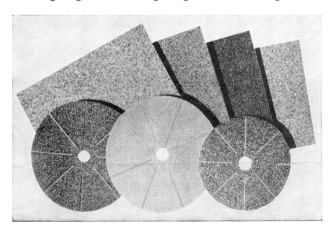

Fig. 15. Slotted disks and cut sheets.

45 degrees, the material goes to a "skiving" machine. There one end passes under a grinding wheel which removes the abrasive coating for about ½ inch without causing injury to the backing. This is done to prevent the joint from becoming thicker than the belt. After skiving, the belt is stamped with an arrow to show its proper running direction. The operator next brushes a uniform film of adhesive on one end, unites the two ends and applies pressure under a joint press. The smallest belt may be as narrow as ¼ in., the widest up to 84 in. Their lengths are sometimes made in excess of 100 feet.

The majority of disks for metal working are made with fiber combination backing. Disks are cut from "jumbo" rolls by means of automatic gang presses, which cut four or five disks at a time, complete with (or without) center holes and slots.

Besides the finished items listed here, there are many others adapted to thousands of different uses.

307. The Use of Coated Abrasives in Woodworking.*   In the woodworking industry three types of abrasives are generally used: *garnet, aluminum oxide,* and *flint. Garnet* is the standard abrasive for sanding *wood by hand.* Garnet cabinet paper is most appropriate for sanding "in the white." Although the grit range is from No. 3½ (very coarse) to No. 4/0 (fine) the popular grits on wood are No. 1/2 and No. 0. These are coarse enough to remove most tool marks and prepare the surface for finishing with No. 2/0 and No. 3/0 cabinet paper.

Garnet finishing papers are open coated on light paper backing of great flexibility. The available grit range is from No. 0 (medium) to No. 8/0 (very fine). These papers are used for the final light sanding in the white, and for sanding between finish coats. The open coating allows sanding shellac and varnish without clogging the grains. The extreme flexibility and toughness of the finishing paper backing make this product ideal for sanding turned work and moldings.

Aluminum oxide papers are in use in many industrial plants in preference to garnet cabinet and finishing paper due to the fact that they are much more durable.

As stated earlier, *flint paper* is weak in structure and does not have nearly the sharpness of garnet. About the only use for which flint paper is suited is the removal of paint and varnish by hand. But in this type of work, the sheet is loaded well before its cutting life is exhausted. Due to its low cost, flint is used quite extensively in school laboratories and by the amateur woodworker. It is available in grit ranges from No. 3 (coarse) to No. 3/0 (fine). These grit numbers *do not* correspond with the numbers given to

---

* *Ibid.,* pp. 36–49.

garnet and electric-furnace abrasives. For wood sanding *by machine,* two minerals are in common use, *garnet* and *aluminum oxide.* Backings of paper, cloth, or combination may be required, depending on the character of the work and the type of machine.*

----

* NOTE: For a more complete discussion of sanding and sanding machines, see: Hjorth, H., and Holtrop, W. F., "Operation of Modern Woodworking Machines," Chapter 10. Also: Holtrop, W. F., and Hjorth, H., "Modern Machine Woodworking," Chapter 7.

REVIEW QUESTIONS, CHAPTER 12

Possible score 50 points

Your score . . . . . .

PART I. COMPLETION QUESTIONS. Complete the following statements:

1. Any hard, sharp material that wears away a softer material is called an . . . .
2. The first true abrasive of which there is any record is . . . .
3. The early Chinese, for lack of a better abrasive, used crushed . . . .
4. Abrasives fall into two convenient classifications, natural and . . . .
5. A natural abrasive found in New Hampshire and Maryland is . . . .
6. A much better abrasive, ... is found in the Adirondack Mountains in New York State.
7. The scale which measures abrasives for hardness is the . . . . scale.
8. Another natural abrasive, found in Turkey and Greece is . . . .
9. In 1891, chemists succeeded in producing the first artificial abrasive, ...
10. To produce this abrasive, two ingredients needed are coke and . . . .
11. Aluminum oxide is made from a raw material called . . . .
12. The backings used for abrasives are either paper or . . . .
13. The strongest paper backing is made of old . . . .
14. The two grades of cloth backings are . . . . and . . . .
15. In the manufacture of coated abrasives two types of glue are used, hide glue and . . . .
16. To separate the various grit sizes, manufacturers use screens made of . . . .
17. The finest of these screens, No. 220, have . . . . openings to the square inch.
18. The very finest particles of abrasive are separated by water and . . . .
19. When separated by water, the process is called . . . .
20. The first thin coat of glue applied to the backing is called . . . . coat.

PART II. TRUE-FALSE QUESTIONS. Indicate, by encircling T or F, whether the following statements are true or false.

21. Electrocoating is one of the most significant developments in the abrasive industry.   T   F
22. In this process an electrostatic field is built up between the positive and negative electrode.   T   F
23. After the electrostatic process the abrasive product goes next to the drying racks.   T   F
24. Abrasive grains can be thought of as a series of little chisels.   T   F
25. Open coating means that the abrasive grains are closely placed together.   T   F
26. The narrowest belt that can be cut from a large roll is one inch wide.   T   F
27. Spliced belts are first cut at angles of 60 degrees and then joined together.   T   F
28. Of the two abrasives, flint and garnet, the first is the most durable.   T   F
29. For lack of another material, sea sand would be satisfactory as a basis for abrasives.   T   F
30. The grit numbers on various kinds of abrasive papers always correspond with each other.   T   F
31. Of the two abrasives, aluminum oxide and flint, flint is the more expensive.   T   F
32. At one time, crushed glass was used as an abrasive.   T   F
33. Gray flint was used by the American Indians in making arrow and spear heads.   T   F
34. Garnet crystals, before crushing, are about the size of a golf ball.   T   F
35. The best grade of garnet is found in the Kentucky Mountains.   T   F

PART III. MULTIPLE-CHOICE QUESTIONS. Select, by encircling the correct letter, the answer which completes each statement:

36. Emery is essentially a mixture of:
    A. Silica and clay
    B. Iron oxide and corundum
    C. Flint and garnet
    D. Bauxite and coke

37. Of the following, which one is the strongest as a paper backing for abrasives:
    A. Kraft paper
    B. Manila paper
    C. Jute paper
    D. Rope paper

38. Of the following silk screen sizes, which one has the coarsest mesh:
    A. No. 220
    B. No. 160
    C. No. 60
    D. No. 50

39. When preparing a batch of hide glue, one of the following should not be practiced:
    A. Heat over an open flame
    B. Soak in water
    C. Heat in double container

40. Spliced belts, cones, and sanding disks are classified as:
    A. Sheet goods
    B. Roll goods
    C. Specialties
    D. Jeans and drills

PART IV. MATCHING QUESTIONS. Match the terms to the left with the descriptions to the right by placing the correct letter in the parentheses:

41. (   ) Emery
42. (   ) Crushed glass
43. (   ) Abrasives
44. (   ) Moh scale
45. (   ) Almandite
46. (   ) Coke
47. (   ) Bauxite
48. (   ) Kraft paper
49. (   ) Jeans and drills
50. (   ) Sedimentation

A. Are classified as either natural or electric furnace.
B. The best grade of garnet.
C. The Old Testament refers to this mineral as Shamir.
D. One of the ingredients to produce silicon carbide.
E. Grades of cloth backings.
F. A Swiss attempt to make abrasives with this material.
G. A paper backing made from wood pulp.
H. The scale that determines the toughness of a backing.
I. The process of grading fine abrasive particles by means of water.
J. The base material for aluminum oxide.
K. The process of grading fine abrasive particles by means of air.
L. The scale that determines the hardness of minerals.

CHAPTER 13

Wood Finishing

Wood finishing is the last step in the completion of a piece of furniture, and a very important one. It was formerly a part of the cabinetmakers' trade, but now requires so much skill and knowledge that it has developed into a distinct trade. During the past decade or two, a great many discoveries, both chemical and mechanical, have made this trade one of the most important specialties in the furniture industry.

While nowadays the professional cabinetmaker seldom "finishes" a piece of work himself, yet it is important that he should know something about finishing methods. To the student and nonprofessional woodworker, this subject should be of particular interest.

Modern methods of finishing are too numerous and complex to be treated in this volume. Only the simplest and most common will, therefore, be described in the following.

Wood finishes are either transparent or opaque. The finishing processes of the first type, with which we are principally concerned, fall into three main divisions: staining, filling, and polishing.

Opaque finishes are produced by paints, colored lacquers, or metallic leaf or powders.

310. Procedure for Preparing the Surface. While the different parts of a piece of furniture should be prepared for finishing during the process of construction, especially those that are inaccessible after gluing, it is, nevertheless, of the utmost importance to give the piece a thorough inspection when all the toolwork has been completed, so that any little damage or defect may be repaired. Check the following points:

1. See that every trace of glue is removed from around the joints, because stain does not penetrate through glue. Any speck of glue, therefore, leaves a light mark on the stained surface. Use the blade of a cabinet scraper or a chisel, with the edge bent over, to remove glue from corners that are not easily accessible.

2. Inspect the surfaces thoroughly for any dent or bruise. A dent in the wood often may be removed by the application of a small pad of cotton waste soaked in hot water. Leave the pad on the bruise for a few minutes, and repeat. The water will fill the cells in the wood near the surface and cause them to swell, thus bringing the bruise to the level of the surrounding surface.

3. A quicker way of taking out dents is to use steam. This may be done by placing a small pad of wet cotton waste over the dent, and then applying a hot soldering iron to it. The steam generated will enter the pores and cause them to swell more rapidly than if only water had been applied. If a soldering iron is not available, an ordinary flatiron, placed on several layers of wet paper, will serve the purpose.

4. Look for any marks left by the cabinet scraper or any scratches caused by sanding across the grain. Nothing shows up more prominently and is more unsightly when the finish is applied than scratches across the grain. It is usually necessary to use a scraper to remove them entirely, and then resand the surface.

5. See that there are no spots of oil or grease on the surface, because they will prevent the stain from penetrating. They should be removed by rubbing with naphtha or benzine.

6. Any holes, cracks, or other defects should be filled with crack filler, which is also known as wood cement or stick shellac. It is sold in sticks of different colors, and is composed largely of shellac and resin. It is melted into the hole to be filled like sealing wax, or by holding a heated iron against it until the drops melting off fill the crevice to above the level of the surface. Work it in with the hot iron. It hardens in a moment, and should then be cut down almost to the level of the surface with a very sharp chisel or scraper. Finish with sandpaper until the surface is perfectly level and smooth.

7. Give the piece of furniture to be stained a final but thorough sanding, using No. 2/0 sandpaper (see Ch. 12). Hold the work toward the light, and

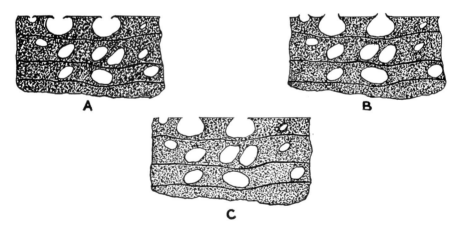

Fig. 1. Magnified cross section through wood. Upper edge planed. A, pores cut through and fine edges bent down by plane or scraper; B, edges of pores bent upward after staining with water stain; C, projecting edges cut away with fine sandpaper.

see that no imperfections remain on the surfaces. If water stain is to be used, wet the work before this final sanding, because water raises the grain of the wood and makes the surface rough.

8. Wood is composed of millions of little cells, the great majority of which run lengthwise. When the surface is planed, a great many of these cells are cut through and their fine, hairlike edges are bent down by the pressure of the tool (A, Fig. 1).

9. When water is applied to the surface, the hairlike edges of the cells bend upward by capillary attraction, and this makes the surface rough to the touch (B, Fig. 1).

10. When dry, the surface is given its final sanding with No. 2/0 or 3/0 sandpaper. The object of the sanding is to cut the hairs off and make the surface smooth. Use a piece of new, sharp sandpaper and rub very lightly at first. Then fold the paper around a cork sanding block and, using both hands, apply plenty of pressure (Fig. 2).

End grain is sanded smooth, by moving the sanding block in one direction only (Fig. 3). In this way, the wood fibers are flattened down and the surface can be made as smooth as that of length grain wood.

11. When the hairs are cut off, the wood looks like C in Figure 1 under a microscope. When water is again applied a second time, less hairs will bend up and the surface will therefore not be so rough.

Too much care cannot be given to this final preparation and inspection for, contrary to the popular belief, imperfections in the surface are not covered by the finish. Rather, they appear as if magnified. An extra hour spent in preparing the surface for staining is, therefore, well spent, and often saves many hours of tedious refinishing.

Fig. 2. Sanding length grain.

Fig. 3. Sanding end grain.

Stains

The purpose of staining usually is to produce a rich and mellow color on freshly-cut although seasoned wood. Oftentimes certain species of wood are stained to imitate others more costly, provided their grain and texture are similar. Many species of wood, for example, are stained to imitate mahogany or black walnut. Furniture stained with this end in view is labeled by the honest manufacturer as "mahogany finish" or "walnut finish," as the case may be. In any case, stains are always transparent and do not obscure the grain of the wood.

Stains are classified according to the material of which they are made. The following are the most common:

311. Water stains are made by dissolving powdered aniline colors in *hot* water. They are clear, penetrate deeply, and do not fade. As they are also inexpensive, they are widely used at the present time, especially on high-grade work. The only disadvantage in using water stains is that they raise the grain of the wood. This is overcome by sponging the wood with water, and sanding it again after drying. The stain should be applied cold, brushed dry, not wiped, and allowed to dry for about six hours.

312. Spirit stains also are made from aniline colors, but the solvent used is alcohol. They dry so rapidly that it is difficult to cover a large surface without showing laps or streaks, except with an air brush. They are used chiefly for shading and for refinishing old work, because they penetrate more readily than water or oil stains. They are liable to fade when exposed to the light.

313. Oil stains are made by dissolving oil aniline colors in turpentine, benzine, or benzol. Asphaltum and naphtha also are among the ingredients of these stains. They usually are bought ready-made, and are very easy to apply because they take a longer time to dry. They may fade or change color when exposed to the light. Oil stains should be wiped dry with a clean cloth as soon as they begin to show streaks and become flat. Allow 24 hours for drying.

Aniline and benzine are coal-tar products; naphtha is distilled from petroleum; asphalt is a mineral pitch found around oil wells, and turpentine is an oil produced from the sap of long-leaf pines.

NOTE: On account of the fire hazard, oil-soaked rags should be deposited immediately in a special metal container with a self-closing lid (Fig. 4). Under certain conditions, oily waste and rags may even ignite by **spontaneous combustion.**

Fig. 4. Container for oil-soaked rags.

314. Acid stains or stains due to chemical action were used a great deal in former years, but are very seldom used commercially at the present time. They are dangerous to use, and do not produce as good results as the more modern water stains.

Some of the most common acid stains are as follows: *Bichromate of potassium* dissolved in water gives oak and mahogany a brownish color. Oak and mahogany contain tannic acid which reacts with the bichromate of potassium.

Permanganate of potash dissolved in hot water also produces brown shades of color on oak. A strong solution of **ammonia** allowed to evaporate in a small closed room or box produces a rich brown color on oak called "fumed oak."

Quicklime dissolved in water gives a rich reddish color to mahogany, and is of value for this purpose, because it does not affect the color of inlays. It is applied with a brush. When dry, the surface looks like it had been whitewashed. It should be wiped off with burlap or cotton waste. A coat of boiled linseed oil, thinned with turpentine, will remove the last traces of the lime. This should invariably be applied before the wood filler.

315. General Directions for Staining. 1. Brush with the grain, using a flat brush, and apply the stain rapidly and evenly.

2. Finish all inside surfaces before staining the outside surfaces.

3. Stain all removable parts, as drawers of doors, separately.

4. Brush along the entire length of a surface to prevents laps. When the surface has been covered, brush any water-soluble stain back and forth over it until it gradually dries. If any laps or other unevenness is then discovered, it can be corrected by rubbing the surface vigorously with a wet rag. This will lighten the color, but it will also make it uniform, especially if it is done soon after the stain has dried.

5. After dipping the brush, begin on the unfinished part, and brush toward the finished part.

6. Regular stain should be applied to sapwood parts, and allowed to dry before the general staining. This is because sapwood is generally lighter than heartwood, and needs a second coat to make the staining uniform.

7. To prevent endwood from getting too dark, it may be brushed with water immediately before staining. Staining it while it is wet lightens the color.

8. Sand lightly with No. 3/0 sandpaper after the stain is thoroughly dry.

316. Procedure for Applying Wood Filler. Wood filler is used for filling the pores of open-grain woods like oak, chestnut, ash, walnut, mahogany, etc., so as to produce a perfectly level and smooth surface.

It is manufactured in paste form, and consists of silex ground in japan, linseed oil (Art. 320), and turpentine. The natural color of filler is a light cream, but any color may be obtained by the addition of colors ground in oil or japan.

Wood filler is thinned with turpentine, benzine, or naphtha according to manufacturers' directions.

Silex or silica is a white powder consisting of quartz and sand.

Japan is a drying agent made from various gums, shellac, linseed oil, metallic oxides, and turpentine.

Filler is usually applied after the stain, and in a corresponding color. Sometimes, however, filler is used as a stain, especially on dark woods, by coloring it a little darker than the wood. Two-tone effects can be produced by using a lighter and a darker shade of filler.

1. Take a small quantity of paste filler from the can, add a little solvent, and stir the mixture with a wooden stick, shaped like a paddle, until it has become a homogeneous mass. On oak, 1 lb. covers about 30 sq. ft. Add small quantities of turpentine at a time, and mix well until the filler has the consistency of thick cream or soup. The coarser the grain of the wood to be filled, the thicker the filler should be.

2. Brush it on with a fairly stiff bristle brush, so that it is worked well into all the pores.

3. When the filler, which was first applied, begins to look flat, stop putting on more filler and begin wiping off with some material that does not lie flat on the surface. Coconut hair, sea moss, fine excelsior, burlap, or cotton waste are all useful for this purpose. Wipe first across the grain so as not to lift part of the filler out of the pores (Fig. 5). Finish by wiping lightly with the grain, using a clean soft cloth or cotton waste until a clear,

Fig. 5. Removing filler.

Fig. 6. Wiping with grain.

smooth surface is produced (Fig. 6). If the filler is hard to wipe off, moisten the wiping cloth slightly with the solvent.

4. Stir the filler well before resuming the brushing-on process, because the heavier parts of it will settle to the bottom of the can, leaving only the solvent on top.

5. Remove surplus filler as before, using a pointed wooden stick to clean out corners, recesses, and other irregular surfaces (Fig. 7). So far as possible, all surfaces should be filled in a horizontal position, as this gives the best results.

6. If the filler is lifted out of the pores while it is being wiped off the surface, add a little japan drier to the mixture.

7. Usually 1 coat of filler is sufficient. Allow 24 hours for drying. Close-

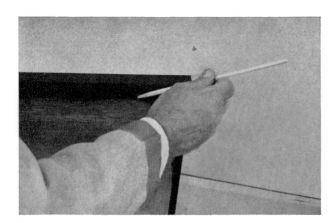

Fig. 7. Removing leftover filler.

grained woods, such as maple or birch, are generally given a coat of shellac instead of filler.

8. An extremely thin coat of shellac, called a "wash coat" is sometimes applied before filling. It is sanded when dry, after which the filler is applied as just described. This treatment prevents a filler smudge on the surface which sometimes results from the filler solvents and color penetrating the wood. If the coat of shellac is too thick, it will glaze the open pores and prevent the filler from sticking in the pores.

317. Production and Manufacture of Shellac. Shellac is produced by an insect called *Tachardia Lacca* (the lac bug, Fig. 8), which is native to the southern part of India. This insect lives on the sap of a few species of acacia trees which are now cultivated in plantations. After being host to a colony of lac bugs, a tree needs several years of rest and care to recuperate.

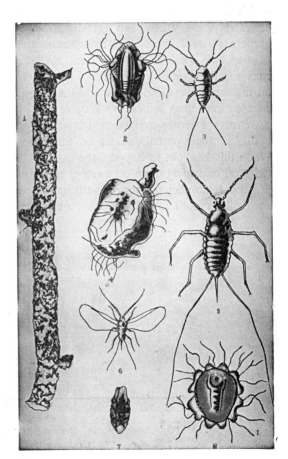

Fig. 8. Lac bug in various stages.

Metamorphosis

Fig. 9.   Stick-lac showing encrustations on twigs.

The lac bug sucks up the sap through a needlelike elongated mouth, which it inserts under the tender bark of young twigs. Through the bug's digestive processes, the sap is changed into shellac which is exuded through numerous pores in its skin. Pretty soon the insect, which is about the size of an apple seed, is covered with shellac. As more shellac is exuded, it runs together with that produced by the hundreds of other insects sitting on the same twig (Fig. 9). Finally the twig and all the insects are completely encased in shellac, but before that happens the females lay thousands of eggs.

When the larvae are hatched from the eggs, they first live off the dead bodies of their parents. Later on they bore their way through the shellac. When this is about to happen, the native workmen break the shellac-covered twigs off and hang them on another tree which is strong and healthy enough to support another colony of lac bugs. Once the lac bugs have inserted their needlelike mouth into a tree, they never move until they die.

Fig. 10.   Seed-lac in cheesecloth bag being heated
and melted.

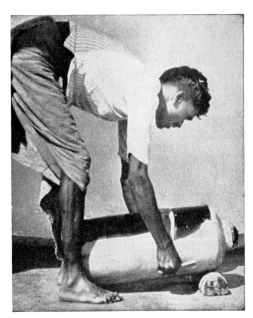

Fig. 11. A "Bhilwaya" spreading molten seed-lac over large porcelain cylinder.

When the new generation of lac bugs have begun their life cycle, the shellac-covered twigs, from which they came, are collected and broken up into small pieces, either by hand or by machinery. The crushed shellac is washed in a large, circular vessel filled with water. Bits of wood and remnants of the dead insects float to the top and are skimmed off, after which the shellac pellets are spread out and dried in the sun. Shellac in this stage is called "seed-lac."

The seed-lac is put into a cheesecloth bag several feet long, but only about 2 in. in diameter. Two men hold the bag in front of an open fire The heat melts the shellac, which drops down upon a marble slab while the men are twisting or wringing the bag (Fig. 10). Another man then picks up the sticky molten mass and lays it on a large porcelain cylinder filled with hot water (Fig. 11), thereby producing a sheet of lac about ¼ in. thick and 2 ft. square. He then takes this sheet, and holding its four corners with his hands and toes, while standing in front of the fire, stretches it to four times its size or about 4 ft. square (Fig. 12). The temperature is so high that it would burn the hands and feet of anyone not trained to do this work. These sheets are then laid on the floor and later are broken into small pieces, cooled, and packed. Shellac of the lightest color is the finest. Garnet lac and button lac is shellac of darker color and inferior quality.

Shellac is dissolved in alcohol only. It is sold according to the number

Fig. 12.
Stretching a
sheet of lac.

of pounds of shellac which are dissolved in one gallon of alcohol. A 4-lb. cut, for example, means that four pounds of shellac have been dissolved in one gallon of alcohol. The natural color of shellac is orange. White shellac is bleached orange shellac.

318. Procedure for Applying Shellac. 1. Prepare the first coat by adding from 25 to 50 per cent of alcohol to a 4-lb.-cut stock solution.

2. As shellac dries very rapidly, it is difficult to brush it on evenly. Use a rubberset brush with medium-size bristles. Start from the top of a piece of furniture working downward. Be careful not to let the shellac run on the edges. Pick up such runs immediately with an almost dry brush. The brush strokes should be with the grain, and doors and drawers should be removed and shellacked separately (Fig. 13).

3. Allow from 2 to 4 hours for drying, and then rub down with No. 3/0 steel wool, or very fine sandpaper. Steel wool is preferable, because the sandpaper "gums up."

4. If a shellac finish is desired, apply two or three coats more, and rub down between coats with No. 3/0 steel wool. Each succeding coat should contain a little more shellac in proportion to the alcohol, but each coat should still be thin enough to brush on evenly. Rub down the last coat in the same way, and apply wax (Art. 319).

Fig. 13. Brushing on shellac.

5. A common mistake is to use shellac too thick and to keep brushing it over the work several times. If used too thick, it will not fill the small pores of the wood, and if brushed over the work too many times it will pile up in uneven layers, which must be scraped off.

6. For a finer, smoother finish, rub the last coat with No. 6/0 waterproof sandpaper and crude oil, using a felt rubbing pad. Rub only a small area at a time, and be careful not to rub through the finish, especially along the edges. Clean off the oily surface by rubbing it with sawdust, because this absorbs the oil.

7. Make a polishing pad by folding a piece of coarse linen cloth over a handful of cotton waste on which very thin shellac has been poured. Rub the surface along the grain, making quick, parallel strokes from edge to edge. A few drops of paraffin oil applied to the surface will help to spread the shellac evenly. Never allow the pad to rest a fraction of a second on the surface, because it will stick to it and spoil the finish.

8. If a duller finish is desired, rub this surface gently with No. 3/0 steel wool. A rubbing paste may also be made by mixing FF powdered pumice stone with vaseline, thinned with paraffin oil to the consistency of thick paint. This paste may be used with the steel wool or with a felt rubbing pad.

319. Procedure for Applying Wax. Wax is composed chiefly of beeswax, paraffin, carnauba wax, and turpentine. Carnauba wax is the best and hardest kind of wax, and is extracted from the leaves of a tree native to South America.

Some waxes are manufactured in paste form, but more modern waxes are manufactured in liquid form.

1. Before a surface is ready for waxing, it must be filled and given a

Fig. 14. Making
a wax pad.

sealing coat of shellac, varnish, or lacquer. If a sealing coat is not given, the wax penetrates into the wood, leaving a dull, uneven finish.

2. Apply the wax, either paste or liquid, with a soft cloth (Fig. 14). Do not put too much on at a time, as it is likely to make the surface greasy and consequently difficult to polish.

3. Allow the wax to dry for about 20 minutes, and then rub briskly with a soft cloth. Finish rubbing with the grain.

4. A second coat may be applied after an interval of 1 or 2 hours.

5. A wax finish is easy to produce, but is not durable. Any liquid spilled on a waxed surface makes a dull spot. In most cases, however, this will disappear if rubbed vigorously with a soft cloth.

320. Procedure for Applying Linseed Oil. Linseed oil is produced by subjecting flaxseed to pressure. The raw oil is very fatty, and dries slowly. Raw oil is used in outside paint. Boiled linseed oil is produced by boiling the raw oil with certain chemicals. Many of the fatty substances which retard the drying qualities of the oil are removed by this process. As boiled linseed oil, therefore, dries faster than raw linseed oil, it is used principally on inside work. Linseed oil dries by oxidation; i.e., contact with the air.

1. Boiled linseed oil, thinned with from 2 to 3 parts of turpentine, is applied with a brush, rag or fingers directly over the wood filler (Fig. 15). The best results are obtained by letting the filler dry 48 hours. Put plenty of oil on the surface, and allow it to soak into the wood for about half an hour.

2. Rub hard and vigorously with a dry, clean cloth, being careful to rub each part of the work absolutely dry. If this is not done, the surface becomes sticky and must be cleaned with turpentine.

3. Allow 24 hours between coats. At least 3 or 4 coats are necessary.

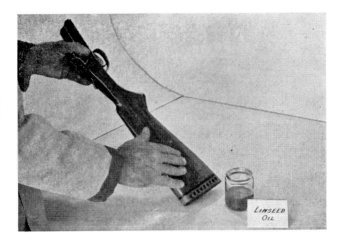

Fig. 15. Re-finishing a gun stock.

This treatment produces a soft sheen, and brings out the color and grain in the wood. It is an old type of finish, very durable and easy to apply, but not used commercially. Another coat of oil may be applied at any time or as often as furniture polish would ordinarily be applied.

NOTE: Be careful about the disposal of rags that have been used with linseed oil, because spontaneous combustion is likely to occur.

321. Lacquer. Lacquer is one of the newer products of the finishing industry. It is composed of many chemicals, some of the most important being nitrated cotton, banana oil, alcohol, naphtha, shellac, or varnish gums.

Banana oil is a complex chemical substance, technically known as amyl acetate. It has many advantages, such as drying quickly, withstanding heat or cold, and not cracking easily. It is difficult to apply, however, and cannot be used over oil stain, varnish, or paint, because it contains some of the ingredients used in varnish and paint remover, and, consequently, dissolves these undercoats. A sealing coat of thin shellac must be brushed over ordinary wood filler if lacquer is to be used, because it dissolves these undercoats, giving the finish a muddy appearance.

Lacquer is a hard and durable finish, but very difficult to apply because it dries so fast. The best method of application is by a spray gun or air brush, but if this is not available it may be applied by hand.

322. Lacquer Spraying Equipment. * Perhaps the most important piece of equipment in the spray method of finishing is the spray gun. It is a tool which, by using compressed air, atomizes sprayable material and applies it to a surface. Air and material enter the gun through separate passages and are mixed and ejected at the air cap in a controlled pattern.

---

* From: "The A B C's of Spray Equipment," The De Vilbiss Co., Toledo, Ohio, 1954, 64 pp.

Spray guns are generally of the separate container or attached container type. In the first, the gun is connected by a hose to a separate pressure feed tank; in the second, it has a small (1 quart) container directly connected to the gun unit.

These two types of guns can further be divided into bleeder and non-bleeder, external and internal mix and pressure, gravity and suction feed guns.

A bleeder type gun is one designed without an air valve. Air passes through the gun at all times preventing any possible pressure from building up in the air lines.

The nonbleeder type gun is one equipped with an air valve which shuts off the air when the trigger is released. The trigger controls both air and fluid flow. It is used wherever a pressure controlling arrangement is present in the compressed air supply system.

An external mix spray gun mixes and atomizes air and materials outside the air cap. This gun can be used to apply almost all fluid materials and is the only type suitable for fast drying materials such as lacquer.

An internal mix spray gun mixes air and material inside the cap before expelling them. This gun is used where low air pressures are employed or where slow drying materials not containing abrasive pigments or particles are to be sprayed.

A suction feed gun is of a type in which a stream of compressed air creates a vacuum allowing atmospheric pressure to force material from an attached container to the spray head of the gun. This gun is usually limited to quart size containers or smaller and is easily identified by the fluid tip extending slightly beyond the air cap. Suction feed guns are used where there are many color changes and small amounts of material involved such as auto or furniture finishing.

A pressure feed gun has an air cap not necessarily designed to create a vacuum. Material is forced to the gun by air pressure from a tank, cup or pump. When large amounts of the same color material are being used, when the material is too heavy to be siphoned from a cup or container by suction or when fast application is required, a pressure feed gun is used. Some examples are, production spraying in a manufacturing plant and applying maintenance paints, or heavier materials such as roof coatings.

In addition to these guns, industry now uses automatic spray guns, mounted on either horizontal or vertical transverse machines.

Figure 16 shows a typical spray gun with its principal components. Delicate as the parts of a spray gun are, one should thoroughly understand each of them and know how to clean and lubricate a gun after use. Air caps can be cleaned by simply immersing them in clean solvent and drying them with compressed air. If the small holes in the air cap become clogged, soak the cap in solvent. Use a match stick, broom straw, or some other soft material to clean out clogged out holes. Never use a wire or nail since the holes may become permanently damaged. A gun should not be completely submerged in solvents, for this would remove the oil from the fluid needle packing, air valve packing and trigger bearing screw. These three parts should be kept lubricated with a few drops of oil.

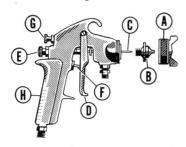

Fig. 16. Spray gun parts. A, air cap; B, fluid tip; C, fluid needle; D, trigger; E, fluid adjustment screw; F, air valve; G, spreader adjustment valve; H, gun body.

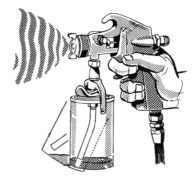

Fig. 17. Jerky or fluttery spray.

323. Care and Adjustment of Spray Guns. Even though the best of care may be given a gun, many things can still go wrong. One of the most common difficulties in spraying is jerky or fluttering spray (Fig. 17), caused by:

A. Lack of sufficient material in the container.
B. Tipping the container at an excessive angle.
C. Obstruction in the fluid passageway.
D. Loose fluid tip or damaged tip seat.
E. Loose or cracked fluid tube in cup or tank.

The following apply to a suction feed gun only:
F. Too heavy a material for suction feed.
G. Clogged air vent in the cup lid.
H. Loose, dirty, or damaged coupling nut or cup lid.
I. Dry packing or loose fluid needle packing nut.
J. Fluid tube resting on the bottom of the cup.

When something is wrong with a gun, the spray pattern is often uneven (Fig. 18). The first pattern shown is a normal spray pattern. The top heavy pattern (No. 2, Fig. 18), could be caused by partially plugged horn holes; by an obstruction on the top of the fluid tip, by dirt on the air cap seat or fluid tip seat. The heavy bottom patterns (No. 3, Fig. 18) may also be caused by partly plugged horn holes. Also by an obstruction on the bottom side of the fluid tip, dirt on the air cap seat or fluid tip seat.

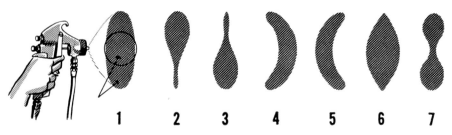

Fig. 18.   Spray patterns.

A heavy right side pattern (No. 4, Fig. 18), could be caused by right side horn holes which are partly clogged. Maybe there is some dirt on the right side of the fluid tip, or, on a twin jet air cap, the right jet.

When the spray pattern is heavy on the left side (No. 5, Fig. 18), it could be caused by the same reasons as listed above except that now the left side horn holes are partly clogged and some dirt could be on the left side of the fluid tip.

A heavy center pattern (No. 6, Fig. 18), could be caused by setting the spreader adjustment valve too low. Other causes for such a defective spray pattern could be, especially with a twin jet cap, low atomizing pressure or a material that is too thick. With a pressure feed gun, a defective spray pattern could be caused by high fluid pressure, or the material flow is in excess of the cap's normal capacity. Also too large or too small a nozzle could cause this pattern.

The split spray pattern (No. 7, Fig. 18) could be caused by improper mixture of air and fluid. As a remedy, reduce the width of the spray pattern by means of the spreader adjustment valve or increase the fluid pressure. This latter adjustment also increases the speed; and the gun must be handled much faster.

As a first remedy toward eliminating faulty spray patterns determine whether there is any obstruction on the air cap or in the fluid tip. Also, by making a series of test patterns and adjustments at the same time, difficulties can often be eliminated.

324. Transformers, Regulators, and Condensers. An air transformer removes oil, dirt, and moisture from compressed air. It also filters and regulates the air. A gauge indicates, by pounds, the regulated air pressure. Placed between the compressor unit and the spray gun, provisions have been made for two outlet valves (Fig. 19).

Transformer parts include: a condenser, filtering device (within the condenser unit), air regulator, pressure gauge or gauges, outlet valves and a drain. This last part is needed in all types of spray finishing operations where a supply of clean, moisture-free, regulated air is needed. Various makes of air transformers may differ somewhat in their inner structure. Dirt, oil, and moisture can be removed by baffles, centrifugal force, expansion chambers, impingement plates and filters. After whatever air cleaning process is used, any accumulated oil, dirt, and moisture is removed by opening the drain valve.

The air regulator reduces air pressure and maintains the required pressure with a minimum of fluctuation. They are available in different capacities, with or without gauges, and in varying degrees of sensitivity. Fluid regulators control and maintain constant and correct fluid pressures to spray guns. They are available with or without pressure gauges and for standard or extra sensitive regulation.

Fig. 19. Air transformer.

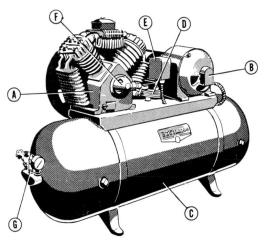

Fig. 20. Principal parts of stationary air compressor. A, air compressor; B, motor; C, air storage tank; D, check valve; E, pressure switch; F, centrifugal pressure release; G, safety valve.

325. Air compressors (Figs. 20 and 21) are specifically designed to pump air from atmospheric to a higher pressure. The types most commonly used in spray operations are either the piston type or the diaphragm type.

Piston-type air compressors develop pressure through the action of a reciprocating piston. Air is drawn in through an intake valve, compressed, then expelled through an exhaust valve to an air receiver or the air line. They are available in single or multiple cylinder and single or two stage

Fig. 21. Principal parts of portable air compressor; A, air compressor; B, engine; C, air receiver; D, unloader; E, wheel, caster, or skid mounting.

models depending on the volume and pressure needed. These compressors are used for heavy duty operations, such as supplying air for industrial plants, service stations, maintenance painting, and automobile refinishing.

A diaphragm-type air compressor develops pressure through the reciprocating action of a flexible disk actuated by an eccentric. A compressor of this type provides sufficient air for use in the home or the small shop. Compressors are driven either by an electric motor or by a gas engine. They are either stationary or portable.

Stationary compressors are permanently located. Usually they are equipped with a larger air tank than the portable type.

Portable compressors are designed for easy movement to a job where their services are needed. They are equipped with handles, wheels, or casters and a small air receiver or pulsation chamber.

For the protection of workers, spraying should be done by either wearing protective respirators or by doing the spraying in or directly in front of a spray booth.

326. Spray booths (Fig. 22) are compartments or enclosures, generally of fire proof construction, built to confine and exhaust overspray and fumes resulting from spray painting or similar operations. Numerous models of booths are designed to suit various materials, objects to be coated and methods of application.

The dry type spray booth (Fig. 22) draws contaminated air through a baffle or removable filters before expelling it directly to the outside. This booth, commonly used for spraying lacquers and other quick drying materials, is used in locations where it is necessary to prevent overspray from being discharged to the outside. Dry spray booths are available in floor, leg, and bench models.

An air washer spray booth (Fig. 22) draws contaminated air through a series of water curtains and baffles to remove solids from overspray before

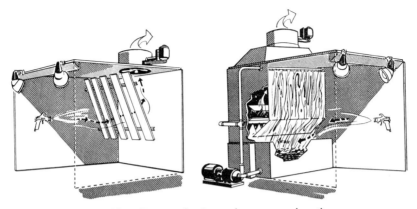

Fig. 22. Dry and air-washer spray booths.

it is exhausted. This booth greatly reduces fire hazards and is used where conditions require that exhaust air be clean when it leaves the stack. Particles of overspray from materials such as varnish and enamels are efficiently removed and confined in the water chamber. This prevents expulsion of spray dust that might be a nuisance outside.

327. Hints on Proper Spray Technique.* The proper application of finishing coats by means of a spray gun requires experience, which is best gained by plenty of practice. The following points of advice are listed here as an aid in acquiring the correct technique as quickly as possible.

1. The gun should be held perpendicular to the surface at all times, keeping from 6 to 8 in. from the surface to be sprayed. A simple method of determining the proper distance is shown in Figure 23.

2. The proper spray gun stroke is made with a free arm motion, keeping the gun at right angles to the surface at all points of the stroke. The ends

---

* *Ibid.,* pp. 56–59.

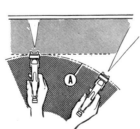

Fig. 23. Determining proper distance.

Fig. 24. Proper gun stroke.

Fig. 25. Spraying corners.

of the strokes are "feathered" out by triggering the gun as shown in Figure 24. Correct triggering involves beginning the stroke before pulling the trigger and releasing it just before ending the stroke. Arcing the gun (A, Fig. 24) results in uneven application and excessive overspray at each end of the strokes. When the gun is arced 45° away from the surface, approximately 65° of the material is lost. For good surface coverage, lap each stroke 50 per cent over the preceding one. Less than 50 per cent overlap is likely to result in streaks on the finished surface. Move the gun at a constant speed while pulling the trigger.

3. Corners are sprayed by holding the gun pointed at the corner, and spraying parts of both surfaces at once (Fig. 25). Then spray each side, blending the side into the sprayed corner area. This method reduces overspray from falling on adjacent surfaces. Inside corners are best sprayed separately. This method prevents material from "piling up."

4. *Orange Peel.* This is a finishing defect common to lacquer and synthetic finishing materials. It is so called because it actually resembles the pimply appearance of an orange. Its general causes are:

    a) Improper thinner. Always select a thinner made by the manufacturer of the finishing material.

    b) Too high or too low atomization pressure.

    c) Holding the gun too far or too close to the work.

    d) Finishing material not thoroughly mixed or agitated.

    e) Drafts in the finishing room, if spraying synthetics or lacquers.

    f) In spraying synthetics, too low humidity.

    g) Improperly prepared surfaces.

5. *Runs and Sags.* Runs result from the material being too thin. Sags are the result of too much material applied on the surface. Also when the gun is tilted at an angle, excessive material will build up and sag where the pattern is closest to the surface.

6. *Mist or Fog.* This is generally caused when the spray material is too thin, or overatomization due to too high an atomizing air pressure for the amount of fluid flowing.

7. We speak of "starving" the spray gun when insufficient air or fluid reaches the gun. Possibly the air transformer is clogged with rust or dirt; air valves may be too small in size or the air lines are clogged. Also the air hose or pipe line may be too small in diameter preventing an adequate air supply from reaching the gun.

328. Procedure for Applying a Clear Lacquer Finish With a Spray Gun.* The following procedure can be used for finishing either closed or open

---

* Soderberg, George A., *Finishing Materials and Methods*, Unit 7, 8, and 9, pp. 214–220.

grained wood. When the wood is open grained, the pores should first be filled with paste wood filler.

1. Prepare all surfaces by careful sanding.

2. Sponge all surfaces lightly to raise the grain. When dry, sand carefully with 5/0 sandpaper.

3. Spray on lacquer sealer. All pores must be filled first, and then all surplus filler must be removed from open grained wood. When dry, seal with sanding sealer.

4. Sand sealer coat with 5/0 finishing paper. Remove all dust.

5. Spray three to five coats of clear lacquer. Sand lightly between coats, removing dust particles that may have settled on the surface.

6. Sand, rub, and polish to produce the desired effect. To produce a satin finish, sand lightly with No. 280 silicon carbide paper and water. Next sand with No. 360 silicon carbide paper using rubbing oil as the lubricant. After cleaning all surfaces, polish with furniture polish. To produce a gloss finish repeat the procedure above but do the final rubbing with commercially prepared lacquer rubbing compound. Use a soft cloth or a piece of soft felt. After cleaning all surfaces, polish with furniture polish.

329. Procedure for Applying Varnish. Varnish consists of copal gums dissolved in linseed oil. It is thinned by adding turpentine. Varnish is made in many grades and for different types of work. A good rubbing varnish suitable for cabinetwork should be transparent, dry hard, and be able to resist heat.

Varnish produces a beautiful finish, and is used on the highest grade of cabinetwork. The disadvantages in using this finish, however, are that it generally cracks and becomes dull and very ugly with age, and that a special, dustproof finishing room is necessary.

Copal gums are fossilized resin deposits from pine trees long since dead. They are found buried in the ground in certain parts of Africa, New Zealand, East and West Indies, and South America.

There are several kinds of varnish. Some are used for exterior work, such as spar varnishes which dry quickly and are not rubbed. Some varnish is made for interior woodwork, and others for furniture. Furniture varnishes are also called "cabinet-rubbing varnishes" and dry slowly.

1. Varnishing must be done in a dust-free room. One cannot be too particular in removing dust from one's clothing, before entering the room, sprinkle water on the floor, and brush off the article of furniture to be varnished. A rag moistened with turpentine is the best thing with which to remove the last vestige of dust from the surface to be varnished.

2. Varnishing should be done at a temperature of about 80 deg. The varnish should be used as it comes from the can. Never shake the can or wipe a brush on its side as this causes air bubbles to form. One single air

bubble may spoil a finished surface. Thinning may cause it to lose its luster. It may be heated by placing the can in a pan of hot water to make it flow more freely. It may be applied directly over the filler if the first coat is thinned with turpentine. Some finishers prefer a sealing coat of thin shellac.

3. Unlike shellac and lacquer, varnish is easy to apply, because it dries slowly. Care should be taken, however, to spread it evenly so as to prevent piling up, runs, and sags. Finish with long, light feathery strokes with the grain.

4. Allow from 24 to 48 hours or more for drying, and sand in between coats. This is necessary in order to get a good bond between coats. Varnish does not adhere to a glossy surface. If waterproof sandpaper is used, the dust produced by rubbing with ordinary sandpaper or steel wool is avoided. Allow 2 hours before applying the next coat, if water is used in rubbing (see directions given in Art. 328).

5. A satin finish is produced with FF powdered pumice stone and rubbing oil, as described in Article 318, step 6.

6. A higher polish is produced by adding rottenstone to the pumice, or by rubbing with only rottenstone and oil.

7. Clean the rubbed surface, and finish by rubbing it with polishing oil.

8. The surface is given a final cleaning by rubbing very lightly with a linen cloth wrapped around a small piece of waste moistened with alcohol. Rub quickly, and never let the ball rest on the surface as the alcohol will burn through the finish. This process is called "spiriting off."

A varnish remover can be made by mixing technical tri-sodium phosphate with water in the proportions of 3 lb. to 1 gallon.

To Paint Furniture and Interior Woodwork

The process of applying inside paint may be divided into the following general steps: preparation of the surface for the priming coat; application of the priming coat; filling of holes and other imperfections in the surface; application of second and third undercoats, and application of the finishing coats.

330. Preparation of the Surface. 1. The surface must be perfectly smooth, well sanded, and free from grease or glue spots (Art. 310).

2. Softwoods, like basswood or whitewood, should be given a coat of thin shellac before the priming coat is applied. The shellac will prevent the wood from absorbing the oil in the paint too rapidly. It will also stiffen and bind the very fine fibers of such woods together, so as to eliminate all fuzziness and produce a perfectly smooth surface when sanded. Sand lightly with No. 2/0 sandpaper before applying the priming coat.

3. Pitchy woods, such as yellow pine, should also be given a coat of

thin shellac in order to prevent the pitch from penetrating, or bleeding through, and discoloring the various coats of paint. Sand the coat of shellac as explained in step 2.

4. Porous woods, such as chestnut, oak, and ash, should be given a coat of paste wood filler before the priming coat is applied (Art. 316).

5. Hard, close-grained woods, such as birch or maple, need no further preparation beyond smoothing and sanding. The priming coat may be applied directly to such woods.

331. Application of the Priming Coat. The chief ingredients of inside paints are white lead or zinc white, boiled linseed oil, and turpentine. To a priming coat is generally added French yellow ocher, a claylike substance, ground in oil, because it covers the surface better.

Primers, paints, and undercoats can be bought ready mixed, and will prove very satisfactory. If it is desired to mix the primer from the raw materials, the following procedure is recommended:

1. Mix some yellow ocher together with the needed quantity of white zinc. The amount of ocher to be mixed with the white zinc depends upon the darkness of the finished color. If the finished color is to be white, no ocher should be used.

2. Add about a tablespoonful of boiled linseed oil to each quart of zinc white, and work it thoroughly together. Then add about one gill of turps and ¼ gill of japan drier to each quart of zinc white, and mix thoroughly. If this mixture is too thick, add boiled linseed oil to it until it has the consistency of cream.

It is very important to take time to mix the ingredients thoroughly because the quality of the paint, and therefore the finished product, depends upon how well this preliminary work is done.

Fig. 26. Applying undercoater.

Zinc white and white lead are both metallic compounds derived respectively from zinc and lead. As white lead is poisonous, it is recommended to use zinc white in its place.

3. Apply the primer and let it dry 12 to 24 hours (Fig. 26); then sand lightly with No. 0 sandpaper until all brush marks have been obliterated and a smooth surface is produced.

332. Filling Holes and Other Imperfections in the Surface. After the priming coat has been applied, any imperfections in the surface will be more noticeable (see last paragraph in Art. 310). These should be filled with a good putty or with Danish whiting mixed with some thin glue. The latter type of putty will dry very hard in a few hours, and will not crack nor shrink if properly mixed. It should be applied with a putty knife and, when dry, sanded with No. 2/0 sandpaper. Nail holes may be filled by using the fingers instead of the putty knife.

Whiting is white, powdered chalk, which is also used as a pigment. Several preparations of this kind are on the market.

333. Applications of the Second and Third Undercoats. Prepare the second coat from the original mixture of zinc white and ocher, but thin only with turpentine, adding a little at a time. Apply this coat, and allow it to dry from 12 to 24 hours before sanding.

For the third coat, which is often unnecessary, use pure zinc white. Add the desired color pigment ground in oil and 1 tablespoon of turps to each quart of zinc white. Stir the mixture thoroughly. Then add a little japan drier and enough turps to give it the right consistency. Apply as before, and allow 24 hours for drying. Sand lightly with No. 2/0 sandpaper.

Ready-mixed paints and undercoats of a good grade will also give satisfactory results. They should be applied according to the directions given by the manufacturer.

Fig. 27. Sanding before applying final enamel coat.

334. Application of the Finishing Coats. The finishing coat generally consists of enamel, which is a colored varnish. Enamel is more transparent than paint, and does not cover the wood so well. For this reason, paint is used for the undercoats, the last of which should be of the same color as the enamel. Enamel, like paint, may be bought to finish either flat or glossy.

1. The first finishing coat should consist of equal parts of enamel and paint used for the last undercoat. Let this dry for 36 hours. Then sand with No. 3/0 sandpaper, and wipe the surface with a piece of moist chamois skin so as to remove every particle of dust (Fig. 27).

2. The last coat should be pure enamel just as it comes from the can. Like varnish it should be applied in a dustproof room, at a temperature of from 70 to 80 deg. (Art. 329).

3. Good enamels dry slowly. It is, therefore, best to let the work stand 4 days before rubbing it down with pumice stone and water.

335. Summary. A perfect finish can only be produced on a perfect surface. Therefore sand thoroughly and look for the following defects: glue and grease stains, dents or bruises, holes or cracks, scratches from tools or sandpaper.

Stains are of the following kinds: water, oil, spirit, and stains due to chemical action as bichromate of potash, lime, ammonia, and permanganate of potash. Brush the work with water and sand before applying any stain soluble in water.

Filler comes either in paste or liquid form. It is used to fill the pores of open-grained woods as oak, chestnut, ash, mahogany, and walnut. Shellac is used as a sealing coat over paste wood filler. It is also used as a filler on woods with small pores as maple, birch, gum, and cherry.

Transparent finishes discussed are shellac, wax, linseed oil, lacquer, and varnish.

336. Summary of Advantages and Disadvantages of the Finishing Coats Described. *The shellac finish* is beautiful, hard, and durable, but it is somewhat difficult to apply by hand methods. No dustproof finishing room is necessary.

The lacquer finish is very transparent, lustrous, and beautiful. It is also hard and durable, and does not mar easily. It is rather difficult to brush on, but improvements in spraying processes are constantly being made to overcome this difficulty. As it dries quickly, no special dustproof finishing room is needed. This is a distinct advantage over varnishing.

The varnish finish is also clear and beautiful, but it is very easily marred, cracks, and becomes dull and ugly with age. It is easy to apply, but great care must be taken to keep the work free from dust. It is used commercially on all fine furniture, pianos, radio cabinets, etc.

The wax finish is very easy to apply, and very easy to repair. It is not durable, however. Finger marks show plainly, and any liquid spilled on it makes a dull spot. It is recommended for beginners on account of the ease with which it is applied.

The oil finish is not so brilliant as the shellac, lacquer, or varnish, but it is very durable and gives furniture a certain charm and quiet dignity, characteristic of antique pieces. Oil finishing was used a great deal on the earlier antiques. It is not used commercially, but is to be recommended for students and amateur woodworkers.

Opaque finishes are paint, metallic leaf and powders, and colored lacquers.*

---

* For a more detailed discussion of wood finishing, see: Newell, A. C., and Holtrop, W. F., *Coloring, Finishing and Painting Wood,* rev. ed., 1961, Charles A. Bennett Co., Peoria, Ill.

REVIEW QUESTIONS, CHAPTER 13

Possible score 55 points

Your score . . . . . .

PART I. COMPLETION QUESTIONS. Complete the following statements:

1. The last big step in the completion of a piece of furniture is the process of . . . .
2. A project, especially when it is to be stained, should be carefully checked for . . . . spots.
3. A dent or bruise in a wood surface can often be removed by the application of a small pad of cotton waste soaked in . . . .
4. A quicker way of taking out dents is to use . . . .
5. A good material to fill holes and cracks, available in different colors, is . . . .
6. End grain is sanded smooth by moving the sanding block in only . . . .
7. Water stains are made by dissolving powdered . . . . in hot water.
8. The solvent used in making spirit stain is . . . .
9. To fill the pores of open-grained wood one uses . . . .
10. Shellac is produced by an insect called lac bug, which is native to the southern part of . . . .
11. The natural color of shellac is orange; when bleached the color is . . . .

12. Flaxseed when subjected to intense pressure produces ....
13. The most important piece of equipment in the spray method of finishing is the ....
14. The tool which reduces air pressure and maintains the required pressure is called ....
15. The machine specifically designed to pump air from atmospheric to a higher pressure is called ....
16. Compartments or enclosures in which spraying is done, are called ....
17. A sprayed coat which has a pimply appearance is called ....
18. The best thinner used for varnish is ....
19. When painting a surface, the first coat is called the ....
20. When color is added to varnish, it is called ....

PART II. TRUE-FALSE QUESTIONS. Indicate, by encircling T or F, whether the following statements are true or false.

21. Wood finishes are either transparent or opaque.   T   F
22. Opaque finishes are produced by paints, clear lacquers, or metallic powders.   T   F
23. Oftentimes, certain species of wood are stained to imitate other more costly woods.   T   F
24. Oilstains are known to fade or change color when exposed to light.   T   F
25. Fumed oak is produced by taking a weak solution of ammonia and allowing it to evaporate in a closed room or box.   T   F
26. Wood filler is removed when the surface takes on a flat dull appearance.   T   F
27. All close-grained woods should be filled with paste wood filler.   T   F
28. To prevent a wood surface from becoming smudgy through filling, a wash coat of shellac can be applied first.   T   F
29. Shellac is basically a mineral product.   T   F
30. When we speak of 4 lb. cut shellac, we mean that 4 lb. of shellac have been dissolved in one gallon of denatured alcohol.   T   F
31. Shellac is brushed on like ordinary paint or varnish.   T   F
32. Furniture waxes are put up in paste or liquid form.   T   F
33. Spray guns are either of the bleeder or nonbleeder type.   T   F
34. An internal mix spray gun mixes air and material outside the air cap before expelling it.   T   F
35. When cleaning a gun, it is good practice to submerge the entire gun in the proper cleaning solvent.   T   F
36. To clean out the small holes in the air cap, use a fine wire or small pointed nail.   T   F
37. A diaphragm-type air compressor develops pressure through the reciprocating action of a flexible disk actuated by an eccentric.   T   F
38. The proper application of finishing coats by means of a spray gun requires experience which is best gained by plently of practice.   T   F
39. One of the basic rules of spraying is to hold the gun at a 45 deg. angle to the work.   T   F
40. A spray gun is "starved" when insufficient air or fluid reaches the gun.   T   F

PART III. MULTIPLE-CHOICE QUESTIONS. Select, by encircling the correct letter, the answer which completes each statement:

41. The main purpose of staining is:
    A. To produce an imitation of another wood
    B. To fill the pores
    C. To produce a rich and mellow color
    D. To cover up mistakes and blemishes
42. One of the following is not a thinner for paste wood filler:
    A. Alcohol
    B. Turpentine
    C. Benzine
    D. Naphtha
43. One of the following is not a characteristic of shellac:
    A. Difficult to brush on evenly
    B. Thinned with alcohol
    C. Deteriorates with time
    D. Extremely waterproof
44. When, in spraying, too much material is applied on the surface, it results in:
    A. Fog
    B. Orange peel
    C. Mist
    D. Sags
45. One of the following should not be practiced in wood finishing:
    A. Apply lacquer over varnish
    B. Apply varnish over shellac
    C. Apply lacquer over sanding sealer
    D. Apply filler over a stained surface

PART IV. MATCHING QUESTIONS. Match the terms to the left with the descriptions to the right by placing the correct letter in the parentheses:

46. ( ) Aniline
47. ( ) Naphtha
48. ( ) Turpentine
49. ( ) Wood filler
50. ( ) japan
51. ( ) 4 lb. cut
52. ( ) Bleeder type gun
53. ( ) Spray pattern
54. ( ) Orange peel
55. ( ) Mist

A. Oil produced from the sap of long-leaf pines.
B. Consists of silex ground in japan, linseed oil, and turpentine.
C. A mixture of 4 lb. shellac and one gallon of alcohol.
D. A gun designed without an air valve.
E. A coal-tar product.
F. Often caused by improper thinner.
G. Distilled from petroleum.
H. Generally caused when the spray material is too thin.
I. A drying agent made from gums, shellac, linseed oil, etc.
J. The manner in which a gun sprays a surface.
K. A mixture of four gallons of alcohol and one pound of shellac.
L. A gun equipped with an air valve.

CHAPTER 14

Project Selection, Design, and Planning

Up to this point the reader of this book should have received a good deal of help in matters pertaining to the construction of his projects. It seems appropriate to include also some suggestions on project selection and design. The steps in planning will be stated and two articles deal with important but often neglected areas, namely: "Identifying parts within a project" and "Layout methods and techniques."

339. Project Selection. For some years the author has used the criteria for the selection of projects as stated by H. A. Allender in his article: "When is a Project Appropriate?"*

Mr. Allender lists the following criteria:

1. *The Project Must Possess Utility When Completed.* Articles should be useful, comfortable, and fulfill our human needs.

2. *The Project Must Include Teaching-Learning Situations.* It is possible to select, design, and construct a project which, when completed, fulfills the criteria of usefulness. But when analyzed and broken down into its various learning units, the number of techniques learned are extremely limited. For example, when a student makes a walnut serving tray, the time spent on removing surplus stock with various gauges and smoothing surfaces with sandpaper is completely out of proportion to that spent on other tool techniques. Projects should be selected so that a maximum amount of problem solving takes place. This approach eliminates the made-to-order project where a student is only required to follow a complete set of plans, and procedures set up by somebody else.

3. *The Project Must Possess Elements of Good Construction.* It is possible to design an article which does not lend itself for construction by the craftsman. Much has been said about the lack of design ability among teachers of woodworking. But the argument also works in reverse. Many designed articles fail to get beyond the design stage, because they are impractical. This may be caused by improper selection of materials, and structural details.

4. *The Project Must Possess Elements of Good Design.* This important criteria will be discussed in greater detail in the following article.

* Allender, H. A., "When is a Project Appropriate?" *Industrial Arts and Vocational Education* magazine, Feb., 1950, page 78.

5. *The Construction of the Project Must Be Within the Students' Ability.* In woodworking, as in all other areas of study, one learns by acquiring sound fundamentals and then proceeding to more detailed and intricate problems. This does not mean that all beginners should make doorstops or bread boards. A project should be challenging, but not to the point where failure can be predicted almost with certainty. The fact that a student has designed some interesting projects in a previous design course is no guarantee that he is capable of constructing these projects in the laboratory, without first acquiring the necessary fundamental skills and a background of related information.

6. *The Project Must Include Available Materials Only.* Some foreign woods make excellent furniture. Their lack of availability, however, makes it an unwise selection. They can be ordered, but the length of time it takes for delivery might seriously cut into the amount of time available to complete the project.

Our supply of native woods is quite adequate, although prices are high. Make your choice from it, and in so doing be sure that there is more where this came from. It is also important to investigate, in advance, certain types of hardware. If a project requires unusual hardware, it is well to order these items well in advance, since it takes time for delivery.

7. *The Project Must Include the Use of Tools and Equipment on Hand.* If a laboratory does not have a thickness planer, it would be unwise to order rough lumber. Lumberyards will deliver, at a nominal charge, lumber surfaced on two sides (S. 2. S.).

Also analyze the project in regard to the various machine processes involved. If shaping and making of edge moldings is required, is there a shaper to do this type of work? The machinery often determines the type of project that can be made, unless one is prepared to do all operations by hand.

8. *The Project Must Fit Into the School Shop Program Relative to Construction, Finishing, and Storage During the Time It Is in the Shop.* Particularly the last two factors should be considered. It would be unwise to insist upon a rubbed varnish finish when there is no dust-proof drying room. It also could prove dangerous to spray lacquer without the use of a well-ventilated spray booth or some other means by which spray dust can be carried off into the open air. When projects, in semistate of completion, must be stored in unsuitable places, sooner or later damage will be done that may require much repair. As a project is selected, try to foresee some of these difficulties.

9. *The Project Must Embrace a Cost That Is Not Prohibitive.* In recent years the cost of lumber has gone up. In planning a project, carefully write out a bill of material and figure the number of board feet. This last figure,

multiplied by the unit cost per board foot, may result in an estimate that is too high.

10. *The Project Must Be One That Can Be Completed in the Allotted Time.* When allowances are made for vacations and school holidays, the average semester in secondary schools and colleges lasts from 15 to 16 weeks. With this as the one definite known factor, it is difficult for teachers and students to determine just how long it takes to complete a certain project. It is ideal to complete all projects by the end of the semester.

11. *The Project Should Be One That Requires a Substantial Amount of the Student's Time and Effort and Also Creates and Maintains His Interest Until Completion.* Assembling and finishing a ready-made or pre-cut project does not satisfy the criterion of effort, while the making of small novelties, time consuming though they may be, does not satisfy the criterion of interest. Students should be encouraged to design their own projects, develop an acceptable set of drawings, and look up references pertaining to construction and finishing. Projects completed in this manner, under the sympathetic guidance of the teacher, will leave the student with a feeling of real accomplishment.

With a typical beginning class in the junior high school, it is unwise to start out by asking students to design and develop their own projects. Much of the time in such a class should be devoted to teaching sound fundamentals and discussing topics of related information. A few carefully selected and well-designed projects serve this purpose. As students reach the senior high school level, and particularly in college, they should be taught and encouraged to design their own projects.

340. Project Designing. Perhaps the most important fact brought out by recent research is what leaders in industrial arts have always maintained, that shop teachers have a definite responsibility to teach "industrial design."

In almost all of the lists stating the objectives of industrial arts, one objective will deal, in one way or another, with design. But still too many teachers of woodworking, because of a lack of confidence in design techniques, continue to rely upon dogmatic rules of design advocated many years ago. These rules give the false impression that only by following them will a successful design evolve.

What is the basic philosophy of contemporary design? When following the evolution of products, large and small, one finds that modern design avoids adherence to rigid rules of proportion, balance, rhythm, and symmetry and rebels against the copying or the adaptation of historic styles. But of vital interest are problems of functional analysis, economy of materials, simplicity, honesty, and the imaginative use of today's materials.

---

* Tinkham, Robert A., "Design in Industrial Arts," mimeographed, 5 pp.

It is creative problem solving rather than blind rule following. Design for today should not be a process of covering good form with meaningless decorations. It is generally agreed that teachers of industrial arts are extremely weak in contemporary design. Fortunately, something is being done about it and most colleges where industrial arts teachers are being trained now have regular courses in design as a part of the curriculum. In the better courses, emphasis is placed upon the need for close co-operation and correlation between the design class and the laboratory. In the ideal situation, a student does his designing under the guidance of his instructor and then goes into the laboratory to complete the actual project.

With a typical beginning class in junior high school it would be unwise to start out by asking each student to design his first project. At this stage he knows little about materials and has not learned any of the basic tool processes. It would be far better to allow him to take his choice from two or three completed, well-designed projects. This would give the instructor an opportunity to demonstrate carefully the tool processes common to these projects, and introduce appropriate topics of related information. Such a procedure would also leave him time to give individual attention to those students who need it. It seems absurd to start a beginning class by saying: "Now what would you like to make?" and let the students pursue some of their poorly chosen projects without any knowledge of the basic processes. This is like buying a youngster his first piano and saying: now what would you like to play. Such an approach is contrary to our basic laws of learning.

The second step in design instruction is taken when the instructor feels that the majority of his students are ready to do some actual designing. The approach is often by means of a project agreed upon by the class, such as a magazine rack made of wood. The assignment is made well in advance so that each student has an opportunity to think about the problem. During this time he has a chance to look up literature and illustrations, to sketch some of his own ideas and answer such questions as: what need does the object serve, how is it used, what must be known about materials, and what operations, either hand or machine, are involved. The final design will be used by all the members of the class with the exception of some students who have shown that they are capable of producing a good individual design.

In the final step, students who have developed a design-confidence through the above procedure should be required to design all of their remaining projects. It should be remembered that designing is a high form of intellectual and creative activity. To be creative, one needs ample time. To expect a student to design a project in too short a time is not likely to produce the best results.

341. Planning Your Project. After a project has been designed, independently or in a design class, a number of steps need to be taken before actual construction can start.

A design drawing usually does not lend itself for construction purposes. Although this drawing shows the appearance as the project will look when completed, it does not show the necessary dimensions and details.

What is next needed is a set of working drawings. This consists of a drawing showing the front, top, and right side view and is called an *orthographic projection*. It shows the true shape of all parts and not foreshortened as is the case in the design drawing.

In an orthographic projection (Fig. 1), the different views are shown by certain types of lines. *Solid lines* outline the body of the object. *Invisible lines* drawn as short, ⅛-in. dashes, indicate a part that cannot be seen from the surface. *Center lines* divide the drawing into equal or symmetrical parts, and are drawn alternately as long (½-in.) and short (⅛-in.) dashes. *Extension lines* extend out from the solid lines to provide lines between which dimensions can be shown. *Dimension lines* have arrowheads at one or both ends and a broken section in the center where a dimension is indicated. They are placed between the extension lines. Generally, there are two types of dimensions. *Over-all dimensions* indicate the full length, height, and depth or width. *Detail dimensions* show the sizes of smaller parts within a project.

In addition to a two- or three-view drawing by way of orthographic

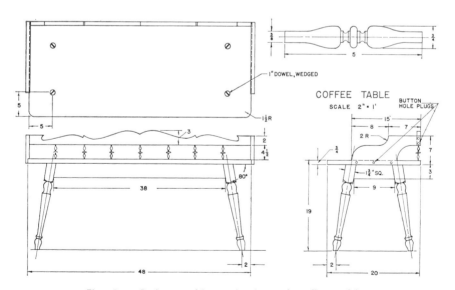

Fig. 1. Orthographic projection of coffee table.

projection, it is often necessary to show certain details. When space permits, *detail drawings* are sometimes placed directly on the orthographic drawing, or they are placed on one or more separate sheets.

The next step in planning is to write out a bill of material. This is a complete list of all the lumber, plywood, hardware, and finishing materials needed. Bills of material are often subdivided into two separate bills, a rough bill of material and a detailed bill. The rough bill of material lists the lumber requirements in standard sizes as it is sold by the lumberyard (Fig. 2).

CHANNEL CITY PLYWOOD & LUMBER CO. No. 7326

730 Punta Gorda St., P.O. Box 718, Santa Barbara, California

Telephone: WOodland 6-1046

SOLD TO	W. F. Holtrop	SHIP TO	Same
ADDRESS	179 Nogal		
CITY	Santa Barbara		

Order Date 7-22-58	Your Order No. Phone	Ship Via Our Delivery V	Customer Will Call	Terms
Shipping Date 7-22-58	Sold By AE	Truck No. 3	Checked By AE	Cash	C.O.D.	Charge V

Quan. Ordered	Quan. Ship	Thick- ness	Width	Length	Description	Feet	Price	Amount Total
V	1	3/4	4 x	8	Birch A2	32	.44	14.08
V	1	3/4	4 x	8	Fir AD	32	210.00	6.72
32 L	26	13/16	RWRL		Birch Lumber	26	.72	18.72
1		2	6	12	D.F.	12	100.00	1.20
1		2	6	16	D.F.	16	105.00	1.68
10 lb.	V				6d. Box Nails		.25	2.50
								44.90
							4% City Tax	1.80
								46.70

All discounts null and void if not paid by . . . .

Your Invoice   Received by . . . . . . WFH . . . . . .

All claims and returned goods must be accompanied by this bill.
All returned merchandise subject to 10% handling charge.

Figure 2. Invoice from lumberyard.

Figure 3 shows the rough bill of material for the coffee table, as prepared by a student.

No. of Pieces Required	Size			Kind of Material
	Thickness	Width	Length	
1	1″	12″	12′-0	Clear Birch or Maple, K.D., rough.
1	2″	6″	4′-0	Clear Birch or Maple, K.D., rough.

Required Miscellaneous and Finishing Materials:

10 Button type hole plugs
1 Quart of clear spraying lacquer
1 Pint of lacquer sanding sealer
1 Quart of lacquer thinner
   Sandpaper No. 1/2 and No. 2/0; 3 sheets each
   Wet or dry finishing paper; No. 400, 2 sheets

Fig. 3. Rough bill of material for coffee table.

By carefully checking and studying the working drawings one prepares the detailed bill of material or cutting list. This list should include, in so far as possible, the exact number and size of pieces which, together, will make the project. When calculating the length of pieces, always make allowances for mortise-and-tenon joints, ¼ inch deep dado joints, some surplus length on turned parts and boards to be glued up into tops and panels.

The detailed cutting list for the coffee table appears as shown in Figure 4.

No. of Pieces	Name of Part	Finished Size
1	Top	¾ x 20 — 48 in.
4	Legs	1¾ x 1¾ — 20 in.
1	Back	¾ x 3 — 47½ in.
2	Sides	¾ x 7 — 15 in.
2	Front and back rails	¾ x 3 — 40 in.
2	Side rails	¾ x 3 — 11 in.
7	Gallery pins	¾ x ¾ — 5 in.

Fig. 4. Detailed bill of material for coffee table.

With the above information the experienced woodworker is now ready to go to work. By experience he knows what to do. But most students are very much at a loss as to where to start. At this point many teachers ask their students to write down, step by step, the procedure for making their project, but this seems to be asking considerable from people who previously have done little with wood. It seems more sensible for a teacher to talk over with a student or the class some of the major problems involved. A group discussion may bring out many points of general or specific interest. Following such a discussion the student is now much more capable of listing some of the basic steps that need to be taken.

The over-all plan of procedure for the coffee table would look somewhat like this:

1. Purchase lumber as listed in the rough bill of material.
2. Lay out, cut, and turn legs and gallery pins.
3. Lay out, cut, and prepare rails, making allowances for 1-in. tenons.
4. Lay out, cut, and prepare sides.
5. Lay out, cut, and prepare back.
6. Lay out, cut, and prepare top, allowing for at least ½ in. over length.
7. Drill all holes, cut mortises, and make a trial assembly.
8. Complete all necessary sanding and assemble.
9. Apply a lacquer finish and rub out to the desired effect.

As the student completes each step he checks it and starts with the next one. Naturally, he still needs, throughout, a great deal of individual attention, but as time progresses he begins to solve some of his own problems. It is often helpful to have each student write down, from day to

Fig. 5. Completed coffee table.

day, some of the problems encountered and the solution found for each one of them. With the help of these notes, he can write out, at the close of the term, a more detailed plan of procedure. Such a plan serves a twofold purpose. It shows by its detailed analysis that the student has learned something, and that the teacher has done a good job of teaching.

Figure 5 shows the completed project.

342. Identifying Parts Within a Project. There seems to be little or no agreement among woodworkers in this country as to how the different parts of a project shall be identified one from another. Books on woodworking offer no assistance in this area either. Nevertheless it is most important to be able to look at a certain part of a project and at a glance be able to tell where it belongs.

If projects were all of the bread board variety, consisting of one piece of wood, the matter of identification would be very simple. But if the builder has to construct out of 1 by 6-in. stock, several 12-in. wide panels, let us say 24 in. long, how is he going to keep the pieces of one panel from becoming confused with those of another. In such a job it could be done by numbering each board, 1 through 10, or higher as the need might be. Or he could go through the greater part of the alphabet by numbering each board A, B, C and so on.

The marking or identification technique presented here was not developed by the author. He was introduced to it while he was a carpenter apprentice in the Netherlands some years ago. Up to the present, this technique is universally used there, and may be in use in other European countries, or unknown to him, in this country.

This marking system uses primarily two or more lines which meet at

Fig. 6. Marking boards to be glued together.

Fig. 7. Second pair of boards marked.

an angle forming a triangle or a pyramid with a face or edge. Two 6-in. boards that need to be glued up into a 12-in. board are marked with two lines as shown in Figure 6. The two boards have previously been planed to their approximate thickness. The marking lines immediately establish which two edges need to be planed straight and provided with a spring joint. If two or more sets of two boards need to be glued up, an additional line is drawn on one side of the triangle (Fig. 7). Since many projects are basically made up of two sides, top and bottom, the number of lines so used generally does not go beyond four. If the number of panels to be glued up is more than four, the lines are substituted by a figure written inside each part of the triangle. By using this technique, a hundred boards can be glued up into pairs, and readily identified by numbers ranging from 1 for the first to 50 for the last (Fig. 8). Naturally, it is seldom that that many boards need to be glued up, unless in a large production shop. When several wide panels must be glued up from three or more narrow boards, the matter of identification becomes proportionately more necessary. A panel of four boards, for example, would necessitate planing six straight edges and making provisions for a spring joint on each one. Unless each board is distinctly marked, one is likely to become confused as to where it should be placed. Again, by putting two lines across the boards as shown in Figure 9, each board is readily replaced after it has been planed. If more than one panel needs to be glued up either follow the procedure as shown in Figure 7 or that in Figure 8.

When making an open shelve utility cabinet or project of similar construction, the inexperienced woodworker has often difficulty in keeping track of the sides and the shelves to be fastened together. It has happened more than once that someone finished with two left sides. Such mistakes are costly, especially if blind dado joints were used. Although it is necessary to keep each shelf in its proper position, a certain amount of rearranging

Fig. 8. Marking and numbering two boards for gluing.

Fig. 9. Marking four boards for gluing.

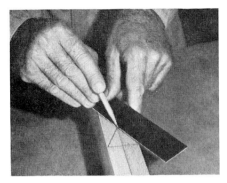

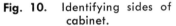

Fig. 10. Identifying sides of cabinet.

Fig. 11. Identifying cabinet shelves.

with these units may be possible. But not with the sides. The builder should definitely remember that once selected, one is the right side, the other the left. For easy identification, place the two sides together and mark them with a triangle as shown in Figure 10. If two utility cabinets need to be made, draw two base lines. Any time the number goes beyond four, place the appropriate number in each half of the triangle. To mark the top and shelves, stack them one on top of the other and mark the edges as shown in Figure 11. If more than one set of tops and shelves needs to be marked, draw two or more lines either to the right or left of the pyramid.

Footstools, benches, and tables usually consist of four legs and anywhere from four to eight (or more) connecting braces or rails. A small bench with upper and lower rails would consist of at least twelve parts, not counting the top. These various parts have to be carefully connected with some type of joint, ranging anywhere from a simple lap joint to mortise-and-tenon or dowel joints. Under production techniques legs and rails would be cut out on a mass production basis, each joint fitting perfectly as the parts come off the machines. But the home craftsman or student in the school laboratory does not follow mass production techniques since he has to make only one bench. The joints he has to make may be all hand-made or machine made with the use of a mortiser and circular saw.

The four legs are first bunched together and next marked in the front as shown in Figure 12. The right side (left side in the picture) is marked similarly, except that two base lines are drawn parallel to each other. In the back, repeat as before but with three base lines; complete marking the left side (right side in picture) like the other sides but now draw four base lines. The upper and lower rails for the bench are marked in pairs

Fig. 12. Marking table legs.

as shown in Figures 6 and 7. Laid out in four sets of two they appear as shown in Figure 13.

The next example shown here of the technique of identification by means of triangles is for a kneehole desk. No attempt is made to consider rules of proper design. The measurements used, however, are standard and were taken from a completed piece of furniture. A typical kneehole office desk 30 in. high, 60 in. wide, and 30 in. deep, generally has two writing tablets, one on the left side and one on the right side. Either on the right or on the left side may be two 12-in.-high drawers, sufficiently wide to hold standard manilla folders, size 9 by 11¾ in. The other side can be divided into three (or four) smaller drawers. In the center there should be sufficient room for a shallow drawer to hold pencils, erasers, and other small items. It should be narrow enough to avoid inconvenience to the person seated at the desk.

Fig. 13. Marking upper and lower rails.

The front of such a desk, in its skeleton form, would consist of the following parts:

    4 legs, 1½ by 1½ in.; 29¼ in. long
    1 top rail, ¾ by 1½ in.; 57¼ in. long
    3 left side drawer rails, ¾ by 1½ in.; 15½ in. long
    4 right side drawer rails, ¾ by 1½ in.; 15½ in. long
    1 center drawer rail, ¾ by 1½ in.; 27¼ in. long

To construct the complete skeleton for such a desk, not counting top, panels, drawers, writing tablets and drawer guides, would require the following parts:

        8 legs;
        2 top rails (one in front, one in back);
       16 drawer rails and
        8 side rails.

This is a total of 34 pieces just for the skeleton frame. Needless to say, some system of marking these pieces must be used in order to avoid confusion.

Basically, the marking procedure is the same as the one used for the bench, except that the desk is made of twice as many legs and more than three times as many rails.

To mark the legs, stack them in two groups of four and lay out the front as shown in Figure 14. Do the same for the sides and back, using 2, 3, and 4 base lines successively.

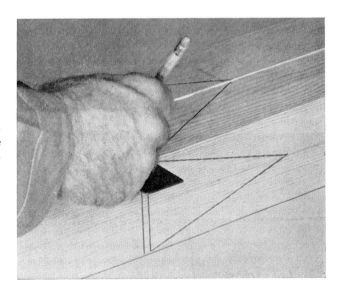

Fig. 14. Identifying knee-hole desk legs.

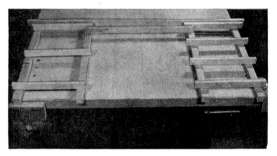

Fig. 16.   Knee-hole desk leg and rail layout.

Fig. 15.   Front rail layout.

Next, group the front rails together. In as much as the front consists of three separate sections (two side sections and the kneehole section) it is not possible to cover all parts with just two lines. To solve this problem, mark the front rails as shown in Figure 15. Also mark the rails to the right with a capital letter R for right, and those to the left with a capital letter L for left.

The markings for the back are like those in the front, but show three parallel lines. The rails for the right and left sides are marked as was done for the bench (Fig. 14). The marked parts for the front of a kneehole desk, laid out in their approximate position, appear as shown in Figure 16.

When several panel doors need to be made the stiles and the rails of the first door are marked (Fig. 17). When the number of doors exceeds four, indicate each set of stiles and rails with the appropriate number symbol.

A small glass door consisting of two stiles, two rails, one vertical mullion, and three horizontal mullions are marked as shown in Figure 18.

The marking or identification procedures presented here will take care of

Fig. 17.   Panel door rail and stile layout.

Fig. 18. Glass door rails, stiles, and mullions marked.

most projects made by amateur woodworkers and students. They also may have their merits in the small commercial shop. In mass production it probably has little or no value.

At first, this system may seem complicated, adding to confusion instead of eliminating it. However, as yet, this seems to be the simplest and most effective solution to the problem.

343. Laying Out Dimensions. Most pieces of furniture consist of a number of separate parts, which, when properly joined together form the completed projects. Some of these parts can be of the exact identical thickness, width, and length. The inexperienced woodworker often makes the mistake of laying out the dimensions on similar project parts one at a time. A much better procedure is to lay out pieces of similar dimension, whenever possible, all at once. For example, the four shelves in a small

Fig. 19. Laying out boards to exact length.

Fig. 20. Laying off exact length
on top board.

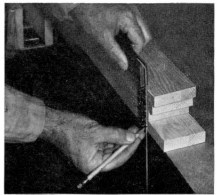

Fig. 21. Laying off length on
all sides.

open cabinet all must be of the exact length if good fitting joints are to
be secured. By laying out the length separately on each board, small
differences in measurements will occur, often significant enough to show
up when the project has been assembled.

To avoid any such discrepancies, stack the shelves along the edge of the
workbench and line up the squared ends with a try square (Fig. 19). Next
lay out the exact length on the top shelf and transfer this dimension to
all the shelves as shown in Figures 20 and 21. From this measurement draw
a square line across the face of each board, which next is cut to exact
length with a sharp crosscut saw. When a cutoff saw or a circular saw is
available, this operation can be completed on these machines by fastening
a stop block on the cutoff gauge (Fig. 10, p. 63).

Table legs, stiles, and rails for doors and windows are readily laid out
and cut to exact length by following this same procedure.

When boards must be reinforced with dowels it is important that the
holes in the edges line up as perfectly as possible. If these holes were to
be laid out individually, slight differences in position would occur, often
significant enough to make the difference between a perfect and a poor fit.
To avoid any differences in position, lay out the dowel centers by first
marking their place (Fig. 22). Notice that the boards have been marked for
easy identification. From these marks in the face of each board, square
lines across the edge and mark the center for each dowel hole with a marking
gauge (Fig. 23). These centers need not be located if a self-centering dowel
jig is used. Simply line up the proper hole in the jig with the lines on the

Fig. 22. Laying out dowels.

Fig. 23. Squaring dowel lines.

edge of each board (see Fig. 47, p. 211). When the holes are drilled on a boring machine, it is important to hold the marked or working face of each board on the supporting table, especially when the various boards differ slightly in thickness (see Fig. 76, p. 97). Figure 24 shows the boards just prior to final assembly.

When one makes a project consisting of two sides, a top and a number of shelves, he first needs to lay out the parts carefully. Assuming that the top and shelves have been cut to the correct length, they are next stacked one on top of the other, or held as shown in Figure 25. The ¾-in. width of the dadoes is laid out on the edge of the top and the ¼ in. that is to

Fig. 24. Final dowel assembly.

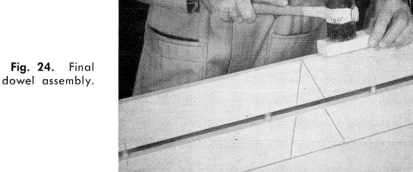

Fig. 25. Laying out top and shelves.

fit in the dadoes to be cut in the sides is laid off on the ends of the shelves (Fig. 25). Notice how the top and shelves have been marked for proper identification.

To lay out the position of the dadoes in the sides, place the two sides in front of you. On the top of the sides make a mark ¼ in. from the top. This is to fill up the dadoes which must be cut in the top. Next lay out the position where the ¾-in. shelves are to be placed. At the bottom end lay out the last ¾-in. measurement which is to become the position of the bottom shelve, to be fastened to the sides by means of a rabbet joint. When the exact positions of top and shelves have been determined, transfer them to the other side (Fig. 26). Figure 27 shows the parts in their approximate position.

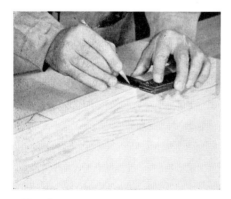

Fig. 26. Cabinet side dado joints.   **Fig. 27.** Layout of cabinet parts.

Fig. 28. Laying out mortises on   **Fig. 29.** Laying out mortises on
inside edges.   other edges.

When laying out the positions of the mortises to be cut in the four legs of a bench, again stack the legs along the edge of the workbench.

They should have been previously marked for easy identification. Stack the legs so that the marked sides do not show in the front. On the top leg, lay out the exact position of the upper and lower rails. With a try square transfer these measurements to all four legs (Fig. 28). Also, at this time, lay out the size of the mortises. Measuring from the top, upper rail mortises are set back from ½ to ¾ in. This procedure avoids showing an opening on the top of each leg, which would weaken the construction. The size of the lower rail mortise is usually set back a ¼ in. from the top. This practice produces a neater looking job. Next, with a try square lay out the mortises on the other unmarked side of each leg (Fig. 29). The tenons on upper and lower rails are laid out by following the same procedure as shown in Figure 25. For legs 1½ in. square, allow tenons of at least one inch length. Lay out the shoulder cut lines on both sides of each rail. The various parts of a bench loosely assembled would appear as shown in Figure 30.

When laying out the position of the mortises in the eight legs of a knee-hole desk, support the four front legs in the vise as shown in Figure 31. Since a great number of mortises will be cut in these legs, a certain amount of shifting may occur, unless well supported. Assuming that the legs have been previously cut to a length of 29¼ in., line them up so that four unmarked sides are face up. These should be the four sides that one could see when looking at the front of the desk. Starting from either top or bottom, lay out the mortises which are to hold the top rail, writing tablet

Fig. 30. Bench loosely assembled.

rails, and drawer rails. If the rails and writing tablet are all ¾ in. thick, and the openings for the large drawers are 11 in. high, the bottom leg dimension should be 3½ in. The other side of the desk is divided to hold a writing tablet and 3 drawers of equal height. If one uses the same dimensions as above, these drawers would be slightly over 7¼₆ in. high. With their position located, lay out the mortises (Fig. 31).

To lay out the position of the mortises in the back, use one of the front legs as a template or guide. The layout and structure of the back resembles that of the front, except that in the back provisions must be made for stationary panels, whereas the front has movable drawers.

The outside and inside panels are laid out by grouping the legs in groups of four and five, the fifth leg being the template. Instead of laying out for

Fig. 31. Laying out mortises for front legs of knee-hole desk.

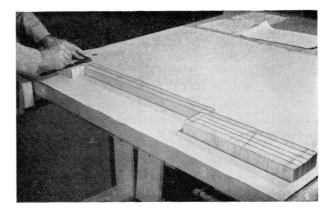

Fig. 32. Laying out front rail tenons.

top, drawer, and writing tablet rails, the as yet unmarked sides are now laid out for top and bottom side rails. Since the sides will be completed with a ¼-in. plywood panel, the mortises for the top rails should be shortened by ¼ in. at the bottom, and the mortises in the bottom rails should be shortened by ¼ in. at the top.

With all the legs marked for mortises, set them out in their approximate position and see whether the layout was executed correctly.

Lay out the tenons on the front rails near the edge of the workbench. The two large drawers should be at least 13 in. wide to accommodate standard size manila folders. After laying out the dimensions on the top rail, mark all rails (Fig. 32). The major parts of the front of the desk laid out in their approximate position appear as shown in Figure 33.

The rails for the back are best laid out by following the procedure as described above, using the front top rail as a template.

The top and bottom side rails are marked in a manner similar to that

Fig. 33. Layout of major members of knee-hole desk.

Fig. 34. Laying out over-all size of mortise.

Fig. 35. Layout of door stile mortises.

shown for the bench discussed above. Allow one inch for the length of all tenons.

When laying out the mortises in the stiles of a small panel door, hold the two stiles in the vise for easier handling. Next lay out the over-all size of the top and bottom mortises by careful measuring or by holding the rails across the edges (Fig. 34). To avoid open mortises, measure in from top and bottom of the stiles for a distance of at least ½ in., and square a line across the edges. Since the door is to be finished with a ¼-in. plywood panel, it will be necessary to shorten the size of each mortise by ¼ in. The completed layout on the edges of the stiles appear as shown in Figure 35.

Fig. 36. Tenons laid out on rails.

If the over-all width of the panel door is known, the exact length of the rails can be determined as follows: subtract twice the width of the stiles from the over-all width; next add three inches for two 1½-in. tenons. Lay out the rails as was done in Figure 32 (also see Fig. 36). The parts of a panel door, properly marked and laid out, appear as shown in Figure 37. The size of the ¼-in. plywood panel should be sufficiently large to fill the ¼-in. grooves which remain to be cut on the inside edges of all four parts.

When one is laying out a small glass door, with, let us assume, one vertical mullion and three horizontal mullions, the layout becomes a little more complicated.

Fig. 37. Position of panel door parts.

Not only that four large mortises and their accompanying tenons must be laid out, but also the mullions must be laid out in stiles and rails. Finally, the mullions themselves must be laid out where they cross each other as well as fit into the stiles and rails. When the shop is equipped with a shaper, mortiser, and a tenoner with coping head, the construction of such a door is a fairly simple job. But when it must be done with hand tools and maybe a mortiser and circular saw, it becomes a job that requires a careful layout and meticulous workmanship.

Procedure, laying out a small door with glass panels: 1. Cut the stiles to the required length.

2. Cut the vertical mullion to the required length by first subtracting the combined width of the upper and bottom rails from the length of stile; add two inches for two 1-in. tenons.

3. Place the mullion and the stiles in the vise of the bench, and lay out the over-all location of the mortises for the rails and horizontal mullions.

4. Shorten the layout of the mortises for the stiles by at least ½ in., at the top and bottom of each stile.

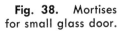

Fig. 38. Mortises for small glass door.

5. Shorten the layout of these mortises by ¼ in. from the inside. This is to take care of the ¼-in. glass groove.

6. Through these points simultaneously draw lines across the mullion and stiles (Fig. 38).

7. Divide the over-all dimension where the three horizontal mullions are located into three parts. If the stock is 1 in. thick, these marks should be ¼ in., ½ in., and ¼ in. apart. Draw lines through these marks.

8. To lay out the rails and horizontal mullions, first cut these parts to their correct length. The length is found by first subtracting the combined width of both stiles from the width of the door; next add two inches for two 1-in. tenons. If tenons should be 1½ in. long, add 3 in.

9. To avoid shifting of parts, hold rails and mullions in the vise.

10. Lay out, from each end, measurements of ¾ and 1 in.

11. Lay out the position of the vertical mullion and carefully divide this measurement of 1 in. into three parts of ¼ in., ½ in., and ¼ in.

12. With the try square draw lines simultaneously through these points (Fig. 39).

13. Remove rails and mullions from the vise and complete the layout of the shoulder cuts on each piece separately. If the glass door is to receive a small decorative molding on one edge and a glass groove on the other edge, draw lines across both faces through the ¾-in. marks. These are the shoulder cut lines. If the edge is to remain plain, draw lines at the ¾-in. mark across the face to receive the glass grove. Draw the other shoulder cut lines through the 1-in. marks on the edge.

14. Complete the outline by drawing four lines clear around the mullions where they will cross each other. Do this with a hard, sharp pencil. To complete the construction of the glass door, see Article 188, p. 220; also see Article 194, p. 234.

Fig. 39. Marking tenons and mortises in rails and mullions.

REVIEW QUESTIONS, CHAPTER 14

Possible score 35 points

Your score . . . . . .

PART I. COMPLETION QUESTIONS.   Complete the following statements:

1. The construction of most projects includes the three basic steps of selection, design, and . . . .
2. One of the basic criteria for a selected project is that, when completed, it is . . . .
3. Projects should be selected so that they are challenging and keep the student's . . . .
4. In a beginning woodworking class a great deal of time should be spent in teaching sound . . . .
5. Shop teachers have a definite responsibility to teach the fundamental steps of proper . . . .
6. After designing a project, it is usually necessary to prepare a set of . . . .
7. These drawings are presented in one, two, or three views, known as . . . .
8. Lines that divide a drawing into equal or symmetrical parts are called . . . .
9. Dimensions are shown as over-all and . . . . dimensions.
10. From a set of drawings one next prepares a detailed bill of material or . . . .

PART II. TRUE-FALSE QUESTIONS.   Indicate, by encircling T or F, whether the following statements are true or false.

11. When calculating the length of pieces, no allowances need to be made for joints and other construction details.   T   F
12. A step by step procedure serves as a guide and often prevents making costly mistakes.   T   F
13. Among woodworkers there seems to be general agreement as to how the different parts of a project shall be identified one from another.   T   F
14. The technique of identifying parts described here is by means of lines, triangles, and circles.   T   F
15. When laying out dimensions on identical pieces, it is most accurate to lay out each piece separately.   T   F
16. The layout of a small glass door can become complicated, especially if the door has a number of mullions.   T   F
17. Regardless of what a student learns, a project is acceptable as long as it is useful when completed.   T   F
18. The selection of a project should not be concerned with the cost.   T   F
19. It is best to design projects along old, well-established rules of design.   T   F
20. Regardless of their experience with tools and materials, students should be encouraged to express themselves freely.   T   F

PART III. MULTIPLE-CHOICE QUESTIONS. Select, by encircling the correct letter, the answer which completes each statement:

21. One of the following lines is placed on a drawing to help in dimensioning:
    A. Invisible lines
    B. Extension lines
    C. Center lines
    D. Solid lines

22. The unit measurement by which most solid lumber is sold is:
    A. Square foot
    B. Board foot
    C. Linear foot
    D. Cubic foot

23. One of the following is not used when identifying parts as described here:
    A. Lines
    B. Triangles
    C. Pyramids
    D. Circles

24. Footstools and benches generally would not be constructed with one of the following:
    A. Rails
    B. Legs
    C. Drawers
    D. Braces

25. A typical French door consists of all but one of the following parts:
    A. Stiles
    B. Mullions
    C. Rails
    D. Gallery pins

PART IV. MATCHING QUESTIONS. Match the terms to the left with the descriptions to the right by placing the correct letter in the parentheses:

26. ( ) Working drawings
27. ( ) Solid lines
28. ( ) Invisible lines
29. ( ) Center lines
30. ( ) Extension lines
31. ( ) Details
32. ( ) S.2.S.
33. ( ) No. 2/0
34. ( ) Mullions
35. ( ) Stiles

A. Outline the body of an object.
B. Lines between which dimensions are shown.
C. Surfaced on two sides.
D. Usually consist of one, two, or three views.
E. Indicates the coarseness of sandpaper.
F. The vertical members of a door, holding the rails.
G. Lines drawn as short dashes.
H. Small parts of a larger whole.
I. Divide a drawing into equal or symmetrical parts.
J. Dividing members in a French door.
K. A grade of lumber.

CHAPTER 15

Wood

It seems but natural and reasonable that a woodworker should have at least an elementary knowledge and understanding of "wood," the principal material with which he works.

Such information will make him more intelligent by increasing his knowledge of the world about him, and will give him certain economic and scientific facts that are useful and necessary both to the art of design and to the mechanics of wood construction.

Wood as a product is taking on an ever increasing importance in our national economy. Through scientific research in the woods and at the processing plants, better and more useful products are being made available.

Particularly since World War II, new uses and new outlets for timber products have been developed. Even so, we are still standing on the threshold of knowledge of wood and its potential for wise and profitable use.

*Versatiliy of Wood.** For more than three centuries, this country of ours has been building a better life with wood. Great forest lands, meeting the nation's expanding need for lumber, have always been one of our most valuable natural resources. Fortunately, with man's help, they always will be. Today, on over 50 million acres of tree farms owned and managed by the forest products industry, more new trees for use of coming generations are growing year by year.

Modern, scientific tree farming is a far cry from logging methods of the past. Commercially useful trees are now raised and harvested as a crop, protected from fire, insects, and disease, perpetually renewed by natural and artificial seeding. This reforestation, guided by research, safeguards our watersheds, wildlife, and scenic heritage. Most important, it assures the availability of wood in abundance, for every human need. Of the nearly one thousand different species of trees on American soil, over a hundred are used for some commercial purpose. The greater part of these are used to construct, beautify, and furnish the houses we live in.

Softwoods provide most of our structural and framing lumber, sheathing, roofing, and sub-flooring. Also from these species we derive most of our siding and trim and much of our interior paneling. Hardwood species give

---

* From: "Livability Unlimited," *National Lumber Manufacturer's Association,* 19 pp.

us most of our flooring and some of the finest woods for furniture, traditional interior paneling, and cabinetwork.

The economy of wood is made possible by its easy workability and availability. The fact that wood is strong, light, and resilient, makes it versatile enough for an architect's most imaginative design. It is durable, too, under almost all conditions of weather and wear, and lends itself to preservation, taking paints, stains, and other protective coatings better than most other materials (Fig. 1). Today, new technological processes continue to increase the usefulness of wood. Wood construction is a lot more than just board sheathing over 2 by 4 studs. It is post and beam, with its architectural precision and planning flexibility; it is plywood with its great diaphragmatic strength; it is lamination, which makes it possible to curve over spans of more than 250 feet. It is a combination of many new products which shape or treat rough lumber into one of the most versatile of all modern building materials.

One of the most outstanding illustrations of the versatility of modern engineered lumber is a judges' stand at Banff National Park, Canada (Fig. 2). This structure has aroused considerable comment in the engineering, construction, and design fields as to the unlimited possibilities of laminated timber construction.*

Rising 70 feet above the skiing slopes of Mt. Norquay, this unique structure is a first in North America. Built to house skiing judges and

---

* "Engineered Timber Beats Competition," *Canada Lumberman,* October, 1959, pp. 34–36.

Fig. 1. Proof of redwood durability. The lower tree was milled into usable lumber after lying on the ground for 1200 years. The second tree grew over it during that time.

Fig. 2. Judge's stand made of laminated supporting members.

the press, the stand was entirely prefabricated in Vancouver, then shipped to Banff for erection.

After having considered a number of preliminary designs, the final design consists of two cabins one above the other supported by four laminated arches and two laminated uprights. The roof area of each cabin is approximately 1200 square feet while the floor area is 800 square feet, comparable in area to a small bungalow. Access to the upper and lower cabins is by ladders.

The selection of wood species for this particular project was very important. Because of exposure to severe elements all material had to be pressure treated. Both West Coast hemlock and Douglas fir were considered as suitable materials. Of these two, hemlock was selected, mainly because of its exceptional record of accepting preservative treatment. Also, from a merchandising point of view, this project presented an opportunity to prove that hemlock was undervalued as a construction material.

The selected hemlock laminating stock was kiln dried at a moisture content of 18–20 per cent. Next it was pressure treated with water-borne Wolman Salts, which meant that the surface area of the stock was impregnated to a depth of ½ inch. A second drying session brought the moisture content down to 10–14 per cent, satisfactory to meet established specifications. Prefabrication now could get under way.

As the stand was required for the opening of the 1959 ski season at Banff, on-site work meant facing subzero weather with temperatures as low as 30 degrees below zero and blizzards adding to the difficulties. Snow fell to a depth of four feet with deep drifts, winches froze, and nuts froze to bolts. The main members and material had to be trucked in over hairpin turns from the Banff Railway station, ten miles from the site, a tedious journey requiring five hours. Once the components of the stand were moved to the base of the hill, movement up to the site was relatively simple, and construction went along without any severe difficulties.

This project, as one among many projects where laminating of wood is involved, offers proof that this technique can be successfully executed under the most difficult circumstances.

The versatility of wood is not only being recognized in home and furniture construction but also in the design and construction of large public and private buildings. Whereas a number of years ago it was common practice to erect two or more story school buildings of concrete and brick, the more recent trend is toward one-story schools primarily built of wood. A combination of comparable low cost, high quality and eye appealing beauty is being achieved today in many parts of this country through construction with wood. Modern developments in wood trusses and glued laminated members make possible exceptionally long spans for gymnasiums, auditoriums, and classrooms of any size.

From the standpoint of fire safety, insurance rates, and maintenance cost these one-story wooden structures compare most favorably with structures of the more conventional type and design.

Historical Development and Present Outlook of Forests and Forestry

The early development of the North American Colonies was characterized by an economy which was primarily provided by fur, fish, farms, and forests. Gold and silver, two minerals which, much later, were to play an important part in the development of the West, were lacking on the Atlantic seaboard. The age of metals, coal, oil, and electricity had as yet not arrived.*

In early colonial days, trapping, fishing, farming, and logging were the main activities of the population. Of these four, three were in abundance, providing the basic needs for food, clothing, and shelter. As the land was cleared, farms were established and small communities gradually sprang up. But the economy was essentially rural, with most efforts spent on the farm, in the forests and at sea.

These natural resources, abundant and cheap as they were, were naturally used liberally and extensively; in fact, they were exploited.

---

* Dana, Samuel T., *Forest and Range Policy: Its Development in the United States,* p. 1.

Forests, with an abundance of game and wildlife, were the dominating feature of the land. With the exception of a few mountain ranges, they covered on area from Maine to Georgia. As to species and size of trees, these forests of the New World were a completely new experience to the European immigrant.

Although the land had to be cleared to start a farm, establish a settlement or build a road, the forest continued to be a veritable storehouse for a wide variety of purposes. From it came wood for fuel, houses, posts, furniture, shingles, masts, and many other products. From certain trees came tar, pitch, and turpentine, potash for fertilizer and soap and bark for tanning purposes. It was but natural, with raw materials so close at hand, that wood-using industries were the first to develop. As early as 1623, the ship "Anne" carried a cargo of clapboards from Plymouth to England.* By 1630 several small saw mills had been established.

With this abundance of lumber, particularly oak for hulls and pine for masts, shipbuilding became the first important industry in the early colonies. At the time of the outbreak of hostilities with England, the colonists were building about 100 ships a year.

Although the forests were practically limitless in their supply of lumber, it soon became clear that even with such abundance some forms of legislature had to be enacted sooner or later. The first forestry act of March 29, 1626, set forth the conditions under which any timber could be sold or transported.** The ordinance clearly reflected the speed by which the forests were cleared away within the immediate surroundings of the young colony. As other colonies were established, they soon set up similar and other legislature. One such legislative attempt was made in 1681 by William Penn, in which he suggested that:

> "One acre of trees must be left for every five acres cleared and that special care must be taken to preserve oak for shipping and mulberry for silk."†

Although the legislative acts passed in those early days showed concern for the timber supply, they dealt, for the greater part, with local, specific situations, and showed as yet no concern as to the possibility of a future timber shortage. It was many years later that a widespread and effective interest in conservation and distribution of timber lands was shown.

346. The Public Domain.†† The land which directly belongs to the U. S. government, acquired by cession, treaty, and purchase, constitutes the public domain. It embraces about one billion and a half acres, disposal and management of which was placed in the hands of Congress. Over the

---

* *Ibid.,* p. 3.   ** *Ibid.,* p. 4.   † *Ibid.,* p. 5.   †† *Ibid.,* pp. 323–350.

years much of this land has been sold or donated to states, corporations or individuals, until today the public domain is made up of some 411 million acres, or slightly less than one fifth of the continental land area. Most of this acreage lies in the eleven Far Western states.

In addition to this land, the government owns some 44 million acres which make up our national forests, wildlife refuges, and military reservations. It also has in trust and manages some 58 million acres of Indian land.

Prior to 1891, the general policy, whether state or federal, was to encourage or at least not to interfere with the unrestricted exploration by private owners. As large areas were transferred from public to private ownership, cutting was done with little or no regard for the future. About the only laws dealing specifically with the cutting practices of timberlands were those of 1817 and 1827, which created reserves for the purpose of assuring an adequate supply of live oak and cedar for naval purposes. With the passing of wooden ships, these few last controls were relinquished until in 1923 the last 3000 acres were passed on to private ownership.

In order to curtail complete disposal, Congress passed, in 1891 and 1897, acts which resulted in the formation of our national park and national forest systems.*

347. Private Ownership and Management. Notwithstanding the early extensive ownership of lands by states and Federal Government, about three fourths of the commercial forest area of this country has now passed into private ownership. Management of these lands for continuous forest production developed slowly.

The turning point in forest management was reached in 1933 with the passing of the National Industrial Recovery Act.** Under Articles I and V of the NIRA, a primary purpose of the Lumber Code was declared to be conservation of forest resources. A conference which was held in Washington, D. C., in October, 1933, was followed by a second meeting in 1934, which resulted in the formulation of the Forest Conservation Code. In the Pacific Northwest a number of meetings resulted, in 1934, in the publication and distribution of the far-reaching "Handbook on Forest Practice."

Even though the NIRA was declared unconstitutional by the U. S. Supreme Court, the lumber industry decided to continue its program of forest conservation as a permanent activity.

In the years that followed some significant changes and improvements came about. Although forest research had long been an important activity of the Forest Service and other federal agencies, the work in that field was greatly strengthened by the establishment of the regional forest experi-

---

* *Ibid.,* p. 323.

** Hagenstein, W. D., *A Quarter Century of Industrial Forestry in the Douglas Fir Region.* Industrial Forestry Association, Portland, Ore., 1959, 8 pp.

ment stations (1908) and the Forest Products Laboratory at Madison, Wis. (1910). Research has always been one of the major functions of schools of forestry. These schools, twenty-four of which were accredited in 1954 by the American Society of Foresters, place increasing emphasis upon breadth of training and graduate work.

It is significant that the many changes in the timber industry came about in the midst of a severe depression. Prior to the 1930's, the utilization of both woods and mills was poor because of low values and a primitive technology. In the light of present day practices, the industry was old-fashioned and antiquated. For example, aerial photography was as yet not used as a forestry and engineering aid. Radio, except in national forests, had not been adapted for forestry communication. Most logging was carried out by railroad and steam equipment. Slash burning was promiscuous, and only one pulp mill was using sawmill leftovers for raw materials. Thinning of timber stands was a textbook subject only, and what little tree planting went on was done in national forests. In short, it was a time of pessimism, lack of incentive and inadequate knowledge. It is miraculous that forest industry leaders, at a time like this, managed to bring the industry up to its healthy position of today. Quoting figures and happenings which apply particularly to the Pacific Northwest here is part of the forestry record:

1. In 1934, the forest industry in Washington and Oregon employed 86,000 people. By 1958 this number had almost doubled.
2. During this same period from 1934–1958, forest industry wages increased eight-fold, while the annual value of forest products made a seven-fold increase.
3. With 4,360,000 acres of nonrestocked land in 1934, by 1958 reforestation had reduced this figure to less than one half (Fig. 3).
4. In 1904 the industry employed 100 foresters. By 1958, there were 1000. When forestry once again became economically attractive, the industry employed men trained in the science and art of forest management.
5. Fires, the industry's worst enemy, decreased significantly. Although 72,000 acres burned over in 1934, only 10,650 acres were destroyed by fire in 1958.
6. In 1934, there were no tree farms. Established in 1941, the Tree Farm Program by the end of 1958 had certified almost 6 million acres as West Coast Tree Farms. This constitutes two fifths of all the region's private forests. Many of these tree farms are also used for recreational purposes by private citizens.
7. In 1934, there was no source of planting stock for private lands. Since the establishment of the Col. W. B. Greeley Forest Nursery at Nisqually, Washington, 103 million seedlings have been distributed, covering nearly 200,000 acres.

Fig. 3. Planting nursery trees.

8. In 1934, the word genetics had little or no meaning. Now better trees are grown through a carefully planned program of genetics.
9. In 1934, the public believed that the forest industry's days were numbered. Now, with the job of forestry being done in the woods at an ever increasing tempo, the industry once again has the full support of the general public which is aware of the importance of tree farming and other forestry techniques for a continuing and expanding economy.
10. Elimination of waste and increased utilization of wood spurs better forestry. Through relogging of old cutover lands, prelogging of old-growth forests to prevent breakage, thinning practices to avoid the natural mortality of young forests and the saving of sawmill and plywood leftovers for pulp and hardboard chips have all intensified tree farming. The day of the big cargo sawmill with its big refuse burner is rapidly giving way to the well-integrated wood-manufacturing unit consisting generally of a sawmill, planing mill, veneer and/or plywood plant and chipper.

348. Wood and Its Importance to Our National Economy.* The following brief statement will indicate the widespread dependence of our economic structure on timber products.

The outlook for forestry in a national setting could hardly be other than favorable. There have been relatively high prices, strong demand and no general depression in recent years. Forestry is being practiced on both private and public lands at an accelerated rate. More and more it is being

---

* U. S. Department of Agriculture, Forest Service, *Timber Resources for America's Future;* Forest Resource Report, No. 14, 1958.

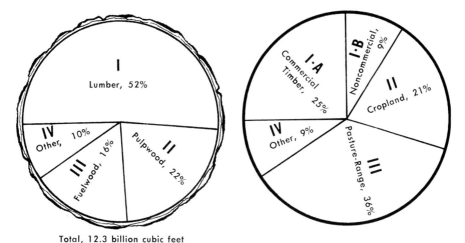

Fig. 4. Consumption of our national timber volume.

Fig. 5. Divided total land area of United States and Coastal Alaska.

recognized that growing timber is economically profitable under certain conditions, particularly in the areas of greatest timber concentration and financial backing.

The manner in which our national timber output is being consumed is shown in Figure 4.

How the total timber acreage in the United States and Coastal Alaska compares with the remaining land area is shown in Figure 5. The extent of this forest land in relation to the total land area is of great economic significance and essential to an understanding of the current timber situation and its future potential.

Three fourths of all the commercial forests are in the East. The total commercial forest area is almost equally divided between softwoods and hardwoods, but the hardwood types are concentrated almost exclusively in the East, where they exceed the area of softwood types by roughly two to one.

As of 1952, three fourths of the commercial forest area is privately owned. This ownership is divided among 4.5 million owners, of whom 75 per cent are farmers.

Although not used for commercial timber growing, noncommercial forest lands have important values for other purposes. The recreational values of the productive but reserved timbered areas of our national forests and parks are very high; but the greatest values of the noncommercial forest lands are for watershead protection and water yield. These lands are also used extensively in the grazing of domestic livestock and afford a valuable habitat for wildlife.

In summary, it can be said that much progress has been made in forestry in recent years. Although meeting projected demands would result in significant impacts on timber resources by the end of the twentieth century, there appears to be no general danger of a timber famine.

Species and Characteristics of North American Woods

Trees on the North American continent are generally classified into two groups, namely: Softwoods or Conifers, and Hardwoods or Broadleafs. Softwoods usually have needle or scale-like leaves and on all but a few species, the fruit is a cone or ball of overlapping closed scales, beneath each of which are found one or more seeds. Because the leaves or needles remain on these trees for several years, they are generally referred to as "evergreens." The botanical name for them is "Gymnosperm."

In the United States and Canada there are roughly 100 species of softwoods, with a little over one third of this number consisting of different species of pines.

It should be pointed out here that the hardness or softness of a specific wood has no bearing upon its classification as a softwood or as a hardwood. Some coniferous (softwood) trees are considerably harder than many hardwoods.*

349. Hardwoods or broadleafs are known for their broad veined leaves. They are deciduous, which means that they drop their leaves in the fall. The botanical name for these trees is "Dycotyledon."

Throughout the world some 99,000 species of hardwoods have been identified, close to 700 of which are found on the North American continent. Only about 250 of this last number is normally available for commercial purposes.

The wood produced from hardwood trees may be either hard or soft in texture but, as in softwoods, the hardness or softness of a wood does not necessarily place it in either classification. For example, basswood and box elder, though classified as hardwoods, are much softer in texture than the wood of many softwood or coniferous trees.**

In Figure 6, the geographic locations are shown of our major forest regions and commercially useful trees in the United States. Although the greater part of the Midwest seems to be completely devoid of forests and trees, there are some timber stands, such as the Black Hills in the Dakotas. But from a commercial standpoint these stands are negligible in value as compared to other areas.

---

* Schoonover, Shelley E., *American Woods*, p. 33.
** *Ibid.*, p. 97.

NATIONAL LUMBER MANUFACTURER'S ASSOCIATION,
"Livibility Unlimited," p. 3.

Fig. 6. Major forest regions and commercially useful trees in the U. S.

I.　DOUGLAS FIR: Douglas fir, west coast hemlock, western red cedar, Sitka spruce

II.　REDWOOD: redwood, Douglas fir

III.　WESTERN PINE: ponderosa pine, Idaho white pine, Douglas fir, white fir, sugar pine, inland red cedar, western larch, Engelmann spruce, lodgepole pine, incense cedar

IV.　NORTHERN FORESTS: maple, birch, beech, northern white pine, eastern spruce, ash, black cherry, jack pine, aspen

V.　CENTRAL AND SOUTHERN HARDWOOD FORESTS: oaks, yellow poplar, gum, hickory, black walnut, basswood

VI.　SOUTHERN PINE: loblolly pine, slash pine, shortleaf pine, longleaf pine, cypress

350. Commercial Woods. The remainder of this discussion will list the major commercial woods as found in the United States of America and Canada.*

Acacia

> *Source:* Many species are grown in America, Europe and India; most are commercially important. Occasionally produced as veneer.
> *Color:* Greenish-brown heartwood.
> *Availability:* Rare.
> *Price:* Moderate.

Alder, Red

> *Source:* Pacific Coast region.
> *Color:* Pale, pinkish-brown to almost white.
> *Characteristics:* Good working properties. Strength between Red Gum and Yellow Poplar. Used in unexposed parts of furniture and core stock.
> *Availability:* Scarce as veneer, plentiful as lumber.
> *Cost:* Low.

Ash, American

> There are many American species of ash, but the three major commercial ones, in order of importance, are: Black Ash, Green Ash, White Ash.

Black Ash

> *Source:* Principally the Great Lakes states.
> *Color:* Warm brown heartwood with a thin white sapwood.
> *Characteristics:* Extremely stable, heavy, rather soft, tough.
> *Availability:* Available to plentiful.
> *Price:* Medium.

Green Ash   Also called Swamp Ash.

> *Source:* Principally South Atlantic states and Mississippi Valley.
> *Availability:* Largely for commercial veneers.
> *Price:* Medium.

White Ash (Fig. 7).

> *Source:* Principally Great Lakes states, also New England and Central states.
> *Color:* Cream to very light brown heartwood with thick, lighter sapwood.
> *Characteristics:* Moderately open grain, heavy, hard, strong, tough.
> *Uses:* Interiors, furniture, tool handles.
> *Availability:* Veneer, rare; lumber, plentiful.
> *Price:* Medium.

---

* Fine Hardwoods Association, *Fine Hardwoods Selectorama: A Guide to the Selection and Use of the Popular Species,* pp. 16–55.

Fig. 7. Quartered white ash.

Basswood   Also called Linden.
Source: Northern United States and Canada.
Color: Creamy white.
Characteristics: Fine grain, very light, fairly soft, glues well.
Uses: Largely as core stock and crossbanding. Drawing boards.
Availability: Plentiful.
Price: Medium.

Beech, American
Source: Great Lakes states and Appalachian region.
Color: Reddish-brown heartwood, thin, white sapwood.
Characteristics: Straight grain, hard, strong, stiff, very close grained.
Uses: Flooring, chairs, shoe lasts, tool handles.
Availability: Plentiful.
Price: Inexpensive.

Birch, Domestic and Canadian   The two commercial species are:

Birch, Sweet   Also called Black Birch, Cherry Birch.
Source: Mainly in Adirondack and the Eastern Appalachian areas up
   to the northern part of the Gulf States.
Color: Brown tinged with red, with thin, yellow sapwood.
Characteristics: Heavy, very strong and hard, close-grained.
Uses: All sorts of cabinetwork where strength and hardness is desired.
Availability: Abundant as both veneer and lumber.
Price: Medium.

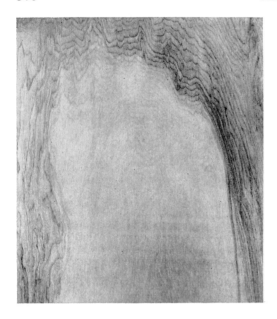

Fig. 8. Natural, rotary, birch.

Birch, Yellow   Also called Gray Birch, Silver Birch, Swamp Birch (Fig. 8).
   Source: Canada and the Great Lakes states and New England to North
      Carolina.
   Color: Cream or light brown tinged with red, with thin, nearly white
      sapwood.
   Characteristics: Plain and often curly, wavy pattern, heavy, very strong,
      hard, closed-grained, even texture.
   Uses: Furniture, interiors, doors, store fixtures and accessories.
   Availability: Abundant. The greater volume produced as "natural birch"
      which contains a normal combination of color tones.
   Price: Medium.
Butternut   Also called White Walnut.
   Source: North Central States and Southern Canada.
   Color: Pale brown.
   Characteristics: Satiny wood with leafy grain, soft to medium textured,
      with occasional dark spots or streaks.
   Uses: Interior finishes of houses, furniture.
   Availability: Somewhat more than rare.
   Price: Medium.
Cedar, Aromatic Red   Also called Eastern Red Cedar, Juniper, Pencil
      Cedar, Tennessee Red Cedar.
   Source: Most of eastern two thirds of United States. Largest produc-
      tion in Southeastern and South central states.

Color: Light red, streaks of light.

Characteristics: Knotty; although brittle, fine wood to work.

Uses: Cedar (hope) chests, lining of closets, pails, lead pencils.

Availability: Plentiful.

Price: Medium.

Cedar, Western Red

Source: Pacific Northwest from Alaska to northern California.

Color: From pure white sapwood to reddish brown heartwood.

Characteristics: Grows to height of 150 to 175 feet, works easily, free from pitch, paints and glues well.

Uses: Bevel siding, light framing, flooring.

Availability: Plentiful.

Price: Inexpensive.

Cherry, Black Also called Rum Cherry, Wild Black Cherry.

Source: Main to Dakotas and Appalachians; production largely Pennsylvania to West Virginia.

Color: Light reddish-brown.

Characteristics: Straight grained, light, strong, rather hard, fine grained.

Uses: Fine furniture, woodwork, engravers blocks.

Availability: Plentiful.

Price: Medium.

Chestnut

Source: Formerly ranged over Eastern United States.

Color: Reddish brown with lighter sapwood.

Characteristics: Straight grain, coarse texture, easy to work, highly durable.

Uses: Character-marked paneling, core stock.

Availability: Only as "wormy chestnut" as lumber; supply largely depleted by "Chestnut blight."

Price: Medium.

Cypress, American Bold Also called Black, Red, Southern, White, and Yellow Cypress.

Source: Southeastern Coast of the United States.

Color: Yellowish-red, often nearly salmon-colored.

Characteristics: Distinct leafy grain, soft open-meshed springwood combines with hard closer-grained summerwood; moderately strong, light, very durable.

Uses: Normally for its great durability against decay; interiors (Pecky Cypress).

Availability: Scarce as veneers, plentiful as lumber.

Price: Medium.

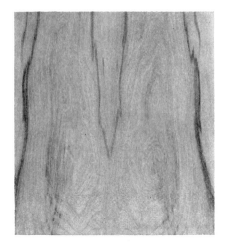

Fig. 9. American brown elm.

Douglas Fir
  Source: Pacific Northwest.
  Color: Light to deep yellow. Weathers to dark gray.
  Characteristics: Tree grows to 300 feet, bark thick, reddish brown, thin layer of sapwood, strong, tough.
  Uses: All-purpose wood, heavy and light construction.
  Availability: Plentiful, makes up half of the nation's softwood output.
  Price: Inexpensive.
Elm, American Also called Soft Elm, Water Elm, White Elm (Fig. 9).
  Source: United States, East of Rockies.
  Color: Light-brownish.
  Characteristics: Conspicuous growth pattern like ash, heavy, hard, strong, tough, difficult to split, coarse grained, bends exceedingly well.
  Uses: As veneers for containers, fine furniture.
  Availability: Plentiful as veneers, available as lumber.
  Price: Medium.
Gum Heartwood and sapwood sold separately as:
Gum, Red Also called Hazelwood, Sweet Gum.
  Source: Commercially produced largely in lower Mississippi Valley.
  Color: Reddish-brown.
  Characteristics: Dark streaks, moderately heavy, hard, straight, close-grained, not exceedingly strong. Red Gum or heartwood often selected for its attractive figure.
  Uses: Outside and inside finish of houses, cabinetmaking, dishes and fruit boxes.
  Availability: Plentiful as veneer; available as lumber.
  Price: Medium.

Gum, Sap

Source: Same as Red Gum.

Color: Pinkish white often blued by sap stains.

Characteristics: Same as above but not as durable.

Uses: Most widely used species for veneers, furniture, TV cabinets,

Availability: Abundant.

Price: Inexpensive.

Hackberry Also called Sugarberry.

Source: New England through Virginia and west through Iowa, Missouri, and Kansas.

Color: Yellowish.

Characteristics: Distinct grain pattern, especially when quartered, heavy, moderately hard, not strong, coarse-grained.

Availability: Plentiful as veneer; available as lumber.

Price: Inexpensive to medium.

Hemlock, West Coast

Source: Pacific Northwest.

Color: White to light yellow.

Characteristics: Height 200 to 225 feet. Fine textured, straight grained, stiff, easily worked.

Uses: Light and heavy construction, bevel siding, flooring, paneling.

Availability: Plentiful.

Price: Inexpensive.

Hickory Most important species is Shagbark Hickory.

Source: From Northeastern United States to the Southwest into Mexico.

Color: White to cream with inconspicuous fine brown lines.

Characteristics: Extremely tough and resilient, quite hard, moderately heavy.

Uses: Skis and bent plywood.

Availability: Scarce as veneer; available as lumber.

Price: Medium to high.

Magnolia

Source: Southern United States, especially Appalachians.

Color: More dark streaks than poplar, sometimes with greenish cast.

Characteristics: Very much like yellow poplar but slightly harder and heavier.

Uses: About same as yellow poplar, wood turning.

Availability: Plentiful.

Price: Inexpensive.

Maple, Bird's-Eye See Maple, Hard

Fig. 10. Bird's-eye maple.

Maple, Hard Also divided into Bird's-Eye Maple, Northern Maple, Rock Maple, Sugar Maple (Fig. 10).

Source: Lake States, Appalachians, Northwest United States, Canada.

Color: Cream to light reddish-brown heartwood, thin white sapwood tinged with reddish-brown.

Characteristics: Usually straight grained; sometimes found highly figured with curly, blistered, quilted, bird's-eye or burl grain, scattered over entire tree or in irregular stripes and patches. Heavy, hard, strong, close-grained, tough. Good resistance to abrasion and indentation.

Uses: Furniture, interiors, flooring, inlays, and overlays.

Availability: Plain maple, plentiful.

Price: Plain, medium; figured, costly.

Myrtle Also called Acacia Burl, Baytree, California Laurel, Oregon Myrtle, Pepperwood.

Source: West Coast of United States, especially Southern Oregon and Northern California.

Color: Golden-brown and yellowish-green. Wide range from light to dark.

Characteristics: Mixture of plain wood, mottle, cluster, blistered, stump and burl figure. Hard, strong, pores the size and distribution of walnut. Magnificent, highly figured veneer.

Uses: Decorative paneling, furniture, novelties.

Availability: Veneers, rare to scarce; lumber, scarce.

Price: Costly.

Fig. 11. Flat sliced red oak.   Fig. 12.   Quartered white oak.

Oak, Red (Fig. 11).
> *Source:* Throughout the eastern United States, especially in the Appalachians, Ohio, and Kentucky.
> *Color:* Slightly redder tinge than White Oak.
> *Characteristics:* Slightly coarser grain, with large rounded open pores. A little easier to finish than White Oak, though both are excellent.
> *Uses:* All the same purposes as white oak except water-tight containers.
> *Availability:* Veneers, plentiful; lumber, available.
> *Price:* Medium.

Oak, White (Fig. 12).
> *Source:* Eastern United States, especially in the Central States and down through the Appalachian region.
> *Color:* From light brown with a grayish tinge in the heartwood to shades of ocher in the sapwood.
> *Characteristics:* A grain pattern with more pronounced and longer rays than red oak. Occasional crotches, swirls and burls. Pores are angular and very numerous, filled with a glistening substance called tyloses, which makes this wood particularly suitable for watertight containers and where water resistance is required. Tannic acid in the wood protects it from fungi and insects. Closer grained than red oak.
> *Uses:* Nearly all common uses of hardwoods, especially where strength and durability are required.
> *Availability:* Veneer, plentiful; lumber, available.
> *Price:* Medium.

Osage Orange

Source: Southwestern United States.

Color: Greenish-yellow.

Characteristics: Seldom cut into lumber, or veneer; very close grained, very hard, strong, and resilient; comparatively inert to atmosphere changes.

Uses: Wheels, archery bows, insulator pins, turnings, and decorative novelties.

Availability: Scarce.

Price: Moderate where available.

Pecan

Source: Southern United States, East of Mississippi.

Color: Heartwood, reddish brown with occasional darker streaks, sapwood, creamy white.

Characteristics: Distinct pattern, close-grained, hard, very heavy and strong.

Uses: Flooring and furniture.

Availability: Veneer, plentiful; lumber, available.

Price: Medium.

Pine, Knotty Also called Idaho White Pine.

Source: Idaho, Washington, Montana.

Color: White, to light brown or red.

Characteristics: Knotty, soft, light, not strong, close, straight grained.

Uses: Construction, interior finish (paneling), some furniture.

Availability: Plentiful.

Price: Medium.

Pine, Jack

Source: Canada.

Color: Creamy white.

Characteristics: Smooth-textured, strong, durable, excellent nail-holding ability.

Uses: House construction, mining timber, railway ties, boxes, and crates.

Availability: Abundant.

Price: Low to inexpensive.

Pine, Southern Also called longleaf, slash and loblolly.

Source: Entire South, from Virginia to Texas.

Color: Creamy white.

Characteristics: Close-grained, dense, fairly hard, wear resistant.

Uses: Decking on boardwalks and wharves, flooring in warehouses, home construction, railway cars, ties.

Availability: Abundant.

Cost: Low to inexpensive.

Pine, White
Source: Canada, Great Lake region of Ontario.
Color: White.
Characteristics: Soft, close-grained, workable, durable, dimensional stability, weather resistant.
Uses: General building, interiors, paneling (knotty white pine), sash and frame, doors.
Availability: Abundant.
Price: Inexpensive to medium.

Redwood, California
Source: Northern California to just over the Oregon line.
Color: Reddish-brown.
Characteristics: Height and size of trees outstrip all trees in the world. Slow-growing, soft, close-grained, durable, light, decay resistant.
Uses: Building and industrial purposes, food processing tanks, cooling towers, roof sheathing, reservoir roofs, core stock laminations.
Availability: Available.
Price: Inexpensive to medium.

Redwood, Burl
Source: California, Northern Coastal region.
Color: Pink to deep red heartwood.
Characteristics: Clusters of eyes (burls), soft, light, close-grained, durable.
Uses: Decorative areas of cabinetry, novelties.
Availability: Veneer, scarce; lumber, available.
Price: Costly as burl veneers.

Sycamore, American
Source: Maine to Central West and the Gulf.
Color: Pale reddish-brown.
Characteristics: Flaky on quartered grain due to wide rays; tough, elastic, bark.
Uses: Lumber often used as drawer sides.
Availability: Veneer, plentiful; lumber, available.
Price: Inexpensive.

Walnut, American (Figs. 13 and 14).
Source: Commercial range largely confined to some fifteen Central States.
Color: Light gray-brown to dark purple-brown.
Characteristics: Produces great variety of figure types such as crotches, swirls, and occasional burls; moderately heavy, very strong, very stable.
Uses: Furniture, interior woodwork, gunstocks, novelties.
Availability: Veneer, abundant; lumber, plentiful.
Price: Medium to costly.

Fig. 13. Plain sliced, narrow heart, walnut.

Fig. 14. Plain, half-round dappled walnut.

Yew, American
Source: Pacific Coast and Southwestern Canada.
Color: Reddish-brown.
Characteristics: Heavy, hard.
Uses: Veneers, decorative areas, archery bows.
Availability: Rare.
Price: Costly.

Conservation and Tree Farming

Each year a considerable part of our timber volume is destroyed by fire, insects, disease, animals, and adverse weather. In addition to these causes, the annual timber output is decreased by poorly executed harvesting techniques and by lack of up-to-date methods of re-seeding and planting (Fig. 15).

To combat these destructive sources, the lumber industry has, for many years, carried out an elaborate program of conservation.

Conservation, in its broadest term, can be defined as the wise use of all our natural resources which include timber, oil, gas, ores, water, and soil. Of these natural resources, timber has received the most publicity and it is for this reason that many people think of conservation as applying to our forests only. To be really meaningful, conservation must be viewed in a much broader sense. But looked at from whatever direction, it comes down to: wise, frugal use and use without waste.

The following discussion will deal with conservation as it applies to our timber supply.

Fig. 15. Example of wasteful harvesting of trees.

351. Fire Prevention, Pest and Disease Control. Fire, insects, and disease are the forest's worst enemies. Of these three, fire ranks as enemy number one.

Fire not only burns and kills standing trees, but scorches many others, making them more susceptible to insect and disease attacks. Worse yet, it burns tomorrow's crop, the young trees, the seedlings and the seed buried in the soil.

It is estimated that a fire breaks out in our forests every five minutes. They are started deliberately by people (49%), by unattended trash fires (17%), careless smokers (15%), thoughtless campers (3%), lightning (1%), railroads (3%), and miscellaneous causes (12%). It is also estimated that 77 of each 100 acres burned are located in the South and that people can be blamed for 99 out of every 100 fires.

Some of the fires in the past were of devastating proportions. For example, the forest fire which occurred at Peshtigo, Wisconsin, in 1871, took the lives of some 1500 people. Oregon's Tillamook burn in 1933 was another one of our worst fires taking one life, and the more recent fire of 1947 in Maine took 16 lives.*

Since the goal of fire fighting is to extinguish the fire while it is still small, private landowners, forest industries, state and federal governments are spending large sums annually on fire prevention, detection equipment, training of fire fighters, and suppression.

---

* American Forest Products Industries, *It's a Tree Country*, p. 30.

As soon as a fire spotter sees a wisp of smoke from his lookout tower, he reports the alarm to headquarters from where it is dispatched to the nearest crew of fire fighters. Depending upon the size of the fire, the alarm may call out an elaborate array of equipment. Many fire fighting units now have at their disposal water-hauling trucks, powerful pumps, bulldozers, and plows. On the spot two-way radios keep fire bosses in touch with lookouts and headquarters. Airplanes may be called in from which smoke jumpers parachute to isolated and inaccessible areas. Probably the most recent development is the use of rotating television cameras in lookout towers.

Despite the efforts put forth in fire protection, the mortality caused by fire and the growth losses constitute a substantial decrease to our timber resources. Normally, the South suffers about four fifths of the losses, both to growing stock and saw timber. Although fires in the West are not as numerous, the potential loss per acre in this area is much greater than in the South, because of the high per-acre timber volume. Furthermore, many western fires are so intense that they kill entire stands of mature trees and devastate large areas that will not again become forest without costly planting projects.*

Although in most sections of this country fire is the number one enemy, in some, insects and disease do the greater damage (Fig. 16). Bark beetles alone kill millions of dollars worth of timber every year. Losses from decay probably will continue to be high until all old growth stands of commercial

---

* United States Department of Agriculture, *Timber Resources for America's Future,* Report No. 14, p. 190.

Fig. 16. Trapping tree-killing beetles.

timber are harvested and replaced by young, sturdy trees. Generally, over-mature trees are more susceptible to disease than younger, more vigorous ones.

Another method of combating tree disease is to develop a stronger strain which can resist the disease. By way of a program of genetics, white pines are now developed which are resistant to blister rust. Crossbreeding of Chinese chestnut with native chestnut has produced a blight resistant strain.

Two effective methods of combating timber losses from insects and disease are by spraying trees with insecticides from low-flying planes, and by cutting down infested trees, which are usually overripe anyway.

Despite the inroads made by fire, insects, and disease, the commercial forests of the United States are growing wood faster than it is being removed by harvest. This historic milestone in forest management was passed during the decade of 1945–1955.

The U. S. Forest Timber Resource Review of 1955 revealed that the amount of wood added to trees in annual growth was 25 per cent greater than the amount removed.*

352. What Is a Tree Farm? A tree farm is a privately-owned forest area of any size, managed to grow timber as a crop under sound and agreed upon forest practices.

Tree farms may be large or small, some no more than ten acres. Others may run into thousands of acres. Some are owned by lumber firms, many by farmers, ranchers, and others. All have the same objective: to grow timber crops, make a profit, and perpetuate the timber stands for future years.

The program of tree farming was started in 1941 by the Weyerhaeuser Timber Company with the establishment of the Clemons Tree Farm in Grays Harbor County in Western Washington. Under the auspices of a national program, the first tree farm so certified was in Alabama in 1942.

To qualify as a tree farm, a tract of timber land must be approved by a certifying agency and meet standards in respect to protection from fire, insects, disease, and excessive grazing. Also the harvesting methods must be of such that they will assure future crops of timber. As of October 1, 1955, there were 7152 tree farms in 38 states with an area of 37 million acres, or more than 10 per cent of the commercial forest land privately owned.**

The tree farm movement has spread to most of the United States (Table 1). In the West it is made up of three timber areas. To the North, along the Pacific Coast, is the Douglas fir region, with West Coast hemlock, Sitka spruce, and western red cedar among the other leading types of trees. In the interior is the Western Pine region, with its great ponderosa, Idaho

---

* American Forest Products Industries, *It's a Tree Country,* p. 14.
** Dana, Samuel T., *Forest and Range Policy: Its Development in the United States.* pp. 311–312.

TABLE 1.   Tree Farms in the United States

American Forest Products Industries, Inc.,
"Tree Farm Progress Report," July 1, 1960

Regions:	Number of Tree Farms Jan. 1, 1960	Number of Tree Farms July 1, 1960	Total Acreage Jan. 1, 1960	Total Acreage July 1, 1960
Southern States	9,512	10,381	33,863,818	35,017,736
Western Pine Region	1,408	1,411	6,836,330	6,893,418
Douglas Fir Region	606	628	5,825,687	5,872,564
Redwood Region	92	109	416,059	597,354
Lake States	1,873	2,044	2,697,084	2,939,081
Central States	1,089	1,210	386,737	433,982
Plains States	410	428	17,316	18,505
Eastern States	1,722	1,814	1,257,090	1,291,545
TOTAL FOR 47 STATES	16,712	18,025	51,300,121	53,064,185

Note: The above report shows the net gains and net losses for the first six months of 1960.

STATES BY REGION

SOUTH: Alabama, Arkansas, Florida, Georgia, Louisiana, Mississippi, North Carolina, Oklahoma, South Carolina, Tennessee, Texas, and Virginia.

REDWOOD: Redwood Region of California.

DOUGLAS FIR: Western Oregon and Western Washington.

WESTERN PINE: Arizona, California (except Redwood Region), Colorado, Idaho, Montana, Nevada, New Mexico, Eastern Oregon, Black Hills of South Dakota, Utah, Eastern Washington and Wyoming.

LAKE STATES: Michigan, Minnesota, and Wisconsin.

CENTRAL STATES: Illinois, Indiana, Kentucky, Missouri, and Ohio.

PLAINS STATES: Iowa, Nebraska, North Dakota, and Plains of South Dakota.

EASTERN STATES: Connecticut, Delaware, Maine, Maryland, Massachusetts, New Hampshire, New Jersey, New York, Pennsylvania, Rhode Island, Vermont, and West Virginia.

white, sugar and other pines. In northern California and southern Oregon is the unique redwood area. Throughout these regions the tree farm movement is well established. Since the start in 1941, western tree farms have developed into a program which embraces some 10 million certified acres. Special attention is being paid to small farm wood lots.

The South is one of the great timber regions of the North American continent, despite the fact that scarcely any part of the original forest remains. Its expanding pulp and paper, lumber and other forest products come almost exclusively from second growth stands, chiefly loblolly, longleaf, shortleaf and slash pine, and considerable hardwoods.

Ten southern states have thriving tree farm programs, in fact, the South has taken the lead in number and acerage of certified tree farms. This acreage totals more than 14 million, divided among 1700 large and small tree farms. In most instances, state forestry departments sponsor the program with strong backing from industrial groups. Originally the program was pioneered in the South by the Southern Pine Association.

The East has known timber harvests for more than three centuries, yet its forests today provide raw materials for large wood industries. Pulp and paper, lumber and wood specialties are the important products. Although the tree farm program is relatively new in this region, seven states had joined the movement by 1951, when the tenth anniversary of Tree Farming was observed. The certified area in this region totals more than 309,000 acres. Since much of the region bordering the Atlantic is under small, ownership, individual tree farms here are relatively small also.

The Middle West, centering on the Great Lakes states, is a varied timber area which, through forest management and protection is rebuilding its timber potential. By 1951, six states in the central region had officially joined the Tree Farm program. They are Michigan, Minnesota, and Wisconsin in the Lakes region, Missouri and Ohio in the central states, and North Dakota in the plains states. Close to 1,400,000 acres have been certified as Tree Farms.*

353. Tree Farms, Wildlife, and Watersheds. Although tree growing and harvesting continue to be the major purpose of the timber land, tree farmers are encouraged also to utilize these same lands for recreation, hunting, fishing, and watershed protection. In a country where camping, hunting, and fishing are three major sports, it is of considerable importance that these outdoor activities be encouraged and maintained.

Today, in planning long-range tree farm programs, foresters carefully consider the problems involved in developing proper watersheds. They recognize the important part that forests play in controlling soil erosion as well as supplying water so necessary for domestic use, hydroelectric power, and irrigation.

354. Our Present Timber Outlook. What are the prospects for adequate supplies of wood in the years ahead? To make definite predictions in the lumber industry has proved risky, and full of uncertainties. But it is possible to point out what is known about today's forests. This is what we know:

1. Our forests are growing wood faster than we are using it.
2. Steady progress is being made in reducing wood losses resulting from forest fires.
3. An earnest and successful attack is being made on forest insect and disease problems.

---

* NOTE: The four geographical areas described here are from "Trees Forever" published on the tenth anniversary of the Tree Farm program in 1951.

4. Methods have been developed by which we grow the maximum amount of quality wood.

5. Trees now harvested are being used almost in their entirety with little or no waste.

6. Private owners are rapidly bringing their forests under good management.

7. We have enough forest land to meet our needs.

8. Forest lands not fully stocked are being built up as wood needs mount.

9. There are still large areas of productive forest that have not yet been opened up to commercial operations because access roads have not been built.

The late Colonel William B. Greeley, former Chief Forester of the United States, voiced his confidence in the future when he said:

"Looking ahead, I am not afraid to entrust our future wood supply to the initiative and profit motive of American industry, with support of the state and federal forest policies already tested out. In this opinion, I rely upon our industrial initiative and skills in wood technology no less than in forestry."*

Modern Logging Practices

Logging practices in different parts of the country vary dependent upon the timber crop that needs to be harvested. In the East, where wood lots are comparatively small, it can almost be a one or two man operation. But in our larger forest regions, logging becomes highly organized.

In the Pacific northwest the growth habits of the Douglas fir tree are such that its seeds will not germinate nor will its seedlings thrive in the deep shade

---

* American Forest Products Industries, *Our Growing Wood Supply,* 1957 edition, p. 22.

Fig. 17. Block cutting of Douglas fir.

of older and larger trees. As a result, planned harvesting in this region is by forest area selection, a system of logging which requires the clear cutting of selected blocks of timber (Fig. 17). Between these blocks, intermittent strips and islands of trees are left to serve as a future seed source. This method not only provides seed for natural reforestation, but also supplies the clean, open, sunlit ground needed to establish a new generation of seedlings. For the fir region this system of block harvesting has proved to be the most effective method.*

The harvesting method used for pine trees in the Pacific Northwest is quite different from the one described above.

In contrast with the dense Douglas fir forests, pine timberlands contain trees of all ages growing in open, parklike stands. The forest floor is covered with a mixture of seedling, young trees and mature trees ready for harvesting. Since the climate of this particular pine country is drier, there are fewer trees per acre than in the more moist fir region. Sufficient sunlight reaches the pine seedlings so it is possible for them to grow alongside the larger trees.

Harvesting of mature pines is done by individual tree selection which calls for the removal of overaged and beetle-damaged trees first. The large trees left standing will continue to grow and increase in volume until such time that they, too, are ready for harvesting. In the meantime, they serve as the natural seed source for any vacant, adjacent areas.

This selective method of tree removal permits more sunlight and rain to nourish the younger trees and improve their rate of growth.**

Harvesting of our hardwoods is generally by individual tree selection but on a much smaller scale than that practiced in the pine regions.

355. Logging in Operation.† Let us imagine that we have been invited to watch the harvesting of a selected crop of pines in the Pacific Northwest. Just what is going on?

Previous to our arrival a skilled forester has marked those trees ready for harvesting. The manner in which he has marked each tree will show the loggers how the tree is to be felled in order to do as little damage as possible to the remaining trees. Also the forest engineer has decided where roads are to be constructed, where the logs are to be loaded, and how much and what kind of equipment is required for this particular operation.

Next into the woods go the loggers. In many cases they drive to and from work in their own car or by way of company cars, called "crummies." Sometimes, when the logging is done deep in the woods, a camp may be built, complete with homes, recreation center, school and medical facilities.

---

* Weyerhaeuser Timber Company, *Tree Farming in the Pacific Northwest*, 19 pp.
** *Ibid.*, p. 12.
† West Coast Lumbermen's Association, *The Story of West Coast Lumber*, pp. 2–15.

But as of today probably not more than two dozen camps operate in the entire West.

The loggers are all trained in a specialized phase of the total operation, each one referred to by such names as: fallers, buckers, high climbers, rigging slingers, choker setters, donkey engineers, hookbenders or whistle punks.

The fallers, working in teams of two or three men, bring down the trees. With a power chain saw or with axes, they notch a tree in the direction they wish it to fall, making sure it will not break other trees, or fall where it will not be hard to handle (Fig. 18). From the opposite side of the tree they next cut through above but toward the base of the notch. Wedges are frequently driven into the cut as it deepens. Pried off balance, the tree leans and then sweeps with a rush to the earth as the familiar logger's cry of "Timber-r-r-r" echoes through the surrounding area.

Once a tree is down, *the bucker* who is an expert at diagnosing the value of this particular tree, cuts it into logs in lengths according to grade and manufacturing facilities.

Sometimes crawler-type tractors are used to skid the logs to the "landing" where they can be loaded on giant logging trucks or railroad flat cars (Fig. 19). Sometimes it is necessary or desirable to use more elaborate equipment, such as a donkey engine, to bring the logs to the landing by way of the "high lead" system. This system is primarily used when the ground is rough, stumps and undergrowth are in the way, or one end of the log, or all of it, must be lifted to pull it toward the landing.

In such a case, wire ropes and blocks are fastened high on a tall, strong tree at the landing. This is the job of the *"high climber,"* a man of cool nerves and great skill. Up the tree he goes, 150 to 180 feet, chopping off limbs as he goes up, assisted only by his climbing spurs and a wire-rope

Fig. 18. Using gas-powered chain saw to fall a tree.

Fig. 19. Tractor used to haul logs.

safety loop around the tree, until he reaches the place where the rigging is to be fastened. Below him the tree has become a spar. He now adjusts his loop or support and saws off the green-branched top. As the top starts falling, its weight pushes the spar backward; next, it springs forward as the weight of the top is released. The climber, clinging precariously to the very top, sways dizzily back and forth (Fig. 20).

With the spar tree topped and the rigging securely put in place, guy wires are spread tentwise to the ground (Fig. 21). Next, from a huge drum on the donkey engine, a wire cable is stretched through the block in the spar,

Fig. 20. "High climber" topping tree 150 feet above ground.

Fig. 21. Log loading boom attached to spar tree.

down to the log which is to be hauled to the landing. By way of a second drum, another wire rope can be led out to the back of the logging area, where it joins up with the hauling line. Thus a sort of endless shuttle system is established between the logging and the landing area.

In the landing area, a crane or swinging boom with huge tongs, picks up the logs and loads them onto waiting trucks or railroad flat cars. When and where satisfactory water transportation can be used, logs are often floated down river toward the nearest sawmill. Here they are stored in mill ponds (Fig. 22).

Fig. 22. Mill pond.

Fig. 23. Cutting log into cants and flitches in head rig.

Of the hundreds of sawmills in the Pacific Northwest, some are very small and others are the world's largest. Whatever its size, the job of a sawmill is to transform logs into lumber for the multitude of uses for which it is intended around the world.

Sawmilling is unlike any other major industry, since no two trees are alike and each piece of lumber has its own characteristics. Some logs will supply lumber of fine appearance; other logs will supply lumber which may not be as good looking, but which is rugged and strong. Each piece has a use for which it is especially adaptable.

As on the logging site, each man in the mill has a definite part to play in the manufacture of a piece of lumber.

Fig. 24. Head rig band saws.

After each log has been unloaded it is brought to *the head rig,* where a large band saw will cut it into various smaller pieces. The head sawer, who, through many years of experience, has become a master craftsman, sizes up the log, and quickly decides whether or not various cuts will supply finish lumber, structural material or boards and framing items (Figs. 23 and 24).

356. Plain- and Quarter-Sawing. A log is sawed in one of two ways, either "plain-sawed," or "quarter-sawed." Plain-sawing means the sawing up of the entire log in a series of parallel cuts. In other words, all the boards sawed in this way, except the middle ones, will be tangential sections of the log, because they are tangent to the annual rings.

When a log is quarter-sawed, its position on the carriage is changed several times (Fig. 25), so that the saw cuts are always made at right angles, or nearly so, to the annual rings. Quarter-sawed boards are, therefore, radial sections of the log.

Plain- and quarter-sawing does not apply to Douglas fir, West Coast hemlock or Western red cedar. In sawing logs of these species, cants and flitches are cut at the head rig to get the highest percentage of vertical grain. Also, cutting of the log at the head rig is most important because every effort is made to get grades of lumber of the highest value. For instance, the deep clear portion of the log will yield all sorts of bundled items, flooring, stepping, casing, siding, paneling. Structural items will come from the courser grained heart of the log and here vertical grain is avoided because of the location of spike knots.

Quarter-sawed boards are more expensive than plain-sawed boards, because the waste by this method of sawing is greater. They have an advantage over common-sawed boards, however, in that they warp and shrink less. In some woods having prominent medullary rays, such as oak, quarter-sawed boards are also more beautiful in appearance. The best pine flooring is quarter-sawed, because on plain-sawed boards the annual rings often come loose, or "shell out."

When the end of the log has been placed in proper position before the saw, the head sawer signals the carriage operator who, by pulling a lever, moves the log into the revolving saw teeth. As the cut is completed, the slice falls onto endless carrier chains and rolls and is on its way to the next operation (see Fig. 23).

This next operation is performed by the gang saw, which cuts the slab or square of timber into a dozen or more slices. Then, trim saws cut off the ends to improve grade and appearance (Fig. 26).

Beyond these machines, the lumber automatically travels the long sorting table where each piece is carefully examined and graded. As the pieces move

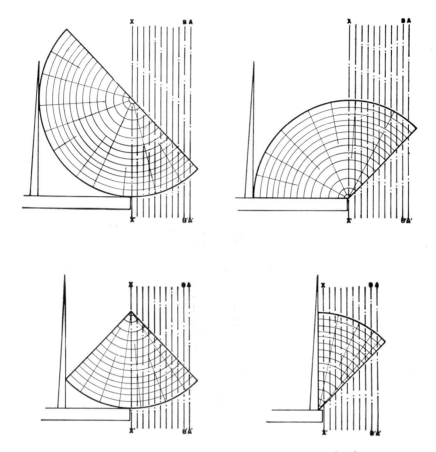

Fig. 25. Common method of quarter-sawing lumber.

along the line, they are removed from the table and stacked according to grade, size, and length.

Some of the green lumber cut in the mill may be shipped out immediately. But most of it is stacked into towering piles for air-seasoning or put into huge kilns for fast drying (see Figs. 32 and 33).

When the lumber is properly dried, it goes to the planing mill where the whir of saws changes to the scream of razor sharp planing knives (Fig. 27). Here the lumber is finished satin smooth, cut to exact patterns and again examined and separated by the graders according to the purpose it may best serve. This is lumber manufacture: sawing, planing, and grading.

Fig. 26. Trim saws.

Fig. 27. Surfacing kiln-dried lumber.

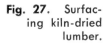

The Structure of Wood

357. Botanical Division of Trees. Botanically speaking, trees may be divided into three general groups:

1. The naked seeds, also known by the less accurate names of conifers or cone-bearing trees, evergreens, needle-leaved, and softwoods. Examples of this group are: pines, cedars, and redwoods.

2. The two-seed leaves, more commonly known as broad-leaved trees, deciduous trees and hardwoods which shed their leaves annually. Examples of this group are: oak, mahogany, maple, and gum.

3. The one-seed leaf, such as the palms, yuccas, and bamboos.

It is in the first two groups of trees, the naked seeds and the broad-leaved trees, that we are chiefly interested, because these groups furnish all the lumber used for building construction, furniture, paper, and manufacture in general. The third group, the palms and bamboos, has little value for the woodworker, and is seldom used by him.

358. Life Function of Trees. A tree consists of three main parts, the roots, the trunk, and the crown. Water and minerals in solution are taken up by the roots and conducted through the trunk to the crown, where they are changed into food material in the thousands of leaves. The crown is, therefore, the most important part of a growing tree. The manufacture of food in the leaves takes place in the following manner: Water and minerals from the soil in solution are conducted from the roots of the cells in the leaves. Carbonic acid gas (CO_2), taken from the air, is also breathed in by these cells. Under the influence of sunlight, which penetrates the green (chlorophyll) cells of the leaves, these inorganic substances enter into various chemical combinations and form an organic substance, sugar ($C_6H_{12}O_6$). Part of this sugar is turned into starch and stored for future use. When it is needed, the starch is again changed into sugar, which is the food of the tree. Sugar, in combination with other chemical compounds, produces cellulose, the principal material of which the cell walls are made, and fatty oils which are contained in seeds and bulbs.

One thousand square feet of leaf surface will manufacture 1 lb. of starch in 5 hours.

During these digestive processes, oxygen (O) and water vapor are given off to the air. This is an important factor in cooling off the atmosphere on warm summer days. The oxygen is used by man and beast for breathing, and is consumed by all kinds of fuels in burning. The water vapor is placed in circulation by the air currents, and moved from place to place.

The daily evaporation of water vapor from trees planted on the banks of lakes or rivers is extremely large. An oak tree, for example, may give off as much as 2000 lb. or 240 gal. of water vapor in 24 hours.

359. Green plants use, therefore, only inorganic materials for their food supply and energy. Man and animals, on the other hand, use organic materials and are dependent on plants for oxygen for breathing; for different kinds of food containing vitamins, sugars, starches, fats, and proteins; for clothing material such as cotton and linen; for lumber, paper, medicines, rubber, alcohol, turpentine, and numerous other products. Moreover, because animals feed on plants, man also obtains such materials as milk, eggs, meat, wool, silk, leather, etc., indirectly from plants.

The Composition of Wood

Of the three classes of trees we have mentioned, the conifers and broad-leaved trees are quite similar in structure. Only the first two classes will be considered in this discussion.

The chemical composition of all woods is approximately the same, that is, the same chemical elements exist in their formation. Wood is primarily composed of carbon, oxygen, hydrogen, nitrogen, potassium, calcium, magnesium, phosphorus, and sulphur. The greater part of all wood is made up of carbon and oxygen. These two elements, with hydrogen, make up about 97 per cent of dry wood. When burned, all these materials disappear into the air except the earthly parts, which remain in the form of ashes.*

360. The physical structure of woods, however, varies greatly. This varia-

---

* California Redwood Association, *Physiology of Trees,* p. 2, 1956.

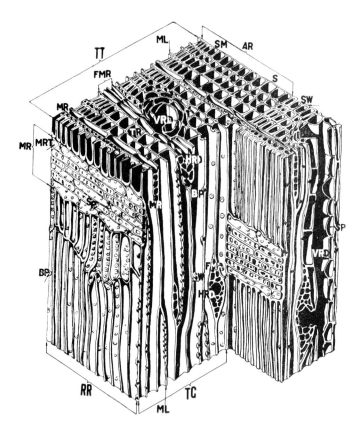

Fig. 28. Microscopic section of a softwood. TR, cells carrying water; S, spring wood; SM, summer wood; AR, one annual ring; MR, medullary rays.

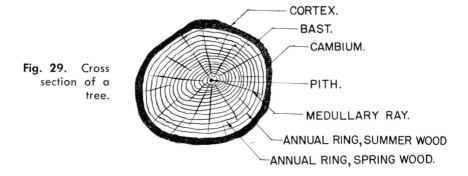

Fig. 29. Cross section of a tree.

CORTEX.
BAST.
CAMBIUM.
PITH.
MEDULLARY RAY.
ANNUAL RING, SUMMER WOOD
ANNUAL RING, SPRING WOOD.

tion in structure is primarily responsible for differences in the properties of the various species. And the study of these properties enables us to analyze uses of wood for specific purposes.*

361. Cell Formation. Examining a cross section of wood under a microscope (Fig. 28), the wood will be found to consist of innumerable small cells growing in a vertical direction. Some of these cells are small and some large. The larger cells have thin walls, and grow rapidly during the spring. The smaller cells have thick walls, and grow less rapidly during the summer.

362. Annual Rings. Looking at a cross section of a tree (Fig. 29) with the naked eye only, the small thick-walled cells, or summer wood, appear as thin concentric circles, and the thin-walled cells, or spring wood, as wider circles or rings alternating with the first ones. One year's growth, or one "annual ring," as it is called, consists of one narrow and one adjoining wide ring. In this way, by counting the rings, anyone is able to tell the age of a tree. Sometimes a hand lens is required to see the rings.

The exact age of a tree is difficult to determine, since the seedling stages are not recorded at this limited height. Also, during the early or "grass" stage of some species, such as long leaf pine, no distinct annual rings are produced in stem or root. This "grass stage" may last anywhere from 4–12 years or more. Growth increments show up in wood in varying degrees because the rate of growth of the wood produced within a tree is not uniform throughout the growing season. Generally, the increase is most rapid at the beginning of the season, when rains are more frequent. It slows down significantly as the season progresses. That portion of the growth ring formed in the spring is commonly called *early or spring wood*. Wood pro-

* *Ibid.*, p. 2.

duced later in the season is called *late or summer wood* and is usually denser and darker.*

363. Heartwood and Sapwood.   The inner core of a tree trunk is called the "heartwood" and the outside part the "sapwood." The center of the heartwood is a white, soft substance called the "pith." The sapwood is usually of a lighter color than the heartwood. The sapwood conducts the water, called "sap," from the roots to the crown. As the tree grows older, and new outside layers of wood are added, the inside part of the sapwood gradually turns into heartwood. The cells then clog up and no longer serve to conduct the sap to the leaves. Through infiltration of chemical substances into the cells, the heartwood turns a darker color.

This infiltration of chemical deposits makes the heartwood more durable. These deposits are often toxic to fungi and repellent to insects, making it more or less immune to attack. Generally, the deeper the color of heartwood, the greater its durability.

364. Cambium.   Between the sapwood and the bark is a greenish, slippery, slimy layer called the "cambium." The cell formation takes place in the cambium. When a cambium cell grows to maturity, it divides into two parts, one of which always remains cambium. The other part forms either wood or bark; most frequently wood.

365. Bark.   Outside the cambium lies the bark. It consists of a thick outer part, called the "cortex," and a thin inner part, called the "bast." Both the cortex and the bast are important commercial products. The cortex furnishes such materials as cork, tannic acid, medicines, etc. Bast is used in the weaving of mats, cloth, rope, etc.

366. Medullary Rays.   On some woods, notably oak, some bright lines crossing the annual rings will be seen to radiate from the center. These lines, when seen under the microscope, will be found to consist of a horizontal series of cells. The function of these cells, which are called "medullary rays," is to store and distribute food material horizontally. These cells appear in all species of wood, but are not visible to the naked eye in all instances.

When a tree trunk is cut lengthwise through the center, a section called a "radial section" is formed (Fig. 30). In this section the annual rings appear as a series of parallel lines, and if the medullary rays are prominent, they appear in various patterns and lines crossing the annual rings. When a tree trunk is cut lengthwise, but not through its center, a section called a "tangential section" is formed, because all lengthwise cuts from a solid trunk, that do not go through the center of the trunk, are tangent to some annual ring.

---

* Brown, H. P., Panshin, A. J., and Forsaith, C. C., *Textbook of Wood Technology.* Vol. 1, Chap. 3, pp. 35–36.

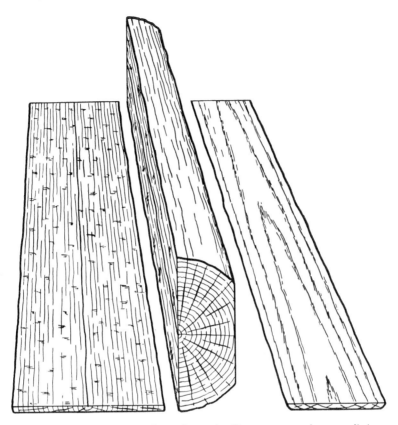

Fig. 30. Boards cut from log. A, Quarter-sawed or radial section; B, plain-sawed or tangential section.

In the tangential section (Fig. 30), the annual rings, which are the grain of the wood, appear in pleasing patterns, especially in the center of the section. Near the edges, the annual rings are more straight, having the appearance of a radial section.

367. Porous Woods. The chief difference between the structure of conifers and broad-leaved trees is that the first are simpler in structure and nonporous, and the second more complex in structure and porous.

The cells in nonporous woods are so small that they cannot be seen without the aid of a magnifying glass. The pores in porous woods, on the other hand, are large sap-conducting vessels consisting of several cells joined together. These pores usually can be distinguished with the naked eye (Fig. 31). In some woods, oak, chestnut, and ash, the pores appear mostly in the spring wood; in others, mahogany, beech, or maple, they seem to

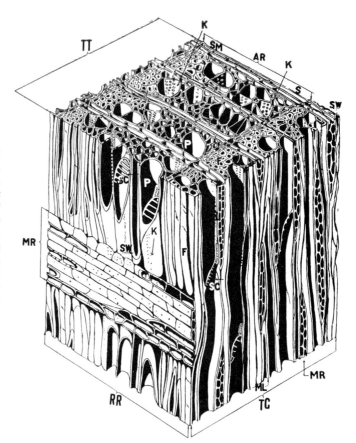

Fig. 31. Micro-
scopic section
of a hardwood.
P, pores; S,
spring wood;
SM, summer
wood; AR, one
annual ring; MR,
medullary rays;
TT, cross section;
RR, radial sec-
tion; TG, tan-
gential section.

be distributed through both the spring and summer wood. The first of these groups is called "ring-porous wood" and the second "diffused-porous wood."

Paste wood filler is used only on porous woods, which in the lumber trade are called "hardwoods."

368. Weight of Wood. From the foregoing, it should be clear that wood is not a solid mass, but a combination of very complex cell structures. Wood is generally thought to be lighter than water, because, under normal conditions, it floats on water. A simple experiment will show that air is contained in the cells.

Fill three glasses with water. Drop a little sawdust in the first, some very thin shavings in the second, and a small block of wood in the third. The sawdust sinks almost immediately, the thin shavings sink within a few minutes, but the block continues to float.

The explanation is simple. Sawdust consists of such small particles of wood, that the cells are partly destroyed and open. Therefore, they fill up with water immediately. The cells of the thin shavings also fill up readily, because they are practically all on the surfaces. But the interior cells of the block cannot be reached, and, therefore, it continues to float. If a freshly cut log is placed in water, it will sink in a comparatively short time, because so many of its cells are filled with sap, a condition known as "water logged." A seasoned log, on the other hand, will float for months or years, before enough of its cells can be filled to make it sink.

The wood substance found in both heavy and light woods is heavier than water. Different authorities state that it is from 1.5 to 1.6 times as heavy as water. Heavy woods are more compact and contain more wood substance per cubic inch than do light woods. Some tropical woods are so dense that they do not float on water, even after seasoning.

Products Derived From Trees*

Most people are familiar enough with wood to recognize that it is a most versatile and useful commodity. Not all of us, however, recognize the fact that, as a result of recent research, this material is now being used in ways unheard of a few years ago. In modern laboratories, scientists are extracting from wood a number of products totally unknown before.

369. Sawmills. Just what happens to a tree after it has been felled in the forest? The bulk of all trees goes either to sawmills or to pulp mills. At the sawmills choice logs are cut into a large variety of useful products, such as:

Heavy timbers, to be used in: bridges, building foundations, dams, docks, warehouses, mines, schools, ships, trailers, trucks.

Construction lumber, is used as: beams, boards, dimension stock of all kinds, flooring, form lumber, joists, light house framing, planks, posts, rafters, sheathing, sills, subfloors, walls.

Finished lumber includes: baseboards, battens, casing, flooring, laths, paneling, siding.

Ties, used as: railroad crossties, mine ties, switch ties.

370. Specialty Mills. Some of this lumber, finished or semifinished, goes to so-called *specialty mills.* Here, the lumber is transformed into all types of useful articles.

It is impossible to list all the specialty mills and the items they produce. The following manufactured items should give some idea as to the great scope of goods produced: airplane parts, agricultural implements, athletic equipment, bowling pins, butcher's blocks, cabinets, caskets, clothespins, doorjams, doors, dowels, furniture, housetrailers, matches, millwork, novel-

---

* Source: Chart, "Products of the Treefarm," American Forest Products Industries, Inc.

ties, pencils, playground equipment, scientific instruments, flight decks, stage scenery, toothpicks, venetian blinds, and all sorts of woodenware.

Other mills specialize in items for the cooperage industry producing the material used for: barrels, buckets, kegs, silos, tanks, tubs.

In addition to these there are a great number of specialty mills which produce a variety of miscellaneous items such as: elevators, fence pickets, reels, shingles, stakes, mine props, wood turnings, and wood chips for making wood pulp.

A few years ago it was common practice to burn sawdust, shavings, and all sorts of leftovers from the sawmills. But the modern sawmill of today has found good use for what were once considered waste and residue.

371. Pulp Mills.   The raw materials used by pulp mills are primarily pulpwood in the form of small logs, sawmill slabs and chips. From these the modern pulp mill produces a variety of pulps most of which are used in the manufacture of paper. Some of the more important pulps are: *sulphite pulp,* used for such items as: paper for bags, blotters, printing papers, boxes, bristol board, envelopes, fruit wrappers, paper napkins, photo processing paper, stencils, wallpaper, and all sorts of wrapping paper. This type of pulp is also used in the manufacture of: cellophane, explosives, lacquers, plastics, photofilm, rayon.

Sulphate pulp is used for many of the items listed above. The two pulps differ primarily in the chemical treatment to which each is exposed.

Semichemical pulp is used in making: corrugated paper, egg cartons, insulating board, wallboard, glossine paper.

Groundwood pulp is the base for such materials as: absorbent paper, building and insulating papers, newsprint, wood cement boards and blocks, wrapping papers.

Residues from pulp mills are liquor containing leftover cellulose and lignin not used in paper manufacture.

Sulphite liquors are used in making: adhesives, building briquettes, dyes, cement, paint and varnish remover, plastics.

Sulphate liquors are used in making: acetic acid, acetone, methyl alcohol, pine oil, turpentine, pharmaceutical chemicals.

372. Veneer and Plywood Mills.   A third type of mill which uses primarily choice logs and bolts is the veneer and plywood mill. The manufacture of veneer and plywood is discussed in detail in Articles 401 and 405.

Through modern chemistry, the leftovers, waste materials, and residues from sawmills, pulp mills, and plywood mills are used in the manufacture of a great variety of items unknown a few years ago. The laboratory most responsible for developing new uses from wood is the Forest Products Laboratory of the U. S. Department of Agriculture, at Madison, Wisconsin. This laboratory was founded in 1910 as the world's first institution devoted exclusively to research in wood utilization. In a vast building on the University of Wisconsin campus more than 450 scientists and other workers spend their full time in research.

It is primarily through the pioneering efforts at the above-mentioned laboratory that a number of plants now find it commercially profitable to extract from wood wastes various useful items. The process is either by distillation or by hydrolysis.

373. Wood distillation plants use for their raw material bolts, limbs, saw-mill edgings, and tree stumps. In the hardwood distillation process some of the following products are made:

Acetic acid, used in: the manufacture of rayon, film, lacquers, plastics, perfumes, textile dying.

Acetone, used in explosives and as a solvent.

Charcoal, used in: black powder explosives, fuel, livestock and poultry foods, medicines, water purification.

Methanol, used as: antifreeze, dry-cleaning agents, paints, shellac, varnishes.

Pitch, extensively used as an insulation in electric transformers.

Tar oil, used as: flotation oils, paint and stains, preservatives, wood creosote.

In the softwood distillation process some of the following products are made:

Cedar oil, primarily used as a furniture polish.

Charcoal, with uses similar to those of charcoal made through hardwood distillation.

Creosote oils, used as: cattle and sheep dips, disinfectants and medicines.

Dipentine, a solvent for reclaiming old rubber.

Lacquer solvents, used in finishing materials such as: lacquer, paints and varnishes.

Pine oil, used as: disinfectants, dying, paints.

Pine tar, used as: coating and binding materials, medicines, soap.

Rosin, for paper sizing, varnish, soap, greases, waterproofing, linoleum.

Wood turpentine, primarily used in paint and varnish manufacture.

374. Wood hydrolysis plants also use wood wastes such as sawdust, slabs, edgings and trimmings as their basic materials. In these plants the raw materials are subjected to a chemical process of decomposition which involves the addition of water. Through the process of wood hydrolysis we derive such products as:

Acetic acid, used in: textile manufacture, white lead pigments, perfumes.

Baking yeast, for bakery products.

Butadiene, used in synthetic rubber.

Ethyl alcohol, used as solvents.

Animal food, for cattle and poultry.

Glycerine, used in medicines and industrial chemicals.

Sugars, as additives to stock feed.

Through wood condensation we derive a product called Furfural, a material used in the resin and plastic industry. Also soil conditioners are produced through this process.

375. Hardboard and Particle Board Plants. In addition to these two types of plants which use wood wastes primarily as their raw material, a great deal of waste material is used by hardboard and particle board plants. Hardboard, either tempered or untempered, is produced by chipping wood scraps into flakes, spraying them with a resinous glue and forming them under heat and pressure into boards. When this material is made with evenly spaced holes, it is called "peg board," popular for display purposes.

Particle board is also made from wood chips and flakes. In various thicknesses and degrees of hardness it is used as: acoustical board, door cores, molded furniture parts, paneling, sheathing, subflooring, window displays.

These are some of the products derived from trees and tree wastes. Although the list is indeed extensive, scientists continue to seek more and better uses for wood. Especially at the Forest Products Laboratory at Madison, Wisconsin, this search continues. The scientists there realize that wood as a raw material still holds many useful secrets.

The Seasoning of Wood

Lumber, as it comes from the sawmill, is literally saturated with water. Except for a few instances, this "green" wood is not ready for consumer use and correct seasoning becomes one of the most essential steps. All lumber shrinks as it dries, and the place for this shrinkage to occur is at the manufacturing plant and not in a newly built permanent structure. A few years ago retail lumber dealers used to carry large stocks of lumber in their yards. When they received green lumber from the mill, it was carefully stacked for air drying. Although this practice continues to a lesser degree, with today's fast building pace, lumber is often loaded in trucks or freight cars at the mill for direct delivery to the building site. This is especially true for construction lumber.

Modern construction practices make the control of moisture much more important today than ever before. Homes are built more rapidly, and requirements are more rigid because of such features as central heating, and air conditioning. No longer is it possible for lumber to dry out during the construction period. If a house is to be soundly constructed, the lumber must be properly seasoned before it is used.

In addition to these needs for seasoning, lumber should be properly cured for the following reasons: dry lumber has greater strength and stiffness; it has greater resistance to wear, stress and strain; it has better nail and glue holding power and higher resistance to decay.

376. How Wood Dries.* Those in charge of curing lumber should have some understanding of what causes moisture to move in wood and the factors that influence the rate of moisture movement. Water in wood normally moves from areas of higher to areas of lower moisture content. This is illustrated by the fact that wood dries from the outside in, which means, that the outside surface of the wood must be drier than the inside if moisture is to be removed. In the drying process, the surface fibers of the heartwood of most species attain the so-called "equilibrium moisture content" corresponding to the immediate surrounding atmosphere almost as soon as drying begins.

Equilibrium moisture content (EMC) is the state of balance of the moisture content of a piece of wood with that of the atmosphere. The surface fibers of sapwood also tend to reach a state of balance with the surrounding drying atmosphere early in the drying process. This is especially true if the air circulation is fast enough to evaporate the water as rapidly as it comes to the surface of the wood. However, if the air circulation is too slow, a longer time is required for the surfaces of sapwood to attain EMC. To reduce the drying time, the initial EMC condition in the kiln should be as low as possible to avoid serious end and surface checking.

Moisture in wood moves through several kinds of passageways in any direction, longitudinally as well as laterally. Generally, the lighter, porous woods dry more rapidly than the heavier, less porous ones, except in porous woods where passageways are plugged with resins and gums.

The drying time in kilns for different wood species varies considerably. The approximate drying time for green 1 inch lumber of most of the commercially important woods ranges from 2–40 days. The time for thicker stock is more than proportional to the increased thickness. A general rule is that 2-inch stock takes about four times longer to kiln-dry as does 1-inch stock.

377. Green Lumber and Timber** are only used under conditions where the wood is maintained at a high moisture content or where shrinkage and defects caused by drying in place have been considered in the design of the structure. It may be feasible, for example, to use green timber for piling that is submerged in water.

Large timbers that would require an exceedingly long and mild seasoning

---

* U. S. Department of Agriculture, Forest Products Laboratory, *"Properties of Wood Related to Drying,"* No. 1900–1901, June, 1951, pp. 9–11.

** U. S. Department of Agriculture, Forest Products Laboratory, *Moisture Content of Wood in Use,* No. 165, 1955, pp. 2–3.

period to dry without serious defects are generally used green and allowed to cure in place. Such timbers are commonly used in construction of bridges, trestles, and mill buildings, where shrinkage, splits. checks, and other defects do little or no damage to the structure.

The greatest hazard connected with the use of green, untreated lumber is decay, particularly at joints and contact points.

378. Air-Dried Lumber.* In most parts of this country, the minimum moisture content that can be generally obtained in air-drying is about 12 to 15 per cent. Air-dried lumber is mostly used for those items that are not ordinarily subjected to the artificial heat of buildings or where some shrinkage can be tolerated. All types of outbuildings, such as sheds and barns, can usually be safely constructed of air-dried lumber.

When air-dried lumber is used in house framing, it is recommended that it be installed at a moisture content below that usually attained in air-drying. If not, any shrinkage may result in plaster cracks and other difficulties. Air-dried lumber is also satisfactory for boxes and crates, parts of agricultural implements, and wagon, truck and trailer bodies. Poles, crossties.

---

* *Ibid.*, p. 3.

Fig. 32. Lumber piled for air drying.

and timbers that are to receive preservative treatment should be partially air-dried. Stock for steam bending should be partially if not thoroughly air-dried.

In air-drying the boards and planks are carefully stacked. A small open space is left between the edges, and sticks, ⅞ by 2 in., are placed crosswise between each layer. This allows the air to circulate freely. Often each pile is protected against sun, dampness from the ground and rain (Fig. 32).

379. Kiln-Dried Lumber. A kiln is an oven in which lumber is dried or seasoned. Every important sawmill and woodworking factory is equipped with one or more of these kilns (Fig. 33). The purpose of kiln drying, which is a very complex process, is to produce a rapid evaporation of the moisture contained in "green wood." This evaporation depends upon three factors: heat, humidity, and circulation. The control and application of these factors in the correct proportion is the main problem in kiln operation, and spells success or failure for the finished product. Kiln-dried lumber is recommended for all uses that require a moisture content below 12 per cent. In most parts of the United States, this will include nearly all interior woodwork, such as flooring, trim, furniture, stairway stock, panels, and cabinet-

Fig. 33. Dry kiln.

work that is used inside heated buildings. Common grades of Douglas fir, West Coast hemlock, and Western red cedar are kiln-dried to a moisture content of 19 per cent.

380. Determining the Moisture Content of Wood.   The usual method followed in kiln drying is to determine the moisture content of the boards to be dried just before entering the kiln and at various stages of the drying process. This is done as follows: A cross section of a board 1 in. long is cut at least 2 ft. from the end of the board. This is necessary because the wood dries faster at the ends. A section cut from the end of a board would, therefore, not be a true sample of the moisture content in the middle. This sample is carefully weighed on a sensitive scale, after which it is heated in a small electric oven at a temperature of 212° to 221° F. until it no longer loses weight. The difference between the two weights is then divided by the oven-dry weight, and reduced to per cent by multiplying by 100. For example, if the original weight is 195 units, and the weight after drying is 150 units, the difference in weight is 45 units. This 45, divided by 150 and multiplied by 100, gives a result of 30 per cent. During the drying process, the moisture content is calculated in a similar manner by cutting and weighing samples from the kiln.

High-grade lumber is usually air-dried for some months, before the process is completed in the kiln. The moisture content of lumber varies with changes in the relative humidity of the surrounding atmosphere.

Air-dried lumber also will absorb moisture from the air until a state of equilibrium is reached. Kiln-dried lumber will again absorb some moisture from the air, and air-dried lumber will lose more moisture if stored under heated conditions. Paint or varnish finishes do not prevent changes in moisture content, but they considerably delay the rate at which the changes take place.

381. Shrinking and Swelling of Wood.*   Wood normally shrinks as it dries and swells as it absorbs moisture. This is the reason that windows and doors often stick in the winter, but usually have sufficient clearance in the summer. Sometimes this swelling and shrinking of wood can be used to advantage. Swelling is employed to close the seams in barrels, tubs, tanks, and boats and to tighten handles on tools. This means of tightening is only temporary as it causes compression of the wood followed by greater than normal shrinkage.

Briefly, shrinkage occurs as follows. Wood grows in a tree under moist conditions, and water not only is held in the wood fiber openings but saturates the fiber walls also. These fiber walls can be thought of as consisting

---

* U. S. Department of Agriculture, Forest Products Laboratory, *Shrinking and Swelling of Wood in Use,* No. 736, 1952, pp. 1–9.

of small units in the form of relatively long strands between which water lodges. As water leaves the spaces between the strands in drying, the strands are drawn together, causing the fiber walls to be reduced in thickness and the fibers themselves to be reduced in girth. This contraction of the fibers causes the whole piece of wood to shrink. Wood shrinks most in the direction of the annual growth rings (tangentially), somewhat less across these rings (radially), and very little, as a rule, along the grain (longitudinally).

Formerly, the smaller amounts of radial shrinkage in quartersawed lumber as compared with the greater shrinkage in plain-sawed lumber was attributed to the wood rays, which are strips of cells extending inward from the bark. It was believed that these cells did not shrink much in length. Since their length lies in the radial direction, they were believed to oppose radial shrinkage. Now, however, it is known that the structure of the walls of the wood-ray cells permit considerable lengthwise shrinkage.

The difference between radial and tangential shrinkage may also be accounted for on the basis of the strands in the fiber walls being bent around the pits that predominate in the radial walls of the fibers, rather than being parallel to the long axis of the fiber. This arrangement of the strands permits maximum tangential shrinkage but lessens radial shrinkage (Fig. 34).

Beside causing changes in dimensions, shrinking and swelling frequently result in severe harmful effects. Inadequately seasoned lumber in a house may cause loosening of fastenings and settling of the building. The result is plaster cracks, distorted openings, uneven floors, and unsightly openings

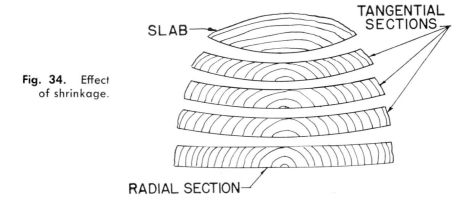

Fig. 34. Effect of shrinkage.

around trim and moldings. Shrinkage of studs, sheathing and siding decreases the weather tightness of walls and reduces their strength and stiffness.

In products such as furniture, interior finish, flooring, sash and doors, swelling and shrinking may cause splitting and cracking, warping, opening of joints and spoilage of carefully applied finishes.

For these and many more reasons, scientists at the Forest Products Laboratory have attempted for many years to overcome these drawbacks. The advent of the cross-laminated plywoods gave improved stability to this type of wood, and made possible the development of the modern hollow-core door. But plywood is as yet not free from warping.

The recent development of new synthetic glues has opened up new possibilities. Through impregnation and bonding of veneers with these new resin glues, a wood can now be produced so stable that it is used to make die models for automobile bodies.

In another attempt to improve the stability of wood, scientists at the Forest Products Laboratory have developed a process which is a combination of resin treatment and wood compression. In this process 60 to 70 per cent of the wood's bulk is removed. The resulting wood, called Pakkawood is extremely hard and dense, and is being used successfully in knife handles and similar articles which are constantly exposed to hot water and soaps. The 16 layers of hardwood veneer, of which a typical knife handle is made, show no signs of swelling, warping, or cracking. As yet the two materials described here are still too expensive for widespread use.*

382. Defects in Wood Due to Improper Seasoning.**   When green wood dries, the first water to leave it is the free moisture in the cavities of the cells. During this early drying stage, no noticeable dimensional changes take place. When, however, the drying continues below the fiber saturation point, shrinkage, and often warpage, occurs resulting in a change in the dimensions of the wood. The fiber saturation point is by definition: the point at which the cell wall is saturated, but no free water remains in the cell cavity. Unfortunately, as wood continues to dry, either in the open air or in a kiln, the shrinkage is not equal in all directions. It is this inequality in shrinkage that sets up a number of strains, which, if becoming too great, cause actual fractures and damage in the wood tissues known as seasoning defects.

The following are some of the defects which may be found in seasoned lumber:

Checks.   These are ruptures in the wood along the grain. They are of two types, *end checks* and *surface checks*. As the name implies, end checks are

---

* Stouffer, Lloyd, "New Wonders from Wood," Chemistry, March, 1960, pp. 1–6.
** Brown H. P., Panshin, A. J., and Forsaith, C. C., *Textbook of Wood Technology.* Vol. I, pp. 310–324.

noticeable in the ends of a board. They may be 2 to 12 inches deep or deeper. In production, checked ends are cut off for whatever length is necessary. Naturally this results in some waste.

Surface checks result from the separation of the thinner walled springwood cells. They extend into the wood for varying distances. They also may be found over the entire flat surface of a board, making it useless for certain jobs.

Checking can be minimized by setting up drying procedures that result in a less rapid but uniform evaporation of moisture. In air-drying this may be done by reducing the circulation through the lumber pile and by shading. Often the ends of boards are painted with a moisture-resistant coating. In kiln-drying it can be avoided by maintaining adequate circulation, proper temperature and humidity conditions.

Warping. A board is warped when as a result of seasoning, distortion from the true plane occurs. The more common types of *warping* are *bowing, crooking, cupping, twisting,* and *diamonding.*

Bowing can be defined as a flatwise curvature, from a straight line, drawn from end to end of a board.

Crooking, by comparison, shows an edgewise curvature. These two defects are very common in lumber that is known to have an irregular grain pattern. However, they may occur in what appears to be perfectly grained stock.

Cupping is the curving of a board so that it assumes a trough-like shape with the edges remaining parallel. It is caused primarily by the more rapid drying of one face of a board as compared with the other. Cupping is often noticeable in floors laid with plain-sawed lumber, where the top of the floor is exposed to the indoor temperature of the house and the underside faces the cool, moist ground. Also, when boards are finished on one side only, cupping is often the result.

Twisting occurs when one corner of a piece of wood twists out of the plane of the other three. This defect is most prominent in cross or irregular grained wood.

Diamonding can be described as uneven shrinkage, and usually develops in square stock. Although square when green, some pieces of wood become diamond shaped during the curing process. This change in shape is due to the difference in radial and tangential shrinkage.

Casehardening in wood develops on account of too rapid drying. Stresses between the core and outer surface of a piece of wood cause the interior wood to stretch while the outer layers are being compressed. This defect occurs most often in kiln-dried stock. It may show as surface checks or as interior pockets.

Casehardened lumber is especially undesirable because, when resawed, the individual pieces have a tendency to cup and bow.

Collapse is a defect that often develops when very wet heartwood in certain species is dried. In extreme cases, the sides of the lumber may cave in, leaving irregular depressions and elevations on the surface and internal checks and splits (Fig. 35). This defect is most frequent in redwood, western red cedar, bald cypress, red gum, and cottonwood. Research is now in progress at the University of California's Forest Products Laboratory in Richmond, California, to find a solution for collapse in such California hardwoods as tan oak, California black oak, Pacific madrone, and a number of other

Fig. 35.   Drying defects. Upper piece shows collapse;
two lower pieces show honeycombing.

species.* The recovery treatment, known as reconditioning, consists of sub-jecting collapsed wood with a moisture content of about 15 per cent after drying, to live saturated steam at 212 degrees Fahrenheit for several hours. This process, which in exploratory tests proved highly successful, may eventually open up a vast and largely untapped treasury of 6 billion board feet of California hardwoods.

Honeycombing, also called "hollow horning," is a defect traceable to internal checking and splitting. Generally, these splits do not extend all the way to the surface but deepen and broaden in the interior of the wood (Fig. 35).

The defect is caused by internal stresses, developed in casehardening and collapse.

Modern Methods of Preserving and Fireproofing Wood

The three greatest destroyers of wood are fungi, insects, and fire. Fungi are low forms of plant life that develop and grow from spores just as higher plants do from seed. These microscopic spores are found everywhere in the open air. They lodge in favorable places on untreated lumber with which they come in contact. There they germinate, and send out hyphae, or strands, that spread through the wood. These plant-like growths break down the wood substance, converting it into food required by the fungus for develop-ment. Like all forms of plant life, the spores of wood-destroying fungi must have air, suitable moisture, and a favorable temperature as well as food in order to survive. Deprived of any one of these four essentials, the spores cannot develop, and wood remains sound.

When wood is completely submerged in fresh water it cannot decay be-cause the necessary air is excluded. Neither will decay progress if the wood has a moisture content of less than 20 per cent of its weight. Decay is also progressively checked as the temperature drops below that generally favor-able for plant growth and stops completely as freezing temperatures are approached. Because it is often impossible to exclude air and moisture and to control temperatures, effective preservation of exposed structures is ob-tained by impregnating the wood with chemicals that are poisonous to fungi, insects, wood borers, and other pests.

Spores of fungi may be dormant in the crevices of wood for years while conditions for development remain unfavorable, only to come to life and begin their destructive activities whenever favorable surroundings are re-stored. This explains why, when there is a lowering of the water table, decay sometimes occurs in the tops of untreated wood piles that have been sub-merged for years.

---

* From: "Views and Projects," University of California Bulletin, Vol. 8, No. 32, Mar. 28, 1960, p. 159.

383. Chemicals Used in Wood Preservation. Creosote, distilled from coal tar, is one of the most effective toxic chemicals used for wood preservation. It has been in continuous use in Europe and in this country for more than 100 years. It is very stable and, when injected into the wood by an approved pressure process, remains effective for long periods of time, depending on the degree and type of exposure. When sound timbers are pressure creosoted, all the spores on the surface or in crevices are completely destroyed. Since spores cannot survive in close proximity to creosote, such timbers will continue to be sterile to any form of life. Creosote preservatives are particularly recommended for use in structures subject to attack of marine borers.

Salt preservatives are carried into the wood by a solution, with water or volatile solvents. Their use is generally recommended when a clean, odorless, paintable product is required.

*Copper sulfate and sodium arsenate** are used in solution with water. This is a new and simple method, called double diffusion, which requires the soaking of green wood alternately in water solutions of these two chemicals. The chemicals react with each other deep in the wood to form insoluble, toxic, copper arsenate, which is highly poisonous to any living organism. Because it is insoluble, this poison remains permanently in the wood to kill anything that might attempt to feed upon it. Success of this method is quite likely to result in the routinely soaking of all sorts of construction timbers, particularly that used in termite-infested areas.

384. Fireproofing Methods. Wood which is pressure treated against decay has been found to be more fire-resistant than untreated wood. Ignition of wood may also be retarded by fire-retardant paint. The newest approach to fireproofing of wood uses certain chemical salts, such as ammonium and boron.** These chemicals are forced, under high pressure, far enough into the wood to give it a protective shield.

Wood is now being chemically fireproofed by a number of plants throughout this country. But as yet the process is too expensive for wide application. Where it has been used, it has resulted in changes in building codes and a lowering of fire insurance rates.

385. Treatment Methods. Several methods can be used to preserve wood. Perhaps the most common method, especially for small jobs, is by simply *brushing, mopping,* or *spraying*. But such methods offer little penetration. A better way is to dip lumber in open tanks and leave it to soak there for several days. In the *diffusion method,* toxic salts are applied to the surface of green lumber where the salts diffuse with the water particles still contained

---

* Stouffer, Lloyd, "New Wonders from Wood," *Chemistry,* Mar.. 1960. pp. 1–6.
** *Ibid.,* pp. 2–3.

in the wood. This makes fairly deep penetration possible. When this procedure is used in dry lumber, the penetration is not nearly as deep.

The best method is by *pressure treatment,* using either steam or creating a vacuum. These treatments can only be done in plants with special equipment and skilled personnel.

In the pressure process the lumber to be treated is loaded on cars and run into long, steel cylinders. When loaded, the cylinders are sealed and filled with preservatives. Through carefully controlled combinations of temperature and pressure, the preservative is injected into the wood. After sufficient length of treatment the load is removed and a new one made ready.

Modern Methods of Bending and Laminating Wood*

Wood bending is an ancient art and to this day of great importance in the furniture, boat, shipbuilding, and sporting goods industry. Wherever curved parts of wood are needed, bending is the cheapest and most economical, and produces articles of great strength.

Despite its long practical history, there is as yet no method of wood bending that guarantees 100 per cent success. Commercial operators often experience serious losses due to breakage during the bending operation or the fixing process, owing to a lack of knowledge of proper wood selection, seasoning and plasticizing of wood, and a lack of efficient machinery.

386. How Wood Is Bent. It is common knowledge that a very thin strip of wood can be easily bent to quite a sharp curvature. But when thick, solid pieces of wood must be bent to a certain shape, it is first necessary to soften it by means of steam, hot water, or plasticizing chemicals. This softening permits the wood to adjust itself to the distortions created by the bending operation.

When a piece of wood is bent, it is stretched along the outer or convex side of the bend, and compressed along the inner, or concave side. These distortions are accompanied by stresses that try to bring the bent piece of wood back to its original, straight shape. The purpose of softening wood by means of hot water, steam, or plasticizing chemicals is to restrict the development of these stresses. Since plasticized wood can be compressed considerably but stretches very little, the objective in bending is to compress the wood as much as possible in order to prevent it from stretching along the convex side. This is usually accomplished by placing a metal strap around the convex face of the piece and pressure blocks at its two ends.

387. Selecting Bending Stock. The selection of bending stock is largely

* Peck, Edward, *Bending Solid Wood to Form;* U. S. Department of Agriculture, Forest Products Laboratory, No. 1764, 1955, pp. 1–24.

determined by the species of wood used in making the article in which the bent parts are to be used. Bending quality varies widely, not only among different kinds of wood, but also in material of the same species. As a rule, hardwoods bend better than softwoods, and certain hardwoods have better bending quality than others. The following American woods of known good bending quality are listed here in order of descending quality: American elm, white oak, locust, American beech, yellow birch, and red oak. Mahogany from Central America is listed as having moderately good bending quality, and is superior to African mahogany, in this respect.

The wood species commonly used in industry for making bent parts are: white oak, red oak, elm, hickory, ash, beech, maple, walnut, mahogany, and sweetgum. As a rule, softwoods have poor bending quality, and are not often used for this purpose. Yew and Alaska cedar are two exceptions. Also, such softwoods as Douglas fir, Southern yellow pine, Northern and Atlantic white cedar and redwood, after steaming and soaking, are often bent to moderate curvatures for ship and boat planking.

Bending stock should be physically sound. Wood with such defects as decay, cross grain, knots, shakes, pith, surface checks, and brash wood generally prove unsuitable for bending purposes.

388. Seasoning Bending Stock. From the standpoint of the bending operation alone, most curved parts could be produced from green stock, or wood with considerable free water in the cell cavities. Only when sharp bends are made and the wood needs to be severely compressed is a large amount of water present a handicap. In such cases, hydrostatic pressure is likely to cause the wood to wrinkle along the concave face.

Theoretically, wood probably bends best when its moisture content is at the fiber-saturation point, which means that it has a moisture content of about 30 per cent. Wood in this condition is water-swollen to its fullest extent. But the cell cavities are empty, and bending can take place without hydrostatic pressure. Such wood, however, is likely to check, split, and shrink excessively during the drying and fixing process.

On the other hand, wood that is too dry, as is most kiln-dried lumber, is not suited for bending. Ideally, bending stock should be air-dried to the desired moisture content, generally 12 to 20 per cent and stored under controlled conditions.

389. Plasticizing of Bending Stock. The purpose of all plasticizing treatments is to soften wood sufficiently so it will bend to a desired shape. Despite considerable experimentation with various chemicals, steam and hot water remain the most practical and satisfactory to soften wood for bending purposes. It is rarely, if ever, necessary to soften wood to its maximum degree of plasticity for bending purposes. In fact, excessively softened wood may fail sooner than wood that is not so soft. The temperature of saturated steam at atmospheric pressure, about 212° F., is generally sufficient to soften wood for bending. Treatment of wood with boiling or nearly boiling water is approximately as good as the steam treatment.

The steaming or boiling period is influenced by the thickness, moisture content, and species of wood used. The degree of plasticization needed is also dependent on the severity of the bend.

Several chemicals, such as urea, urea-aldehyde, tannic acid and glycerine, have been tried as wood plasticizers. Experiments have proved that soaking wood in tannic acid solution has no great effect. In experiments at the Forest Products Laboratory, glycerine also failed to give favorable results. Treatment with urea, alone or together with formaldehyde or dimethylolurea, causes wood to become highly plastic. Generally, chemically treated woods bend less successfully than steamed wood. They also develop more tensile failures during drying and fixing.

390. Bending. There are two broad classes of bends: free bends made without end pressure, and those that are made under end pressure. Free bending is feasible only where the curvature is slight, and the difference in length between convex and concave faces of the bent piece is not more than 3 per cent.

Boat frames and planking are often steamed or boiled, and after bending installed and forced into their proper position. Free bends are not highly permanent, even after drying and fixing, since the deformation obtained during bending is relatively slight. In such instances it may be necessary to overbend slightly.

For most bending, end pressure is necessary to secure the required compression and to prevent tensile failures. End pressure can be applied in several ways. The most common is by means of a metal strap with end fittings, such as blocks and clamps. Many other devices and machines have been made for bending wood. Some machines consist of rollers between which the strips of wood are passed. Hot plate presses are widely used in the furniture industry. These presses consist of metal male and female forms or platens which are heated by steam. The stock is first placed between these forms; next hydraulic pressure is applied. The bent pieces are held in this position until dry.

391. Drying and Setting. When a piece of wood has been softened and bent to a curved shape, the stresses built up within the wood are not evenly distributed. If such a bent piece was released immediately, it would tend to straighten in order to relieve these stresses. To overcome this, it is necessary to hold the piece in shape with tie rods, wood stays, or presses and leave it there long enough until thoroughly dry. Chair manufacturers often provide heated rooms for drying purposes. Such rooms should be equipped with thermostats and humidity controls. Particularly during this drying process many things can go wrong. The difficulties experienced here are somewhat similar to those encountered in kiln-drying of flat lumber.

*Wood Laminating**

Glued-laminated wood construction, often referred to as "glulam," is one of several wood building techniques that has developed in recent years. Extensive research by forest products laboratories and private industry, plus many years of experience by fabricators in Europe and in the United States and Canada, have brought glulam to maturity as an important structural material (Fig. 36).

Fig. 36. Hyperbolic paraboloid shapes made of two layers of one-inch Douglas fir — 75 foot span and no supports.

Glulam is a way of building up large structural members by gluing several layers of dressed lumber together (Fig. 37). It differs from plywood in that the laminations are laid up with their grain parallel; in plywood, the alternate piles are placed to that their grains run at right angles to one another. The advantage of glulam over natural timber is not only its greater strength and stiffness, but this technique makes possible the construction of structural members of a size and shape heretofore unheard of. Sawn timbers are limited in size by the size of the trees they are cut from. But glulam, constructed from small pieces, makes large members possible, whether straight, curved, or tapered.

Originated by Hetzer in Germany in the early part of this century, glued laminated wood arch construction has been used for framing churches, railroad stations, factories, and warehouses for some time before it was intro-

---

* Selbo, M. L., and Knauss, A. C., *Wood Laminating Comes of Age*, U. S. Department of Agriculture, Forest Products Laboratory, 1954, pp. 1–8.

Fig. 37. Glue laminating.

duced in America. In America, the widely accepted use of wood construction and a readily available lumber supply have enabled the laminating industry here to outgrow its European counterpart. Most of the American production is of Douglas fir and Southern yellow pine. In Europe, native spruce, fir and pine is used.

Much of the research in wood laminating in this country has been done at the Forest Products Laboratory in Madison, Wisconsin, dating back to World War I. Since then, research and industry have succeeded in producing many products such as arches for big buildings, curved barn rafters, ship keels, baseball bats, bowling pins, tennis rackets, shoe lasts, and vehicle parts. The recent development of new and improved glues has been greatly responsible for the tremendous growth of the laminating industry. Important improvements have been made in the resistance of glue bonds to water, heat, and decay. Also the strength properties and use characteristics of the glues have been greatly improved.

The most recent glue developed for laminating wood structural members is resorcinol resin or phenol-resorcinol resin combinations. These glues are derived from the distillation products of coal. They can be used to bond any commercially used species of wood and are fully durable under any exposure to moisture, heat, and chemicals. Although they do not protect the wood against fire or decay, it is now possible to treat laminated members with wood preservatives, without harmful effect to the glue.

Manufactured and Graded Lumber

In addition to being processed into plain boards, planks, and timbers, lumber for the building and furniture trades is also made into a great variety of special items. In order to protect the eventual buyer, the lumber industry has set up an elaborate system of standard dressing and grading rules. It will be impossible to present here all the details, since grading practices are highly diversified for the wide variety of woods.

Because of the nature in which a tree grows, no piece of timber is completely free from defects. Knots, for example, are unavoidable, and other defects are traceable to unfavorable growing conditions, outside forces such as wind or frost or to attacks of organisms such as fungi, insects, and marine borers.

392. Knots have a definite bearing on the quality and value of wood and are the most common cause for lowering the value of lumber. Also, they affect the working qualities of wood, cause twisting and checking and often decrease the strength of structural timber.

In lumber, knots are classified as to form, size, quality, and occurrence. As to form, they are round, oval, or spike. A spike knot is one cut either lengthwise of the knot or diagonally across it. As to size, knots are classified as pin, small, medium, and large. The smallest of these, pin knots are not larger than approximately ½ in., a large knot measures over 1½ in. in diameter.

As to quality, knots are either sound, unsound (decayed), tight, intergrown, or not firmly fixed. The last one of these is one not held tightly in place by growth, shape, or position.

As to occurrence, knots may be observed as clusters of two or more, as star checked knots where seasoning checks run from the pith toward the edge of the knot or as well spaced and scattered.

393. Grain. Serious lumber defects are often caused by the direction of the grain. Whenever the fiber alignment differs from a direction parallel to the long axis of a piece of wood, it is said to be cross grained. The degree of cross grain is measured as an angle. We speak of vertical grain or quarter-sawed lumber when it is sawed at approximately right angles to the annual growth rings. Lumber continues to be so classified as long as the rings form an angle of 45 degrees or more with the flat surface. Flat grain or plain-sawed lumber is cut approximately parallel to the annual growth rings. The angle of rings and flat surface here is less than 45 degrees.

Grain can also be mixed, spiral, or diagonal. The last defect is especially serious when wood with such grain is used for skis and other articles that need to be bent.

A number of imperfections and blemishes in finished lumber are traceable to faulty manufacturing processes. Some of these are: *torn grain,* where the surface has been torn or broken in the planer; *raised grain,* where the hard summerwood is raised above the springwood; *loosened grain,* where a part of a surface has been partially loosened; and *machine burns,* which is a darkening of the wood due to overheating by machine knives and rolls. These and other causes make careful grading of lumber necessary.

394. Grades and Uses of Lumber. It already has been mentioned that it would be quite impractical to show here the many grades of lumber and list the various uses for each one. As an illustration, one of the many items produced from Douglas fir is given in detail here, namely Douglas fir flooring.

395. General Characteristics.* D. F. Flooring is customarily shipped kiln-dried (KD). One-inch flooring is usually dried as closely as practicable to an average moisture content of 10 per cent or less; 1¼ in. flooring is usually dried to an average moisture content of 12 per cent or less.

396. Vertical Grain Flooring Grades. There are three grades of vertical grain flooring, "B and Better," "C," and "D." In vertical grain lumber the grain on the face of a piece of wood appears as alternate strips of light springwood and dark summerwood, providing a good surface for paint retension and wear resistance. "B and Better" vertical grain flooring is recommended and widely used where the combination of the fine appearance and highest resistance to wear is required. Pieces of this grade are sound wood. Most pieces are entirely clear or have only a few minor characteristics, such as occasional very small pitch pockets. *"C" vertical grain flooring* is recommended where a combination of excellent appearance and high resistance to wear is required. It is often used in conjunction with "B and Better" flooring. Pieces of this grade are only slightly lower than the "B and Better" grade. "D" vertical grain flooring is recommended for use where good resistance to wear is desirable but where appearance is not of primary importance. Pieces of this grade are only slightly lower than "C" grade.

397. Flat Grain or Mixed Grain Flooring Grades. There are three grades of flat grain or mixed grain floorings: "C and Better," "D," and "E." In flat grain lumber the annual growth rings viewed from the end are parallel with the wide face or form an angle up to 30 or 45 degrees with the wide face. This results in an interesting and varied pattern of grain on the exposed face. Flat grain flooring is used where wear-resistant requirements are less exacting.

---

* West Coast Lumbermen's Association, *Douglas Fir Lumber Grades and Uses,* pp. 8–9.

"C and Better" flat grain or mixed grain flooring is recommended and widely used where a combination of fine appearance and good resistance to wear is required. Most pieces of this grade are entirely clear or have only a few minor characteristics, such as occasional small, tight knots and pitch pockets.

"D" flat grain or mixed grain flooring is recommended for use where good resistance to wear is desirable but where appearance is not of primary importance. Pieces of this grade are only slightly lower than "C and Better" grade.

"E" mixed grain flooring is recommended for subfloors, sheathing, lining of clothes closets and similar uses. Pieces contain characteristics too large or numerous to be accepted in the higher grades. Short lengths of good quality may be obtained from it, however, and its utility value is good.

398. Standard Sizes of Flooring. Flooring is usually bundled at the mill for shipment and sale. The lengths of pieces range from 3 ft. to 6 ft. or longer. Table 2 shows the nominal and actual sizes of Douglas fir flooring.

TABLE 2. Sizes of Douglas Fir Flooring

Sizes

Nominal		Actual	
Th	W	Th	W
1	x 3	$^{25}/_{32}$	x 2⅜
1	x 4	$^{25}/_{32}$	x 3¼
1	x 4	$^{25}/_{32}$	x 5³⁄₁₆
1¼	x 3	1¹⁄₁₆	x 2⅜
1¼	x 4	1¹⁄₁₆	x 3¼

In addition to these written specifications, which give the general characteristics, grades and size of each lumber item, the lumber industry has developed for many items a grade stamp, which is another guarantee that the buyer receives an approved product. These stamps may be found on the ends of timbers, on the face of boards or on the outside wrapping of bundled goods. In abbreviations, such stamps give the name of sponsoring associations, the mill by number that produced the item, and the grade (Fig. 38).

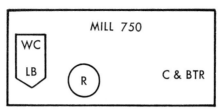

Fig. 38. Grade stamp for grade "C and Better."

399. Abbreviations.* With such detailed specifications for each item, the lumber industry has developed a long list of abbreviations, which, when understood, give a precise picture as to the characteristics of each item. The following is a partial list of abbreviations and their brief explanations:

AD   Air-dried. Lumber dried in the open air as distinct from kiln-dried lumber. Air-dried lumber generally has a moisture content of about 12 to 15 per cent.

AW & L   All widths and lengths.

BD. FT.   Board feet. Also called board measure. Lumber is sold by the standard unit of measurement, the board foot. Each board foot is the equivalent of a piece of lumber measuring 1 in. in thickness, 1 ft. in width, and 1 ft. in length. To calculate board feet, multiply the thickness and the width of the board in inches by its length in feet, and divide the product by twelve. The easiest method of doing board measure is to use cancellation. The dimensions of lumber are always written in the order of thickness, width, and length. On the cheaper grades of lumber, ½ in. is disregarded and counted as 1 in. Generally, a board less than 1 in. thick is counted as 1 in. A board thicker than 1 in. is figured to the nearest larger quarter inch in thickness. Thus 1⅛ in. is calculated as 1¼ in., 1⅜ in. as 1½ in., etc.

Sample problems:

1 piece ⅞″ × 3″ × 10′ 0″ = 1 × 3⁄12 × 10 = 2.5 board ft.
1 piece ¾″ × 6″ × 17½″ = 1 × 6⁄12 × 18⁄12 = .75 board ft.
1 piece 1¾″ × 6¼″ × 12′ 0″ = 2 × 6⁄12 × 12 = 12 board ft.
2 pieces 1⅜″ × 7½″ × 10′ 6″ = 2 × 3⁄2 × 9⁄12 × 21½ = 21 board ft.

CLR	Clear
DF	Douglas fir
D & M	Dressed and matched
FG	Flat or slash grain
FOB	Free on board (named point)
Ft	Foot

* West Coast Lumbermen's Association, *Standard Grading and Dressing Rules for Douglas Fir, West Coast Hemlock, Sitka Spruce, Western Red Cedar,* pp. 293–295.

FT. BM	Feet board measure
FT. SM	Feet surface measure. All flat stock, such as plywood, is measured by the square foot.
KD	Kiln-dried. Lumber so indicated has received additional drying in a heated room. The moisture content of kiln-dried finish lumber is generally below 12 per cent; common grades average 19 per cent
M	Thousand
M.BM	Thousand (ft.) board measure
MC	Moisture content
MLDG	Molding
RDM	Random. Lumber so specified is of different thickness, width, and length.
RL	Random lengths
RW	Random widths. Lumber supplies for school laboratories are often purchased as random widths and lengths. Such lumber is generally more economical than the standard sizes.
SG	Slash or flat grain
SEL	Select
SQ	Square
S 1 E	Surfaced one edge
S 2 E	Surfaced two edges
S 1 S	Surfaced one side
S 2 S	Surfaced two sides
S 4 S	Surfaced four sides
T & G	Tongued and grooved

Veneers and Plywood

400. Veneers are very thin sheets of wood, usually cut from rare stock. They are glued to the more common woods, either for the sake of appearance, or durability of construction. Veneer is most extensively used for plywood facing.

Wood has been cut into veneers for a long time.* Records show that the Egyptians practiced this art probably 3000 or more years ago. Its early use was primarily confined to ornamentation, for bringing out the figure of the wood.

401. Thickness of Veneers. Modern veneers are produced on a lathe, a slicer, or a saw, and, dependent upon the manner of cutting, is referred to as "rotary," "sliced," or "sawed" veneer. On these machines it is cut in many thicknesses, ranging from $\frac{1}{40}$ to $\frac{5}{16}$ in. For special purposes it is cut

---

* U. S. Department of Agriculture, Forest Products Laboratory, *The Manufacture of Veneers*, No. 285, pp. 1–8.

as thick as ⅜ in. and as thin as ¹⁄₁₁₀ in., or even less. The large bulk of soft-wood rotary veneers is cut in thicknesses ranging from ³⁄₁₆ to ¹⁄₁₀ in. Rotary hardwood veneers for plywood cores range in thickness from ¹⁄₁₂ to ¼ in., depending on the density of the wood and the type of plywood to be made. Rotary-cut hardwood face veneers are commonly ¹⁄₂₀ to ¹⁄₂₈ in. thick.

Sliced veneers for use in plywood and furniture construction generally range from ¹⁄₃₂ to ¹⁄₁₆ in. in thickness, whereas sliced face veneers are usually ¹⁄₂₈ in. thick. The great bulk of sawed veneers is cut into thicknesses of ¼ to ¹⁄₂₄ in.

402. Cutting Veneers. Logs intended for veneer cutting are generally cut into the same length as sawmill logs. In Douglas fir, the 34-foot length is popular, because it permits the cutting of four bolts, each 8 ft. 6 in. long. This length permits "spurring" the ends in the lathe to a uniform length of 100 inches, and trimming of the finished plywood panel to 96 inches, the standard length of a 4 ft by 8 ft. sheet of plywood.

Usually veneer logs are not allowed to dry out before they are cut into veneer. For some wood species it may be necessary to soften the logs through heat treatment. Generally, hardwoods need to be heated to a higher temperature than the soft. Softwoods such as cottonwood and basswood may be cut satisfactorily at room temperature. Depending upon the kind of wood, the heat treatment may last from one day to a week.

For rotary cutting, the bolts are first cleaned and heated with the bark on, because in this condition the bark is more easily removed. Wood to be sliced is first cut into "flitches" or portions of the log. For sawing, the wood need not be heated, and a high moisture content is not essential.

The typical veneer lathe (Fig. 39) consists of a heavy steel bed on which is mounted at each end a framework for the support of the bearing spindles. These spindles are equipped with chucks for gripping the log, which is

Fig. 39. Modern veneer lathe.

hoisted by mechanical power into position. An extremely sharp knife and pressure bar extend the full length of the machine. When the log is revolved against the knife, a continuous sheet of veneer is peeled off. As the knife cuts, the pressure bar placed directly ahead of the knife compresses the wood, and in so doing prevents excessive checking of the veneer. By an automatic geared arrangement, the knife and pressure bar unit move slowly into the log, cutting the veneer to the desired thickness. As the veneer leaves the lathe, it is picked up on a wide conveyor-type table and moved on to the next operation.

Most rotary lathes operate at speeds from 50 to 60 revolutions per minute. The speed at which the band of veneer leaves the machine is from 200 to 400 feet per minute for hardwood and as high as 1000 feet per minute for softwood.

On a typical veneer slicer (Fig. 40), the part of the log called "flitch" is moved downward over the stationary knife. In some designs, however, the knife is moved by power and the flitch moves only to regulate the thickness of cut. Veneer produced on a slicer comes in long, narrow strips, which may show a variety of grain patterns depending on the manner in which the flitch was mounted with respect to the knife.

Most veneer slicers operate at speeds of 35 to 50 strokes per minute. The process of sawing veneers is similar to that of sawing green logs into boards and timbers. The saw used is especially designed for this purpose. Even so, this operation wastes material and time, and is chiefly used when certain high grade finish and furniture woods must be cut into veneers. Softwood veneers are primarily used for the production of plywood for structural and other purposes. Its manufacture is concentrated in the Pacific

Fig. 40. Veneer slicer.

Northwest, where most of it is cut from Douglas fir and other softwood logs.

The hardwood veneer industry is widespread in the eastern half of the United States, with its heaviest concentration in the Southern and South-eastern States. More than half of all hardwood veneers is used for furniture and high-grade plywood manufacture. The remainder is used for millwork, musical instruments, radio and TV sets, chairs, seats, vehicles, aircraft, and many more. As single ply, it is used for decorative purposes and in making all sorts of small items, such as boxes, barrels, and hampers.

Wood Figuration*

Broadly speaking, any design or distinctive markings that appear on the surface of a piece of wood may be described as *figure*. In the trade, how-ever, figure signifies only such decorative designs as are prized in the furniture and cabinet-making industries.

If a log is sawed so that the exposed surface is approximately tangent to the annual rings, *plain* or *flat-sawed* lumber is produced. If the cut is more or less at right angle to the annual layers, the stock is said to be *quarter-sawed*. By changing the plane of cut to a position where it is neither tangential nor at right angles, a number of intermediate figures can be produced.

Fig. 41. Quarter-sawed veneer.

Plain-sawed figures are characterized through the center of the board by *nested angular* and *parabolic designs,* the tips of which are directed toward one end of the board, or by concentric cones of irregular shape. The extent to which these designs are noticeable is greatly due to the difference in springwood and summerwood. When the seasonal growth increments are poorly defined, the resulting plain-sawed stock will show little or no figure, but the opposite will hold true when this distinction is pronounced.

The characteristics of quarter-sawed wood with rays of normal size are also due to successive growth increments. These growth layers appear as parallel stripes (Fig. 41). Since in quarter-sawing the plane of the cut is in

---

* Brown, H. P., Panshin, A. J., and Forsaith, *Textbook of Wood Technology,* Vol. I, Chap. 11, pp. 267–281.

the same direction as that of the rays, the pattern will follow these rays for a considerable distance producing in such woods as oak and sycamore a figure called *ray fleck*. In some woods, these flecks reflect light more than the surrounding tissues, a characteristic which is referred to as *silver grain*.

403. Types of Veneers. When various techniques are used, a number of interesting figures are obtained in the manufacture of veneers and plywoods. As was explained before, *rotary-cut veneer* is obtained by rotating a log against a knife in such a way that a continuous sheet of veneer is unrolled. Since logs, even those of large trees, usually possess some taper, a sheet of rotary-cut veneer generally displays portions of several different growth layers.

Most rotary-cut veneer is of the "commercial veneer" type; it is used for the central plies of plywood or for concealed parts in furniture; seldom for exposed surfaces. Such veneers are classified as *plain-rotary-cut veneers.* When rotary cutting is done to produce exposed surfaces, it is either plain or figured, depending on the prominence of the pattern. The bird's-eye quilted, curly, and blister type are examples of *figured rotary-cut veneer.*

Half-round veneer is also cut on a lathe. The material to be sliced is usually the split half of a log, a flitch, or a section of a crotch or stump.

Cone-cut veneers are shaved from a cylindrical bolt of wood, like sharpening a pencil. This method lends itself to some interesting designs, particularly for circular table tops.

The figures described above are obtained by making cuts perpendicularly

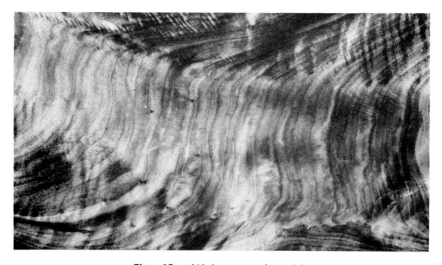

Fig. 42. Walnut crotch swirl.

from the tree. When the grain deviates from the perpendicular, or when the cut is made from irregularities of grain caused by burls, crotches, and stumps, a variety of interesting figures results (Fig. 42).

404. Figures. A number of distinctive patterns also arise as a result of wavy appearances in the direction of the fiber arrangement. *Wavy, curly, blister, quilted,* and *bird's-eye* figures belong in this category.

Wavy and curly figure is due to wavy appearances in the direction of fiber alignment. The radial-split faces of such a wood are wavy or corrugated. When the corrugations are close and abrupt, the resulting pattern is called *fiddle back* figure and appears mostly in maple and mahogany. It has long been used for the backs of violins.

The term *blister figure* is used to indicate a peculiar type of figure that quite frequently occurs on flat-sawed lumber and rotary-cut surfaces. It consists of small, more or less widely spaced, elevated or depressed areas of rounded contour. This type of figure occurs in a number of native species, especially in maple and birch.

Quilted figure is a pattern that resembles blister figure but differs in that the whole surface of the wood is involved. It is obtained from selected Oregon maple.

Bird's-eye figure is due to local distortions in fiber alignment that are shown as conical indentations. These indentations extend from the surface of the bark inward toward the pith and, once started, continue in successive growth layers for many years, frequently throughout the length of the tree and even into the branches. It is most common in hard maple, but is also found in soft maple, birch, and white ash. No satisfactory explanation of the cause of bird's-eye figure has yet been given (Fig. 10).

Various figures are produced in wood as a result of twisted grain. Perhaps the most unusual patterns of this kind are obtained from crotches, burls, and stumps, and are highly prized for matched veneers.

Crotch figure comes from the segment of a stem that forks, usually shaped somewhat like a Y. Among domestic woods, ornamental crotch figures are obtained almost exclusively from black walnut.

Burls or *burrs* are large abnormal bulges that form on the trunk and limbs of a tree and may occur on almost any species. The fiber alignment of burls is very irregular giving the burl a more or less gnarled appearance. This irregularity of grain produces very striking figures which are highly prized for veneer and turned articles. Among native species, burls of Oregon myrtle, maple, walnut, and redwood are the main sources for this figure (Fig. 43).

Stump wood comes from the bell-shaped base of a tree just above the roots. Among native species, figured walnut stumps bring an unusually high price.

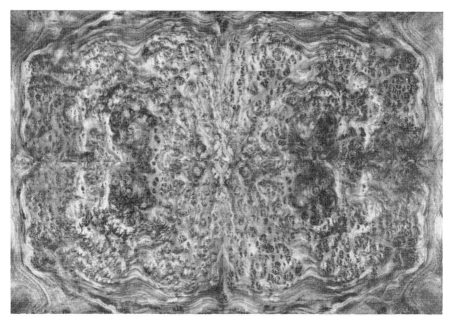

Fig. 43. Burl, four pieces matched.

Plywood

405. Manufacture and General Characteristics.* Plywood is manufactured by bonding thin layers of wood (veneers) together with adhesives
in such a way that the mechanical and physical properties of the wood are
redistributed. The veneers commonly produced in this country range in
thickness from 1/100 in. to more than 1/4 in. They are cut from many kinds
of wood, both softwood and hardwood species and are carefully classified
and graded. The adhesives available for bonding veneers together to make
plywood panels are classified according to their water resistance and the
temperature at which they set.

Plywood is manufactured in different thicknesses, sizes, numbers of plies,
and grades of lumber. Three-ply panels are 1/4 or 3/8 in. thick, and of various
widths and lengths. Panels consist simply of a core, usually of inferior or
defective wood, to each side of which a sheet of veneer has been glued,
the grain of the core being at right angles to the grain of the veneers.

Five-ply panels consist of a core, to the face and back of which a sheet
of common veneer is glued with the grain running at right angles to that
of the core (Fig. 44). These sheets, next to the core, are called "crossbands."

---

* U. S. Department of Agriculture, Forest Products Laboratory. *Manufacture and
General Characteristics of Plywood*, No. 543, pp. 1–15.

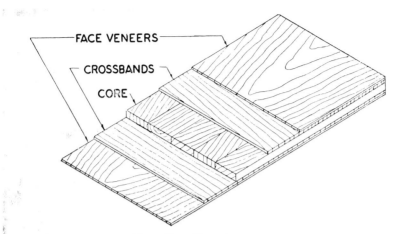

FACE VENEERS

CROSSBANDS

CORE

Fig. 44.   Five-ply veneer.

A sheet of thin veneer, usually of a higher grade, is then glued to each of the crossbands. These outside veneers are called the "faces." The grain of the face veneers runs at right angles to the crossbands, but in the same direction as the grain of the core.

Plywood is manufactured either by the hot or cold press method. In the hot press method, the panels of plywood are placed between heated plates. The time required for the sheets to remain in the hotpress depends upon the thickness of the material to be glued and on the adhesive. Some glues require setting temperatures in the neighborhood of 300° F., whereas others may be cured at 212° F. or less. The time required may vary from 2 to 3 minutes for very thin panels to an hour or more for panels 2 or 3 inches thick.

In cold pressing, the panels are bonded with glue that requires no heat for setting. Pressure is usually applied hydraulically or by rollers (Fig. 45). Once the glue has set, the panels are ready to be trimmed and sanded. In storage they are dried to the proper moisture content and next made ready for shipment.

406. Some Properties of Plywood.   The chief advantages of plywood, as compared with solid wood, are:

1. Its approach to equalization of its strength along the length and width of the panel.

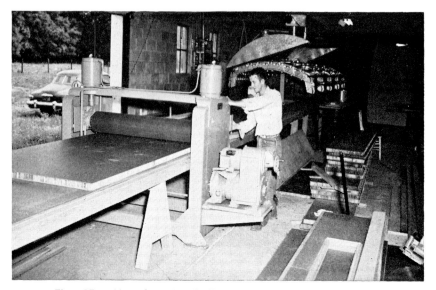

Fig. 45. Manufacturing hollow core doors on rotary press.

2. Greater resistance to checking and splitting.

3. Less change in dimensions with changes in moisture content.

The greater the number of plies for a given thickness, the more nearly equal are the strength and shrinkage properties along and across the panel and the greater is the resistance to splitting.

By using an odd number of plies and by arranging them so that there is a parallel ply of the same thickness, species and properties on the opposite side of the core, one can obtain a balance in construction, which eliminates many faults common to solid stock. Good balanced construction will largely eliminate the tendency of plywood to warp. This is also true for cupping and twisting.

407. Types and Grades of Plywood. As in the lumber industry, the plywood industry has set up standard grading rules for the different types of plywood that are manufactured. Although these rules are not as elaborate as those set up by the lumber industry, they are too lengthy to be included in their entirety here.

Briefly, these rules apply to two classifications of plywood, namely Douglas fir plywood and hardwood plywood (see Table 3). Douglas fir plywood is either classified by type as exterior or interior. Within the hardwood group the classifications are for type I, type II, or type III panels. Glue line quality or the degree of waterproofness determines whether a sheet of plywood belongs in one or the other group.

TABLE 3. Types and Grades of Plywood*

Type	Glue-Line Quality	Typical Glues Used
Douglas fir: Exterior	Permanent under exterior use	Phenol resin
Interior	Water resistant	Soybean or extended phenol resin
Hardwood: Type I	Fully waterproof	Phenol risen or melamine-urea resin
Type II	Water resistant	Urea resin (sometimes moderately extended)
Type III	Moisture resistant	Casein, urea resin (with extension)

The quality of the veneer in a panel determines its actual grade. Douglas fir plywood is classified into grades A, B, C, and D. Firmness, smoothness, and the presence or lack of knots, splits, patches, pitch pockets, wormholes, and other defects, are the determining factors. The best grade of Douglas fir plywood, A-A, has sound, smooth veneers that are free of any defects. It may have well-made patches on each surface.

Hardwood plywood is similarly classified into grades 1, 2, 3, and 4. Grade 1 includes face veneer that meets requirements as to color, pattern, general appearance, and defects, as defined for individual species. Grades 2, 3, and 4 are based on the presence of such defects as knots, knotholes, burls, mineral streaks, and wormholes. The standards for hardwood plywood also include specifications for lumber core panels and edge banding of such panels.**

Plywood standards also cover such subjects as sanding, thickness tolerances, number of plies, standard panel sizes and plywood tests. Manufacturers whose products can meet the standards set up by the manufacturer's association, are so certified and are entitled to carry the stamp of approval on their product.

408. The Use of Plywood.   Today, plywood panels are readily available, not only in many popular and beautiful woods, but also in an interesting variety of grain and figure patterns. With these panels, it is easy to bring

---

* Source: U. S. Department of Agriculture, Forest Products Laboratory, "Manufacture and General Characteristics of Flat Plywood," No. 543, p. 13.

** NOTE: For complete standards of hardwood plywood consult: *Commercial Standard*, CS 35–36, compiled by The U. S. Department of Commerce. Available from: U. S. Government Printing Office, Washington, D. C., 1956, 26 pp.

to interiors and to many products a touch of beauty and contemporary styling that is difficult to duplicate with other materials. In the words of the late architect Frank Lloyd Wright,

"hardwood plywood has emancipated the beauty of wood."*

Plywood panels are available in width from 24 to 48 in. in 6-in. breaks, and in lengths from 36 in. to 96 in. in breaks of 12 in. Longer lengths are made for marine and exterior uses. Panels are also made with the grain running the short way of the panel.

Veneer core construction hardwood panels in 3, 5, 7, and 9 ply are generally available in the following thicknesses:

$$3 \text{ ply} — \frac{1}{8}, \frac{3}{16}, \frac{1}{4} \text{ in.}$$
$$5 \text{ ply} — \frac{5}{16}, \frac{3}{8}, \frac{1}{2} \text{ in.}$$
$$5 \text{ and } 7 \text{ ply} — \frac{5}{8} \text{ in.}$$
$$7 \text{ and } 9 \text{ ply} — \frac{3}{4} \text{ in.}$$

The popularity of plywood as a construction material has been especially advanced by its ease of installation, and its ability to take finishes readily. The recent introduction of pre-finished panels in a variety of colors has now greatly reduced the time formally required for the finishing process. Panels are also available with vertical V grooves cut into the panel, giving a wall the appearance of solid, tongue, and grooved wood paneling.

Glossary of Wood Terms**

Angiosperms: The botanical name for a group of plants that includes the so-called hardwoods; literally the word means "having the seeds enclosed." Terms commonly applied to trees belonging to the angiosperm group: hardwoods, deciduous trees, porous woods, broad-leaved trees.

Annual ring: The growth layer put on in a single growth year.

Blue stain: A bluish or grayish discoloration of the sapwood caused by the growth of certain dark-colored fungi on the surface and in the interior of the wood; made possible by the same conditions that favor the growth of other fungi.

Brashness: A condition of wood characterized by an abrupt failure across the grain without splintering; frequently accompanied by small loads and deformations.

Cambium: The layer of tissue just beneath the bark of the tree from which the new wood and bark cells of each year's growth develop. On the inner side of the cambium the typical wood cells, springwood and summerwood, are formed. On the outer side of the cambium the phloem, or bast, is formed.

---

* Hardwood Plywood Institute, *A Treasury of Hardwood Plywood*, p. 4.
** U. S. Department of Agriculture, Forest Products Laboratory, *Technical Note*, No. 240, 1952

Casehardening: A state of compression in the outer layers of a board or timber accompanied by tension in the center or core, the result of too severe drying conditions.

Cell: A general term for the minute units of wood structure, including wood fibers, vessel segments, and other elements of diverse structure and function.

Cellulose: The carbohydrate $(C_6H_{10}O_5)_\times$ that is the principal constituent of wood and of parts of many plants.

Collapse: The flattening of single cells or rows of cells in heartwood during the drying or pressure treatment of wood; characterized by a caved-in or corrugated appearance.

Compreg: Wood treated (preferably in the form of thin sheets or veneers) with water or alcohol solutions of synthetic resins that are subsequently polymerized by heat simultaneously with the application of pressure. Compreg has great stability with respect to moisture and shrinking and swelling, greater hardness than "Impreg," greater density than "Impreg" or normal wood (depending on the method of processing), and a glossy through-and-through finish that can be redressed by buffing alone when scratched (see "Impreg").

Compression set: A condition in which some of the outer fibers in a piece of wood are permanently compressed as a result of the piece being restrained from swelling while taking on moisture.

Compression wood: Abnormal wood that often forms on the lower side of branches and leaning trunks of softwood trees. Compression wood is identified by its relatively wide annual rings, usually eccentric, and its relatively large amount of summerwood, usually 50 per cent or more of the width of the annual rings in which it occurs. Compression wood shrinks excessively and irregularly lengthwise, as compared with normal wood.

Conifer: A tree bearing seed cones; usually, an evergreen. A softwood.

Crook: That distortion of a board in which the edge is concave or convex longitudinally.

Crossband: To place the grain of layers of wood at right angles in order to minimize shrinking and swelling and consequent warping. Also the layer of veneer at right angles to the face plies, applied particularly to five-ply plywood and lumber-core panels.

Cross grain: Cross-grained wood is that in which the fibers are not parallel to the axis of a piece.

Cut stock: Softwood cuttings similar to hardwood dimension stock as described under "Dimension Stock," but used where softwoods are appropriate.

Decay: The disintegration of wood substance through the action of wood-destroying fungi.

Diffuse-porous woods: Certain hardwoods in which the pores tend to be uniform in size and distribution throughout each annual ring or to decrease in size slightly and gradually toward the outer border of the ring (see "Ring-porous Woods").

Dimension stock: Hardwood squares or flat stock, usually in pieces under the minimum sizes admitted in standard grades, rough or dressed, green or dry, cut to the approximate dimensions required for the products of woodworking factories. Dimension stock should be distinguished from "ready-cut stock," which is defined as material green or dry, sawed, turned, shaped, or otherwise machined to exact conditions and dimensions required for assembly into the various products of wood-using factories.

Dry rot: A term loosely applied to any dry crumbly decay but especially to that which, when in an advanced stage, permits the wood to be easily crushed to a dry powder. The term is actually a misnomer for any decay, inasmuch as all fungi require considerable moisture for growth.

Durability: A general term for permanence or lastingness. Frequently used to refer to the degree of resistance of a species of wood to attack by wood-destroying fungi under conditions that favor such attack. In this connection decay resistance is a more specific term.

Edge-grain: Vertical-grain (edge-grain, rift-grain, comb-grain, or quarter-sawed) lumber is that which has been sawed so that the wide surface extends approximately at right angles to the annual growth rings. Material is considered vertical grain when the rings (so-called grain) form an angle of 45° to 90° with the wide surface of the piece (see "Flat-grain").

Equilibrium moisture content: The moisture content at which wood neither gains nor loses water when surrounded by air at a given relative humidity and temperature.

Fiber-saturation point: The stage in the drying or wetting of wood at which the cell walls are saturated and the cell cavities are free of water. Usually taken as approximately 30 per cent moisture content, based on oven-dry weight.

Fireproofing: Making wood resistant to fire. Wood cannot be treated chemically so that it will not char or decompose at temperatures of about 280° F. and higher. What effective fireproofing does is to make wood difficult to ignite, keep it from supporting its own combustion, and delay the spreading of flame over the wood surface.

Flat-grain: Flat-grain lumber is that which has been sawed in a plane approximately perpendicular to a radium of the log. Synonymous terms: slash-grain, "bastard" grain, plain-sawed, tangential-cut. Lumber is con-

sidered flat-grain when the wide surface makes an angle of less than 45°
with the annual growth rings.

Flitch: A thick piece of lumber with wane (bark) on one or more edges.

Groundwood: Pulp produced by mechanical disintegration of wood on
grinding stones. It is the main constituent of newsprint paper and the
"groundwood-book" type of magazine paper. It is also used in paper
towels, tissues, and paper boards. The pulp yield by the groundwood
process is in excess of 90 per cent of the wood.

Gymnosperms: The botanical name for the group of plants that includes
the so-called softwoods: literally the word means "seeds not enclosed."
Terms commonly applied to trees belonging to the gymnosperm group:
softwoods, evergreens, nonporous woods, needle- or scale-leaved trees,
conifers. Most, but not all, true gymnosperms are needle-leaved, evergreen, and cone-bearing (see "Angiosperms").

Hardwoods: Broad-leaved trees. The term refers to a botanical grouping
and not to the actual hardness of the wood. Some of the so-called hardwoods are in reality very soft. All hardwoods contain pores or vessels,
specialized water-conducting elements not characteristic of softwoods.
Angiosperms is the botanical name for hardwoods.

Heartwood: The wood, extending from the pith to the sapwood, the cells
of which no longer participate in the life processes of the tree. Heartwood
may be infiltrated with gums, resins, and other materials that usually make
it darker and more decay resistant than sapwood (see "Sapwood").

Honeycombing: Checks that occur in the interior of a piece of lumber,
often not visible at the surface. Honeycombing usually occurs along the
rays.

Impreg: Wood treated (generally in the form of thin sheets or veneers)
with water or alcohol solutions of synthetic resins and heat treated to
polymerize the resins. The resins are bonded (chemically rather than
physically) to the wood fibers, so that moisture absorption and shrinking
and swelling are greatly reduced. Hardness is increased.

Laminated wood: A piece of wood built up of plies or laminations that
have been joined with glue and in which the grain of all plies is essentially parallel.

Lignin: The second most abundant constituent of wood, located principally
in the middle lamella. Lignin constitutes 16 to 35 per cent, by weight,
of wood. Its chemical structure has not been definitely determined. Lignin
may be isolated by treating wood with 72 per cent sulfuric acid followed
by dilution with water and hydrolysis to remove the cellulose associated
with the lignin.

Moistureproofing: Making wood resistant to moisture changes. Referring to wood, moistureproofing is a relative rather than an absolute term. No practicable coating or treatment for wood is known that will completely prevent moisture changes.

Naval stores: A term applied to chemically reactive oils, resins, tars, and pitches derived from oleoresin contained in, exuded by, or extracted from trees chiefly of the pine species (genus *Pinus*), or from the wood of such trees.

Oleoresin: The viscous mixture of nonvolatile solids and essential oil secreted by the resin-forming cells of the pines and certain other trees. Oleoresin from long-leaf and slash pine is of great commercial importance, being the raw material of the United States turpentine and rosin production. It is obtained by regularly repeated wounding of the living tree.

Peck: Pockets or areas of disintegrated wood caused by advanced stages of localized decay in the living tree. It is usually associated with cypress and incense cedar (see "Bird Peck").

Plain-sawed: See "Flat Grain."

Plywood: A crossbanded assembly made of layers of veneer or veneer in combination with a lumber core or plies joined with an adhesive. Two types of plywood are recognized, namely, (1) veneer plywood and (2) lumber-core plywood. The grain of adjoining plies is usually laid at right angles, and almost always an odd number of plies are used to obtain balanced construction.

Porous woods: Another name for the hardwoods, which frequently have vessels or pores large enough to be readily seen without magnification.

Quarter-sawed: See "Edge Grain."

Rays: Strips of cells extending radially within a tree and varying in height from a few cells in some species to 4 inches or more in the oaks, in which species they produce the characteristic "silver grain" seen on radial (quartersawed) surfaces. The rays serve primarily to store food and transport it horizontally in the tree.

Ring-porous woods: A group of hardwoods in which the pores are comparatively large at the beginning of each annual ring and decrease in size more or less abruptly toward the outer portion of the ring, thus forming a distinct inner zone of pores known as the springwood and the outer zone with smaller pores known as the summer wood.

Rotary-cut veneer: Veneer cut in a continuous strip by rotating a log against the edge of a knife in a special type of lathe (see "Sliced Veneer" and "Veneer").

Sap: The term commonly used to refer to all of the fluids in a tree, special secretions and excretions, such as oleoresin, excepted.

Sapwood: The (usually) light-colored zone of wood next to the bark, ½ to

3 or more inches wide, that is actively involved in the life processes of the tree (water and sap movement, food storage). Under conditions favorable to decay sapwood is more susceptible to decay than heartwood; as a rule it is more permeable to liquids than heartwood. Sapwood is not essentially weaker or stronger than heartwood of the same species.

Second-growth: Denotes timber that has grown after the removal of all or a large portion of the previous stand whether by cutting, fire, wind, or other agency.

Sliced veneer: Veneer that is sliced off a log or bolt by moving a large knife across a bolt or flitch (see "Rotary-cut Veneer" and "Veneer").

Softwoods: See "Gymnosperms."

Specific gravity: The ratio of the weight of a body to the weight of an equal volume of water at some standard temperature.

Spiral grain: A type of growth in which the fibers take a spiral course about the bole of the tree instead of the normal vertical course. The spiral may extend right handed or left handed around the tree trunk.

Springwood: The portion of the annual growth ring that is formed during the early part of the season's growth. It is usually less dense and weaker mechanically than summerwood.

Starved joint: A glued joint in which, as a result of the use of excessive pressure or insufficient viscosity of the glue, or a combination of these causes, the glue is forced out from between the surfaces to be joined, leaving insufficient glue to make a strong joint.

Sulfate process: An alkaline pulping process, involving the use of caustic soda and sodium sulfide (the latter derived from salt cake or sodium sulfate by a smelting process), used in the production of wrapping papers and container boards from both hardwoods and softwoods (mostly softwoods). The pulp produced by the sulfate process is tough, and for this reason it is used for sacks and wrapping papers and the liners of shipping containers. Bleached sulfate pulp is used in bond, writing, wrapping, and other strong white papers. The yield is about 50 per cent on the basis of the oven-dry weight of chips admitted to the digester.

Sulfite process: An acid pulping process, involving the use of an aqueous solution of sulfur dioxide and calcium or magnesium bisulfite or a mixture of the two, used in the production of newsprint and writing papers from long-fibered softwoods with low resin content, such as spruces, firs, and hemlocks, and such hardwoods as the birches, gums, and maples. The pulp produced is long-fibered and light-colored. The yield is about 45 per cent on the basis of the oven-dry weight of chips admitted to the digester. Sulfite pulp is used unbleached in newsprint paper and numerous other kinds of light-colored papers. Highly purified sulfite pulp is used for making rayon and other cellulose chemical products.

Summerwood: The outer, later-formed, usually denser portion of the annual growth ring.

Tangential section: A longitudinal section through a tree or limb perpendicular to a radium. Flat-sawed lumber is cut tangentially.

Tension wood: An abnormal form of wood found in leaning trees of some hardwood species and characterized by the presence of gelatinous fibers and excessive longitudinal shrinkage.

Transverse section: A section through a tree or timber at right angles to the pith.

Veneer: Thin sheets of wood produced by rotary cutting, sawing, or slicing. Veneer thicknesses to some extent overlap the thicknesses of resawn lumber.

Warp: Any variation from the true or plane surface. Warp includes crook, bow, cup, and twist, or any combination of these defects.

Weathering: The mechanical or chemical disintegration and discoloration of the surface of wood that is caused by exposure to light and to the alternate shrinking and swelling of the surface fibers with continual changes in moisture content due to weather changes.

Wood flour: Wood ground finely enough to pass a 40- to 140-mesh screen, produced by stone mills of the "top runner" type, steel burr roller mills, or any one of the several types of hammer and beater mills; used chiefly in linoleum, dynamite, and synthetic resin products.

Wood preservative: Any substance that, for a reasonable length of time, is effective in preventing the development and action of wood-rotting fungi, harmful insects, and marine borers that deteriorate wood.

REVIEW   QUESTIONS,   CHAPTER   15

Possible score 100 points

Your score . . . . . .

PART I. COMPLETION QUESTIONS.   Complete the following statements:

1. Today, the number of acres owned and operated by the forest industry approaches . . . . acres.

2. Of the more than one thousand different species of trees on American soil, over . . . . are used for commercial purposes.

3. Most of our lumber for structural and framing purposes comes from the . . . . species.

4. The usefulness of wood continues to increase through new processes in wood . . . .

5. One of the most outstanding illustrations of the versatility of modern engineered lumber is a judge's stand at ....
6. The wood selected for this structure was Pacific Coast ....
7. This project was carried out at a temperature as low as .... below zero.
8. The four F's in the early development of the North American continent stood for ...., ..., ..., ...
9. With the exception of a few mountain ranges, early colonial forests covered an area from .... to ....
10. As early as the year ...., the ship "Anne" carried a cargo of clapboards from Plymouth to England.
11. An early legislative attempt to curtail waste of our forest products was made in 1681 by ....
12. Land which directly belongs to the United States government constitutes the ....
13. In order to curtail complete disposal of land, Congress passed in 1891 and 1897 acts which resulted in the formation of a system of .... and ....
14. Forest management reached a turning point by the passing in 1933 of the ....
15. This act was eventually declared unconstitutional by the U. S. ....
16. The major function of schools of forestry has always been ....
17. The Tree Farm Program was started in the year ....
18. The second largest percentage of our timber volume is made into ....
19. Three fourths of all commercial forests in the U. S. are located in ....
20. The botanical name for softwoods or conifers is ....
21. The botanical name for hardwoods or broadleafs is ....
22. Throughout the world, some .... species of hardwoods have been identified.
23. The three main species of American ash are black, green, and .... ash.
24. Another name for basswood is ....
25. Our native supply of chestnut has been largely depleted by ....
26. The more common name of Acacia burl, Baytree, or California laurel is ....
27. The wood obtained from trees which outstrip all other trees in height and size is ....
28. The wise use of all our natural resources is called ....
29. The carelessness of people can be blamed for .... out of every 100 forest fires.
30. The severe forest fire in 1933 in Oregon is known as the ....
31. Probably the most recent development in fire spotting is by means of ....
32. An insect which kills millions of dollars worth of timber annually is the ....
33. A privately-owned forest area, managed to grow timber as a crop under sound and agreed-upon practices is called a ....
34. One of this country's outstanding Chief Foresters was the late Colonel ....

35. Present-day loggers drive to and from work in their own car or in company cars called . . . .
36. Teams of two or three men that bring the trees down are called . . . .
37. After logs are unloaded at the mill, they are next brought to the . . . ., where each log is cut into smaller pieces.
38. The approximate age of a tree can be determined by counting the . . . .
39. The inner core of a tree trunk is called the heartwood and the outside part the . . . .
40. Boards cut from a log are either plain-sawed or . . . .

PART II. TRUE-FALSE QUESTIONS. Indicate, by encircling T or F, whether the following statements are true or false:

41. The bulk of all trees goes either to sawmills or to pulpmills.   T   F
42. As of today, the modern sawmill has little or no use for waste and residue.   T   F
43. Sulphite pulp is used in the manufacture of cellophane, explosives, lacquers, etc.   T   F
44. Choice logs and bolts are primarily used by plywood and veneer mills.   T   F
45. The Forest Products Laboratory at Madison, Wisconsin, functions under the U. S. Department of Commerce.   T   F
46. This laboratory was established in 1910 to do research in wood utilization.   T   F
47. Various useful items are extracted from wood wastes by either the process of distillation or by hydrolysis.   T   F
48. Dipentine is a solvent used in the reclamation of used rubber.   T   F
49. Cedar oil is primarily used as a disinfectant.   T   F
50. Baking yeast is derived from wood waste through the process of wood distillation.   T   F
51. Lumber as it comes from the sawmill is literally saturated with water.   T   F
52. Water in wood normally moves from areas of lower to areas of higher moisture content.   T   F
53. EMC stands for equilibrium moisture content.   T   F
54. Most of the moisture lost by wood during the drying process moves through cell cavities and small openings in the cell walls.   T   F
55. Two inch thick lumber takes twice as long to dry as one inch thick lumber.   T   F
56. The greatest hazard connected with the use of green lumber is decay.   T   F
57. Air-dried lumber generally has a moisture content of 12 to 15 per cent.   T   F
58. Kiln-dried lumber is recommended for all uses that require a moisture content below 12 per cent.   T   F
59. Wood normally swells as it dries and shrinks as it absorbs moisture.   T   F
60. Swelling of wood is employed to close the seams of barrels, tubs, and tanks.   T   F

61. Poorly seasoned lumber in a house may cause plaster cracks and distorted openings.   T   F
62. Plywood is completely free from warping.   T   F
63. Pakkawood is extremely hard and dense and is being successfully used in knife handles and similar articles.   T   F
64. Checks are ruptures in the wood along the grain.   T   F
65. Checking in kiln drying can be avoided by maintaining adequate circulation, proper temperature, and humidity conditions.   T   F
66. Diamonding as a defect usually occurs in rectangular stock.   T   F
67. Casehardening in wood develops on account of too slow drying.   T   F
68. Honeycombing is a defect traceable to internal checking and splitting.   T   F
69. The three greatest destroyers of wood are fungi, insects, and fire.   T   F
70. Fungi are low forms of animal life that develop and grow from spores.   T   F
71. Wood destroying fungi must have air, suitable moisture, and a favorable temperature in order to survive.   T   F
72. When wood is completely submerged in fresh water, it cannot decay.   T   F
73. Creosote, distilled from coal tar, is one of the most ineffective toxic chemicals used in wood preservation.   T   F
74. When sound timbers are pressure creosoted, all the spores on the surface are completely destroyed.   T   F
75. Copper sulfate and sodium arsenate are used as a preservative in solution with water.   T   F
76. Wood which has been pressure treated against decay has been found to be less fire-resistant than untreated wood.   T   F
77. The simplest method to preserve wood is by simply brushing, mopping, or spraying.   T   F
78. The best method of wood preservation is by means of pressure treatment.   T   F
79. Despite its long practical history, there is as yet no method of wood bending that guarantees 100 per cent success.   T   F
80. To bend thick, solid pieces of wood, it is first necessary to soften it by means of steam, hot water, or plasticizing chemicals.   T   F

PART III. MULTIPLE-CHOICE QUESTIONS. Select, by encircling the correct letter, the answer which completes each statement:

81. When a piece of wood is bent:
   A. It stretches along the outer side
   B. It stretches along the inner side
   C. It stretches on neither side of the bend

82. Experience has shown that one of the following American woods bends most readily:
   A. Locust
   B. Red oak
   C. American elm
   D. White oak

83. One of the following woods has poor bending quality:
    A. White oak
    B. Knotty white pine
    C. Maple
    D. Walnut

84. One of the following is also unsuitable for bending purposes:
    A. Green lumber
    B. Kiln-dried lumber
    C. Air-dried lumber

85. Glued-laminated wood construction or "glulam" consists of:
    A. Dressed lumber glued together
    B. Rough lumber glued together
    C. One solid piece of wood

86. The tremendous growth of the laminating industry is primarily due to:
    A. New laminating equipment
    B. New wood species
    C. New and improved glues

87. Of the following three D. F. flooring grades, which one is the best:
    A. "C" vertical grain
    B. "B and better" vertical grain
    C. "D" vertical grain

88. How many board feet are there in a piece of wood, ⅞" x 3" x 10' 0"?
    A. 4 b.f.
    B. 6 b.f.
    C. 2.5 b.f.
    D. 3.5 b.f.

89. One of the following is not a part of a veneer lathe:
    A. Heavy steel bed
    B. Sharp knife
    C. Thin-blade saw
    D. Pressure bar

90. Veneers cut from a bolt like sharpening a pencil are called:
    A. Cone-cut veneers
    B. Rotary-cut veneers
    C. Half-round veneers
    D. Plain-rotary cut veneers

PART IV. MATCHING QUESTIONS. Match the terms to the left with the descriptions to the right by placing the correct letter in parentheses:

91. ( ) Annual ring
92. ( ) Cambium
93. ( ) Casehardening
94. ( ) Cellulose
95. ( ) Conifer
96. ( ) Crossband
97. ( ) Flitch
98. ( ) Hardwoods
99. ( ) Rotary-cut veneer
100. ( ) Warp

A. A state of compression in the outer layers of a board accompanied by tension in the center.
B. The layer of veneer at right angles to the face plies.
C. The growth layer put on in a single growth year.
D. Any variation from the true or plane surface.
E. The carbohydrate that is the principal part of wood.
F. The layer of tissue just below the bark from which the new bark and wood cells develop.
G. A thick piece of wood with bark on one or more edges.
H. A tree bearing seed cones.
I. Broad-leaved trees.
J. Veneer cut in a continuous strip by rotating a log against the edge of a knife.

Selected Bibliography

Bending and Laminating Wood

U. S. Department of Agriculture, Forest Products Laboratory, "Bending Solid Wood to Form," No. 1764, Madison, Wisconsin, 1955, 63 pp.
———— "Wood Laminating comes of Age," Madison, Wisconsin, 1954, 8 pp.

Coated Abrasives

Behr-Manning Co., "Coated Abrasives Today," Troy, New York, 1960, 25 pp.
———— "New Trends in Industrial Woodworking," Troy, New York, 1960, 12 pp.
———— "A Lecture Course on Coated Abrasives for the Artisan, Mechanic and Student," Troy, New York, 1937, 66 pp.
Coated Abrasives Manufacturer's Institute, *Coated Abrasives: Modern Tool of Industry* (New York: McGraw-Hill Book Co., 1958), 426 pp.

Conservation and Tree Farming

American Forest Products Industries, Inc., "Our Growing Wood Supply," 1957 ed. Washington, D. C., 22 pp.
———— "It's A Tree Country," Washington, D. C., 1958, 39 pp.
Brown, Nelson Courtlandt, *Forest Products* (New York: John Wiley and Son, 1950), 399 pp.
Carhart, Arthur H., "Trees and Game — Twin Crops" American Forest Products Industries, Washington, D. C., 33 pp.
Dana, Samuel Trask, *Forest and Range Policy; Its Development in the United States* (New York: McGraw-Hill Book Co., 1956), 455 pp.
Fritz, Emanuel, "Just what is Conservation?" *Journal of Forestry,* 1952, 5 pp.
Hagenstein, W. D., "A Quarter Century of Industrial Forestry in the Douglas Fir Region," Industrial Forestry Association, Portland, Oregon, 1959, 8 pp.
Schoonover, Shelley E., *American Woods* (Santa Monica, Calif.: Watling and Co., 1951), 250 pp.
Titmuss, F. H., *A Concise Encyclopedia of World Timbers* (New York: Philosophical Library, 1949), 156 pp.
U. S. Department of Agriculture, Forest Service, *Timber Resources for America's Future,* Forest Resource Report, No. 14 (Washington, D. C.: U. S. Government Printing Office, 1958), 713 pp.
West Coast Lumbermen's Association, "The Story of West Coast Lumber," Portland, Oregon, 16 pp.

Grading of Lumber

West Coast Lumbermen's Association, "Douglas Fir Lumber Grades and Uses," Portland, Oregon, 42 pp.
———— *Standard Grading and Dressing Rules for Douglas Fir, West Coast Hemlock, Sitka Spruce, Western Red Cedar,* Portland, Oregon, 1956, 343 pp.
———— "West Coast Hemlock Lumber Grades and Uses," Portland, Oregon, 43 pp.
———— "West Coast Lumber Data on Grades and Specifications," Portland, Oregon, 15 pp.
———— "Western Red Cedar Lumber Grades and Uses." Portland, Oregon, 35 pp.

Planning and Design

Allender, H. A., "When is a Project Appropriate?" Industrial Arts and Vocational Education Magazine, February, 1950, p. 78.
Feirer, John L., *Advanced Woodwork and Furniture Making* (Peoria, Ill.: Charles A. Bennett Co., 1954), 399 pp.
Tinkham, Robert A., "Design in Industrial Arts." mimeographed, 5 pp.

Preservation and Fireproofing of Wood

American Wood Preservers Institute, "Pressure Treated Timber Poles," Chicago, Illinois, 1957, 74 pp.
———— "Pressure Treated Foundation Piles." Chicago, Illinois, 1955, 66 pp.

U. S. Department of Agriculture, Forest Products Laboratory, "Study of the Preservative Treatment of Wood," No. 2043, Madison, Wisconsin, 1955, 16 pp.

Upholstery

National Rubber Bureau, "Convert to Comfort with Latex Foam," Washington, D. C., 1959, 21 pp.

Thames, Gena, "Reupholstering Chairs with Foam Rubber," Cornell Miscellaneous Bulletin, No. 20, Ithaca, New York, 48 pp.

Wood Products

Fine Hardwoods Association, Educational Series, "Veneers," Books 1, 2, 3, 4, and 5, Chicago, Illinois, 11 pp. each.

———— "Fine Hardwoods Selectorama; A Guide to the Selection of the Popular Species," Chicago, Illinois, 1956, 59 pp.

Hardwood Plywood Institute, "A Treasury of Hardwood Plywood," Chicago, Illinois, 20 pp.

———— "Hardwood Plywood Handbook," Chicago, Illinois, 1956, 22 pp.

Plywood Corporation, "Weldwood Prefinished Paneling for Fine Interiors," New York, New York, 1957, 23 pp.

U. S. Department of Agriculture, Forest Products Laboratory, "The Manufacture of Veneer," No. 285, Madison, Wisconsin, 1955, 12 pp.

———— "Manufacture and General Characteristics of Flat Plywood," No. 543, Madison, Wisconsin, 1956, 15 pp.

———— "A Hundred Definitions Pertaining to Wood and Other Forest Products," No. 240, Madison, Wisconsin, 1952, 11 pp.

U. S. Department of Commerce, "Hardwood Plywood," *Commercial Standard CS 35–56*, U. S. Government Printing Office, Washington, D. C., 1956, 26 pp.

Woodworking

Cunningham, B. M., and Holtrop, W. F., *Woodshop Tool Maintenance* (Peoria, Ill.: Chas. A. Bennett Co., 1956), 295 pp.

Feirer, John L., *Industrial Arts Woodworking* (Peoria, Ill.: Chas. A. Bennett Co., 1950), 295 pp.

Hjorth, Herman, and Holtrop, William F., *Operation of Modern Woodworking Machines* (Milwaukee, Wis.: Bruce Publishing Co., 1958), 176 pp.

Holtrop, William F., and Hjorth, Herman, *Modern Machine Woodworking* (Milwaukee, Wis.: Bruce Publishing Co., 1960), 280 pp.

National Retail Hardware Association, "Hardware: Advanced Course in Hardware Retailing," Indianapolis, Indiana, 1957, 90 pp.

Scharff, Robert, *Easy Ways to Expert Woodworking* (New York: McGraw-Hill Book Co., 1956), 191 pp.

Wheeler, Charles G., *Woodworking for Beginners* (New York: G. P. Putnam's Sons, the Knickerbocker Press, 1906).

S. A. Woods Machine Co., "Illustrated Catalogue of Woodworking Machinery," Boston, Massachusetts, 1884.

Wood Finishing

The De Vilbiss Co., "The A B C's of Spray Equipment," Toledo, Ohio, 1954, 64 pp.

Newell, Adnah C., and Holtrop, William F., *Coloring, Finishing, and Painting Wood* (Peoria, Ill.: Charles A. Bennett Co., 1961), 478 pp.

Soderberg, George A., *Finishing Materials and Methods* (Bloomington, Ill.: Mc-Knight and McKnight, 1952), 320 pp.

Wood Technology

Brown, H. P., Panshin, A. J., and Forsaith, C. C., *Textbook of Wood Technology*, Vol. I, (New York: McGraw-Hill Book Co., 1942), 652 pp.

"Centennial Gift Shaping Job," *British Columbia Lumberman*, January, 1960, p. 58.

"Engineered Timber Beats Competition," *Canada Lumberman*, October, 1959, pp. 34–36.

Keyser, Carl A., *Materials of Engineering* (Englewood Cliffs, N. J.: Prentice-Hall, Inc., 1956), 502 pp.

National Lumber Manufacturer's Association, "Livibility Unlimited," Washington, D. C., 19 pp.

Stouffer, Lloyd, "New Wonders from Wood," *Chemistry*, March, 1960, pp. 1–16.

U. S. Department of Agriculture, Forest Products Laboratory, "Properties of Wood related to Drying," No. 1900–1, Madison, Wisconsin, 1951, 48 pp.

———— "Longitudinal Shrinkage of Wood," No. 1093, Madison, Wisconsin, 1954, 20 pp.

———— "Moisture Content of Wood in Use," No. 1655, Madison, Wisconsin, 1955, 10 pp.

———— "Shrinking and Swelling of Wood in Use," No. 736, Madison, Wisconsin, 1952, 17 pp.

"Wood in Creative Architecture," *The Lumberman*, November, 1959. Reprint, 17 pp.

Index